Overtures to Biology

The Speculations of Eighteenth-Century Naturalists

The spirit of poetry unveils the mystery of nature.

Frontispiece, dedicated to Goethe, from Alexander von Humboldt, *Al. von Humboldt und Aimé Bonpland's Reise* (1807) (Speck Collection, Yale University Library). Goethe's *Metamorphosis der Pflanzen* (1790) set forth his theory of plant growth in poetry.

Overtures to Biology

The Speculations of Eighteenth-Century Naturalists

Philip C. Ritterbush

Yale University Press 1964

New Haven & London

Designed by Sally Hargrove,
set in Baskerville type,
and printed in the United States of America by
Vail-Ballou Press, Inc., Binghamton, N.Y.

Library of Congress catalog card number: 64-12657
Published with assistance from the Stern Fund.

To my mother
and my grandmother

Preface

The scientist requires discipline to sustain him through exhausting courses of experiment and to resist premature conclusions. Lacking discipline of either kind, the eighteenth-century naturalists indulged their imaginations in an almost poetic outburst of speculation meant to serve the purpose of scientific explanation. They were the first to study the bewildering ranks of lower animals, the sexual anatomy of flowers, the sensitive plant, and the electric fish. Their observations of these strange creatures fired their ambitions for a unified and self-contained explanation of nature and led them to the very heights of surmise.

The narrative centers upon the interconnections and sequences of development in the speculative concepts of the eighteenth-century naturalists. The growth of scientific ideas is influenced not only by observation and experiment, but also by the emotional endowment of the investigator and the temper of his age. I have sought to describe such an intellectual climate in terms of scientific ideas and also to give an account of how the emergence of biology was influenced by more general notions about nature.

Seeking the continuities of thought in eighteenth-century natural history, I found two dominant and recurring themes. The ether of Newton and the subtle fire of Berkeley seemed to be at hand in certain electrical experiments, while the presence of electricity in clouds, volcanoes, and living creatures showed it to be a force of cosmic significance. Would not electricity then cure disease, hatch eggs, promote organic growth, and raise the dead? The other inquiry that fascinated the naturalists was how to explain the life of plants. Fluids circulated within them as in animals. The discovery that plants were differentiated into sexes invited other analogies with animals. Plants were seen to move their leaves and flowers, and some varieties even to react suddenly to the touch. Might not plants then feel and perhaps even think, feel emotions of love, and change into animals and back again?

Thus speculation centered upon the energy of life and its analogies to other energies and upon those relationships among life forms which might betray a unified system of nature. These concerns are very much alive in modern science, although in my view the eighteenth-century notions should be regarded only as historic counterparts and not as the legitimate forbears of modern biological ideas. But there can be no harm in noting their many parallels. In its broader aspects science was then, as it should be now, a vital force in general culture and the arts. The close relationships between the ideas of these early naturalists and romantic nature poetry should invite our attention to the divisions in culture which preoccupy us today.

I wish to thank my supervisor in the University of Oxford, Alistair C. Crombie, and the following, who have been generous with advice and assistance: the late Agnes Arber, Lady Barlow, John R. Baker, Sir Gavin R. deBeer, Peter R. Bell, Bernard Blackstone, John S. Bromley, Arthur J. Cain, Joy Day, Mark L. Franklin, Claude leGrise, G. Evelyn Hutchinson, Johanna Kooymans, Philip McNair, Mr. and Mrs. J. J. Murray, Jr., Joseph Needham, Derek J. deSolla Price, Charles L. Remington, James L. B. Smith, Robert A. Smith, W. T. Stearn, Johanna Stuckey, Pat Tidwell, W. B. Turrill, Jeremy D. B. Walker, J. Steven Watson, William K. Wimsatt, Jr., and Edgar Wind.

P. C. R.

Washington, D.C
September 10, 1963

Contents

Preface vii

1 *"The blaze Newton kindled on the altar of science"* 1

2 *Electricity: The soul of the universe* 15

i. Electricity and the idea of immanence 15

ii. The Leyden jar 22

iii. Electricity and vital energy 28

iv. Animated phials 35

v. The sovereign remedy 43

vi. The climax of speculation 48

3 *Clearing the mysteries of vegetation* 57

i. Analogy as an aid to understanding 61

ii. Plant nutrition and growth 1660–1727 70

iii. Plant generation 1676–1830 88

4 *The triumph of botanical analogy* 109

i. Linnaeus, analogy, and the scale of beings 109

ii. Problematical organisms 122

iii. The super-life of plants 141

5 *From the idea of nature to the science of biology* 158

i. Erasmus Darwin 159

ii. Lamarck: The rejection of analogy 175

iii. Sir Humphry Davy: The rejection of subtle fluids and the romantic imagination in science 180

iv. John Hunter: The first of the modern biologists 186

v. The romantic protest 197

Illustrations after p. 210

Bibliography 211

Index 275

☙ I ❧

"The Blaze Newton Kindled on the Altar of Science"[1]

Figuring prominently in the writings of eighteenth-century naturalists were two speculative beliefs whose history is here presented in narrative form. One belief was that electricity was the most important agent in the economy of nature, sustaining life and perhaps its principal physical cause. The other was that plants were analogous to animals because of their close proximity in the scheme of nature. For convenient reference these notions will be called the idea of immanence and the idea of botanical analogy. Although the authority of science was invoked on their behalf the concepts reflected an improper understanding of organic nature, far exceeded the evidence given for them, and too often led naturalists to neglect observation and experiment in favor of abstract conceptions.

The influence we assign to ideas in the history of science depends upon how we answer many familiar questions about the extent to which scientists should allow themselves to be governed by the needs of theory in planning experiments and explaining observations. The investigators who have unerringly fixed upon a distant theoretical goal and single-mindedly achieved its triumphant realization have been very few. Modern science proceeds through an eminently practical accommodation of theoretical claims to experimental results. Our task

1. Gregory Watt (1777–1804), letter to Humphry Davy, 7 Feb. 1801: Davy, *Fragmentary Remains* (1858), p. 30.

in the present study is not to state the extent to which intuitive goals are a prerequisite to successful scientific inquiry but to explain the fact that for nearly a century in the history of biology two speculative notions did not merely justify inquiry but in effect largely supplanted it.

In modern experimental science, established conclusions are carried only so far as observations permit, and additional intuitions are regarded as hypotheses to be tested. Sir Isaac Newton (1642–1727) advocated the acceptance of this technique of limiting explanation as a normative principle of natural philosophy. He stated laws of gravitation and planetary motion in terms nicely calculated to place no strain on his evidence. They were descriptive statements whose truth did not depend upon any speculations he may have entertained about "the kind or the manner of any action, the causes or the physical reason thereof." [2] In the second edition of the *Principia* (1713) Newton claimed to have limited explanation to justifiable inferences: "for whatever is not deduced from the phenomena is to be called an hypothesis; and hypotheses, whether of occult qualities or mechanical, have no place in experimental philosophy." [3] In a paper published in 1672 he had described the differential refrangibility of light without attempting to determine its physical nature.[4] Newton's assertion that a proposition might be of scientific value without answering all conceivable questions about observed events or accounting for their causes gave needed emphasis to a principle of scientific method. His statement of empiricism was aimed directly at the ambitions of seventeenth-century corpuscularian mechanists.

Robert Boyle (1627–91) had accounted for gaseous diffusion by imagining air particles shaped like springs, and the cohesion of bodies by imagining minute hooks on their particles. Acids fitted into metals as keys into locks. Descartes advanced a simple hydraulic model interpreting organisms as systems of tubes, to ascribe nervous action and muscular motion to pressure and movement in circulating fluids. The mechanists struck a bold pose before nature and devised ingenious models to reduce all observable events to matter in motion. They demonstrated their opposition to systems of scholastic qualities and occult powers but their models had only a temporary usefulness. In order to justify their faith in the possibility of scientific explanation

2. Newton, *Principia* [1687], p. 6.

3. Ibid. [1713], p. 547.

4. See "the best and safest method of philosophizing" (1672), Cohen, ed., *Newton's Papers and Letters* (1958), p. 106.

Descartes (1596–1650), Hobbes (1588–1679), Borelli (1608–79), and others had extended their explanations far beyond conjecture into surmise. While these models did not contribute to understanding, they satisfied desires for knowledge by their comprehensiveness of explanation extending to the most concrete images of physical causation. The mechanists seem to have believed that they had to provide just as comprehensive an account as those they sought to supplant and one that pretended to just as complete a knowledge of the reason for things. These two aims became dissociated from their historical context and exerted considerable influence upon eighteenth-century naturalists as an ambition for "total explanation."

What distinguished the corpuscularian philosophy from its antecedents was the physical nature of the causes described and the susceptibility of such notions to representation by naive mechanical models. Nehemiah Grew, Leeuwenhoek, Robert Hooke, Claude Perrault, and others sought to characterize living bodies as assemblages of gross material corpuscles of a magnitude that suggests the limit of the resolving power of early microscopes.[5] The coarse texture they attributed to organic bodies, an easily recognized feature of the corpuscular philosophy, would be steadily refined by later observers until the level of complexity in scientific explanation coincided more closely with the actual texture of organic bodies. The refinement of explanatory texture began as a reaction against Cartesian mechanism and has been a feature of biological history right down to the present day.

Biologists were long in applying principles of limited explanation wherein accuracy was substituted for comprehensiveness as a regulative value. While Newton advanced the principle of limited explanation as a principle of scientific procedure, he did not apply it to the substance of his own ideas. He did not force such a drastic change upon his immediate successors because his scientific legacy was paradoxical and ambiguous.

Through his intuitions of the interrelatedness of physical forces, which he hoped his successors would fully discover, Newton's natural philosophy enjoyed the appeal of comprehensiveness.

> I wish we could derive the rest of the phenomena of nature by the same kind of reasoning from mechanical principles, for I am induced by many reasons to suspect that they may all depend upon certain forces by which the particles are either mutually impelled towards one another and cohere in regular figures, or

5. See Chapter 3, below, for the change from corpuscular texture in plant physiology to explanation in terms of subtle fluids.

> are repelled and recede from one another. These forces being unknown, philosophers have hitherto attempted the search of nature in vain; but I hope the principles here laid down will afford some light either to this or some truer method of philosophy.[6]

Augustus de Morgan thought Newton "so happy in his conjectures as to seem to know more than he could possibly have any means of proving." [7] There can be no question that Newton suspected more than he could prove by his most rigorous standards. It was to express these intuitions that he advanced the ethereal hypothesis, to advertise the possibility that the cause of gravity, repulsion, the refraction of light, chemical action, and the transmission of nerve impulses might be a highly attenuated universal gas.[8]

In the twenty-first query (1706) of the *Opticks* Newton sought to explain gravity by supposing that ether was rarefied within dense bodies so that pressure "from the denser parts of the medium toward the rarer" caused the bodies to draw together.[9] In a letter to Robert Boyle in 1679 Newton wrote that the close approach of bodies might cause the ether between them to rarefy up to a natural limit, at which point there would be "a reluctance from being brought nearer together." [10] He invoked the persuasive sanction of comprehensiveness by extending the hypothesis to account for a great variety of appearances:

> Now hence I conceive it is chiefly that a fly walks on water without wetting her feet, and consequently without touching the water; that two polished pieces of glass are not without pressure brought to contact, . . . that the particles of dust cannot by pressing be made to cohere, . . . that the particles of tinging substances and salts dissolved in water [are diffused].[11]

It was by means of the ether that heat might be transmitted through a vacuum.[12] In a paper read to the Royal Society in 1675 Newton

6. *Principia* [1713], p. 2.
7. Quoted by Lord Keynes, in "Newton, the Man" (1942), p. 28.
8. The idea of the ether was a hypothesis of the kind Cohen defines as "a supposed mechanism": *Franklin and Newton* (1956), p. 139. Sir Edmund Whittaker refers to it as an "inter-phenomenon": *A History of the Theories of Aether and Electricity, 1* (2d ed. 1951), 30–31. The spelling "ether" was used in the late eighteenth century and is now recommended by the O.E.D.; I retain "aether" in titles and quotations from poetry.
9. *Opticks* (1952), p. 350.
10. *Newton's Papers and Letters,* p. 251.
11. Ibid.
12. *Opticks,* p. 349. Qu. 18 (1706).

maintained that the refraction of light resulted from collisions with particles of ether, bending the course of emerging light particles into a course more nearly parallel to refracting surfaces. The reflection of some light from transparent surfaces was explained by supposing that corpuscles of light "impinging" on the surface of bodies caused vibratory motions in the adjacent ether. If a corpuscle of light moves toward a body in an advancing ethereal wave, "it easily breaks through a refracting surface." If a corpuscle were in a retreating wave it was easily reflected.[13] In the twenty-fourth query (1717) Newton asserted that vibrations of the ether along the "solid, pellucid and uniform capillamenta of the nerves" constituted nervous impulses.[14]

> And thus nature will be very comformable to herself and very simple, performing all the great motions of the heavenly bodies by the attraction of gravity which intercedes those bodies and almost all the small ones of their particles by some other attractive and repelling powers which intercede those particles.[15]

Bernard Cohen writes "that a belief in an ethereal medium, penetrating all bodies and filling empty spaces was a central pillar of [Newton's] system of nature." [16] Cohen supposes that Newton advanced the hypothesis because he "could not resist telling his readers about his thoughts concerning the cause of phenomena." [17] Marie Boas believes "that Newton would have preferred the mechanical explanation" (the ether) but that he excluded it from his account of gravitation in the *Principia* "for want of experimental evidence." [18]

While refining the texture of scientific explanation from gross particles to subtle fluids, Newton upheld total explanation by the comprehensiveness of his hypothesis and the possibility of its action as a proximate cause. He closed a door on corpuscles but left cracks for his own ether to slip through. In the thirty-first query of the *Opticks* he stated his opposition to corpuscular models.

> [The] vast contraction and expansion [of gases] seems unintelligible, by feigning the particles of air to be springy and ramous, or rolled up like hoops, or by any other means than a repulsive power.[19]

13. Ibid., [1704], pp. 280–82.
14. Ibid., p. 354.
15. Ibid., p. 397. Qu. 31 (1717).
16. *Newton's Papers and Letters,* p. 13.
17. *Franklin and Newton,* p. 143 n.
18. "The Establishment of the Mechanical Philosophy" (1952), p. 519.
19. P. 396. See [Peter Browne], *The Procedure, Extent, and Limits of Human Understanding* (1728), pp. 207–09 for similar remarks on the mechanists.

In physics a number of natural philosophers went beyond Newton's mere refinement of explanatory texture to accept the principle of limited explanation. Among the possible reasons for this commendable development was the delay in publishing such significant descriptions of the ether as his letter to Boyle (not until 1744), the second paper on light and colors (1757), and the letter to Bentley disavowing action at a distance (1756). Marjorie Nicolson has shown that poets made Newton their ally against Cartesianism.[20] Henry Pemberton's *View of Sir Isaac Newton's Philosophy* (1728) expressed a widespread conception of Newton's writings:

> This philosophy professes modestly to keep within the extent of our faculties and is ready to confess its imperfections . . . [without] the vain ostentation of rash and groundless conjectures.[21]

In natural history (the most convenient term for the descriptive natural sciences before 1800) the degree of complexity to be attributed to organic tissues was a central issue. The change from corpuscles to fluids meant a retreat from the most advanced salients of seventeenth-century mechanism. This process was aided by a reaction against Cartesian physiology, which was thought to be crude and overambitious.[22] A refinement of texture did not necessarily imply a gain for the principle of limited explanation. To many naturalists it seemed that a chaos of particles was to be exchanged for a cosmos of interrelated fluids; their reasons for welcoming the change were not conducive to empiricism. The cosmic synthesis conferred infinite suggestiveness on insubstantial experiments and encouraged the belief that physical and vital forces were interchangeable. Ambitions for comprehensiveness survived to influence a generation of speculators who did not forswear ambitions for total explanation.

The belief that all physical forces were interrelated contributed to much eighteenth-century physiological speculation on behalf of an ideal of metaphysical harmony. For example, physiologists were to use the ether to resolve Cartesian dualism such as that shown by John Harris (1666?–1719) in his Boyle Lectures of 1698. He had maintained that body or matter was "a sluggish, insensible, passive, and unintelli-

20. *Newton Demands the Muse* (1946), pp. 132–44.

21. P. 18.

22. See Auguste Georges-Berthier, "Le mécanisme Cartésien et la physiologie au XVIIe siècle," *Isis, 2* (1914), 37–79, and *3* (1920), 21–58. Also Lawrence, *Lectures on Physiology* (1819), 72. Also Darwin, *Zoonomia, 1* (1794), 1. Also Boas and Hall, "Newton's 'Mechanical Principles' " (1959), pp. 168–69. Also A. R. Hall, *From Galileo to Newton 1630–1720* (New York: Harper & Row, 1963).

gent thing, not possibly able to move of itself." Any "motion and activity" must arise "by communication from something that is without it or distinct from it."[23] Harris held that the motivating spirit was "more akin to motion . . . for the active cause of motion may be very well said to be incorporeal, or the Deity itself."[24] Ethereal fluids would be found capable of resolving the difference between matter and spirit. Speculators were to forsake dualism in favor of analogies between mind and matter, between spirit and corporeal substance. Newton wrote,

> Thus may therefore the soul, by determining this ethereal animal spirit or wind into this or that nerve, perhaps with as much ease as air is moved in open spaces, cause all the motions we see in animals.[25]

Newton's conjecture that the ether might mediate between soul and body was elaborated by John Cook in his *Anatomical and Mechanical Essay on the Whole Animal Economy* (1730); while the thinking faculty of animals was "immaterial" it was nonetheless "clothed with a material vehicle, or rather united and inseparably mixed therewith." Cook described the ether as an "intermediate vehicle," "another and finer body than what we visibly carry about with us."[26]

> This fine ethereal vehicle of the soul . . . receives motions from the animal spirits, or [corporeal] liquid of the nerves, and impresses them after a peculiar and unknown manner on the soul or thinking substance that possesses it; and as the nervous liquor acts on this subtle chariot of the soul in the brain . . . so likewise the soul acts as its own vehicle, thereby agitating the nervous fluid.[27]

The ether might be impressed with the "marks or signatures" of memory. Were it not for this medium, sensation would be "beyond all mechanical laws." Cook imagined a "fine subtle material vehicle, which the soul is incorporated with, which received tremors and impressions from the nervous fluid."[28] Speculations about ether gave

23. *The Atheist's Objections Against the Immaterial Nature of God, and Incorporeal Substances, Refuted* (1698), 4th lecture, p. 5.

24. Ibid., p. 32.

25. Second paper on light and colors (1675), *Newton's Papers and Letters,* p. 184.

26. 2, 160.

27. Ibid., p. 159.

28. Ibid., pp. 165–66.

Cook the same satisfactions that corpuscularian philosophers had derived from naive mechanical models.

We may observe the seductive influence of the synthesis of physical forces in the writings of Bryan Robinson of Dublin (1680–1754). In 1732 he published *A Treatise of the Animal Economy,* a studied exercise in limited explanation, describing the movements of blood and perspiration as they varied with heat or exercise, but speculating not at all on their causes. After he read Newton's *Opticks,* Robinson abandoned his cautious position and tried to develop the ethereal hypothesis into a universal explanation of physics and life.[29] In *A Dissertation on the Aether of Sir Isaac Newton* (1743), he proposed a set size and density for ether particles, discussed their manner of acting on bodies, and then proceeded to demonstrate the laws of gravity and planetary motion as a necessary effect.[30] He watched heated hairs contract and supposed that the ether in all animal fibers caused them to contract when heated. A vibration "raised by the power of the will" on the nerve ends in the brain would be transmitted along the nerves in "an instant" and "raise a like vibrating motion" in the muscles.[31] Robinson is our first example of a speculator who abandoned limited explanation in a headlong rush to describe gravity, light, heat, muscular motion, and the transmission of nervous impulses in terms of a single fluid. He justified his attempt by appealing to the desirability of comprehensive explanation: "By how much the more general any cause is, by so much the stronger is the reason for allowing its existence." [32] Newton had advanced the ether as a hypothesis; Robinson deduced consequences from it as though its existence and properties were demonstrated facts.

The interrelatedness of harmonious forces constituted the basis for a great deal of speculation; we must try to understand the appeal

29. Robinson does not say in so many words that he changed his mode of investigation as a result of having read the *Opticks.* I draw this inference because while he quoted it frequently in 1743 he did not do so at all in 1732. In 1745, after he had read Newton's letter to Boyle, he provided extracts from it in *Sir Isaac Newton's Account of the Aether.*

30. P. 32. See also Georges Louis LeSage, "Lucrèce Newtonien" (1782). Also Thomas Percival, "Facts and Queries Relative to Attraction and Repulsion" (1785). Also *Letters of Euler to a German Princess on Different Subjects in Physics and Philosophy,* Henry Hunter, trans. *1* (London: for the translator and H. Murray, 1795), 243, 298, 347. The ethereal hypothesis was found deserving of refutation by S. Vince, *Observations on the Hypotheses Which Have Been Assumed to Account for the Cause of Gravitation from Mechanical Principles* (Cambridge: by R. Watts for Deighton, and Nicholson, and by Lunn of London, 1806), pp. 14–26.

31. *Dissertation on the Aether,* p. 110; he cites the 24th query of the *Opticks.*

32. Ibid., "Preface."

of this notion to eighteenth-century writers. Their chief motive was the desire for comprehensive explanations. Cadwallader Colden (1688–1776) defended an elaborate hypothesis in physics by claiming that it would "show agreement with nature in every instance." [33] Rogerio Boscovich supposed that his model for particles of matter, which expressed force as an extended property of matter, was sufficient foundation for "a system that is midway between that of Leibniz and that of Newton . . . undoubtedly suitable in a marvellous degree for deriving all the general properties of bodies." [34] After he had attributed to matter a power of repulsion and a power of attraction Joseph Priestley (1733–1804) thought it possible to claim, "Ultimately one great comprehensive law shall be found to govern both the material and intellectual world." [35] In the *Système de la nature* (1770), d'Holbach (1723–89) supposed that life was caused by "ce fluide qui les [animaux] environne, qui les presse, qui les pénètre, qui leur donne du ressort." [36] Once he had assumed that the fluid really existed he found satisfaction in stating that the growth of plants and the crystallization of minerals might be explained by the same cause. Only by the assumption of active powers within particles of matter could a harmonious metaphysical system be constructed:

> Si par la nature nous entendons un amas de matières mortes, dépourvues de toutes propriétés, purement passives, nous serons,

33. *An Explication of the First Causes of Action in Matter* (1746), p. 41. Colden imagined a third kind of matter, to which motion was essential; cf. *The Principles of Action in Matter* (1751), p. 12. His debate with Samuel Johnson (1696–1772) of Yale College affords excellent insight into how Newton's principles and those of Berkeley (upheld by Johnson) were interpreted. Also William Kenrick's article in the *Monthly Review, 21* (1759), 500–12. Also the very extensive *Cadwallader Colden Papers;* the New-York Historical Society owns many more of Colden's unpublished scientific papers and documents. Also E. Edwards Beardsley, *Life and Correspondence of Samuel Johnson* (1874). For Colden and his scientific circle, see Alice M. Keys, *Cadwallader Colden* (Columbia Univ. Press, 1906), pp. 10–16. The greater comprehensiveness of a hypothesis, according to the principle of simplicity, may be a valid reason for preferring it to another one. But many eighteenth-century speculators tried to devise explanations that explained all appearances, rather than experimental data, as later examples will show.

34. *A Theory of Natural Philosophy* [1758], p. 35. Also H. V. Gill, *Roger Boscovich, S.J. (1711–1787)* (1941).

35. Priestley, "A General View of the Doctrine of Association of Ideas," *Hartley's Theory of the Human Mind . . .* (London: J. Johnson, 1775), p. xxv; also xx. Also *Disquisitions on Matter and Spirit* (1777), pp. 4–5. Also Sir John Pringle, "A Discourse on the Different Kinds of Air . . . ," *Six Discourses Delivered by Sir John Pringle* (London: W. Strahan and T. Cadell, 1783), p. 40. Also Richard Barton, *Lectures in Natural Philosophy . . .* (Dublin: for the author and George and Alexander Ewing, 1751), pp. 38–46.

36. *1,* 35.

> sans doute, forcés de chercher hors de cette nature le principe de ses mouvements; mais si par la nature nous entendons ce qu'elle est réellement, un tout dont les parties diverses ont des propriétés diverses, qui dès lors agissent suivant ces mêmes propriétés, qui sont dans une action et une réaction perpétuelles les unes sur les autres, qui pèsent, qui gravitent vers un centre commun, tandis que d'autres s'éloignent et vont à la circonférence, qui s'attirent et se repoussent, qui s'unissent et se séparent, et qui par leur collisions et leurs rapprochements continuels produisent et décomposent tous les corps que nous voyons, alors rien ne nous obligera de recourir à des forces surnaturelles pour nous rendre compte de la formation des choses, et des phénomènes que nous voyons.[37]

The speculative naturalists, in physiology and in general theories about the nature of the physical world, were largely to rely on this synthesis of forces. They were devoted to a monistic and comprehensive metaphysic based upon assumptions of extra powers in matter.

David Hartley (1705–57) based his celebrated theory of the association of ideas upon conspiring vibrations in ethereal substance. "The attractions of gravitation, electricity, magnetism, and cohesion, with the repulsions which attend upon the three last, intimate to us the general tenor of nature." [38] Hartley confessed that his comprehensive system of analogies rested upon slender grounds:

> Let us suppose the existence of the ether, with these its properties, to be destitute of all direct evidence; still, if it serves to explain and account for a great variety of phenomena, it will have an indirect evidence in its favor by this means. Thus we admit the key of a cypher to be a true one, when it explains the cypher completely . . . and this without any direct evidence at all.[39]

Hartley's words indicate the complacent temper which we find characterized many eighteenth-century naturalists. Powers inherent in matter were assumed in order to permit the harvest of a complete account of proximate causation based upon analogies between vitality and the energies of matter. Physiologists who wrote that motion was essential to some kinds of matter or assumed the existence of subtle

37. Ibid., p. 25. On monism in eighteenth-century French natural science see Mornet, *Les sciences de la nature en France au XVIIIe siècle* (1911), pp. 81–84.

38. Hartley, *Observations on Man, 1* (1749), 28.

39. Ibid., pp. 15–16. Cf. David Hartley, fils, in *Observations on Man . . . , 3* (3d ed., London: J. Johnson, 1791), xii.

fluids usually forsook limited explanation and went on to maintain a synthesis of light, heat, electricity, gravity, and life.

> We hear of bodies so exceedingly fine that their very exility makes them susceptible of sensation and knowledge, as if they shrunk into intellect by their exquisite subtlety, which rendered them too delicate to be bodies any longer. 'Tis to this notion we owe many curious inventions such as subtle ether, animal spirits, nervous ducts, vibrations, and the like, terms which modern philosophy, upon parting with occult qualities, has found expedient to provide itself, to take their place.[40]

We must not expect to encounter the modern empirical awareness that science must be faithful to the disclosures of experiment and leave unity to shift for itself, as has happened with quantum theory and the Bohr atom for example. What mattered most to the eighteenth-century speculators was the adequacy of their key to the cypher of nature.

A more vitalistic, impassioned concept of subtle fluids was that of George Berkeley (1685–1735), whose *Siris* (1744) was to exercise a noticeable influence on later speculations about electricity. Berkeley's skeptical philosophy successively disposed of all physical causes for human sense impressions in order to appeal to spiritual intervention. If the cause of ideas could be neither adventitious ideas nor material substance, "It remains therefore that the cause of ideas is an incorporeal, active substance or spirit." [41] He relied upon the same argument in *Siris,* which presented a hermetic concept of God as the soul of the universe employing fire as his instrument. Berkeley attacked "some corpuscularian philosophers of the last age" who had attempted to explain "the formation of this world and its phenomena by a few simple laws of mechanism." [42] He noted that the "extreme minuteness of the parts" of Newton's ether "and the velocity of their motion are thought to qualify it for being the cause of all the natural motions in the universe" (par. 224). It was an "uncouth explication"; physical forces are "abstract, spiritual, incorporeal," "prescinded from gravity and matter" (par. 225). Berkeley preferred to think of an immaterial agent closely associated with God's will, more like fire than matter. He wrote of a "fine subtle spirit" (par. 150), "some active subtle

40. James Harris, *Hermes: or a Philosophical Inquiry Concerning Language and Universal Grammar* (London: J. Nourse and P. Vaillant, 1751), p. 393.

41. *A Treatise Concerning the Principles of Human Knowledge,* part 1 (Dublin: by Aaron Rhames for Jeremy Pepyat, 1710), p. 67–68, par. 26.

42. *Siris,* par. 232.

substance; whether it be called fire, ether, light, or the vital spirit of the world" (par. 147). Berkeley held that his fire was immaterial and altogether different from Newton's ether (par. 221–30, 238, 250). This was not altogether true; there were many parallels.

> Being always restless and in motion, ["this ether or pure invisible fire"] actuates and enlivens the whole visible mass, is equally fitted to produce and to destroy, distinguishes the various stages of nature and keeps up the perpetual round of generations and corruptions, pregnant with forms which it constantly sends forth and resorbs. So quick in its motions, so subtle in its nature, so extensive in its effects, it seemeth no other than the vegetative soul or vital spirit of the world [par. 152].

Berkeley advanced the distracting contention that the fluid of life was distilled by evergreen trees and stored in "viscid resin or balsam" (par. 121) which might be dissolved to make tar-water, a panacea for the diseases of mankind. The volatile plant soul of tars and resins, soluble in water (par. 47), could easily penetrate the human body (par. 48, 54), bringing to bear upon any illness the sun's heat as well as the patient maturity, mellowness, and serenity of old evergreens (par. 35–45).

> [Tar-water] possesseth the most valuable qualities ascribed to the several balsams of Peru, of Tolu, of Capivi, and even to the balm of Gilead; such is its virtue . . . it is the best medicine I have ever tried [par. 21].

Berkeley's hopes for the remedy were characteristic of eighteenth-century benevolence, but not of empiricism. He produced numerous accounts of cures and paid no heed to negative evidence.[43] He reasoned directly from the importance of fire in the economy of nature to its supposed curative properties, an argument we are to encounter again in writings on medical electricity.

Siris is a disjointed and enthusiastic statement of Berkeley's mature metaphysical inclinations. The argument is uncritical and subjective, like Robinson's arguments from the existence of a universal ether. He was deeply involved in mystic chemical and Neoplatonic notions but did not sustain them for a philosophical audience, relying instead upon the appeal of a folk nostrum supported by conjectures about

43. For a bibliography of the pamphlet war on tar-water see Jessop, *A Bibliography of George Berkeley* (1934), pp. 48–51. Also Burton Chance, "Bishop Berkeley and His Use of Tar-Water," *Ann. Med. Hist.*, 3d ser., *4* (1942), 453–67 and frontispiece.

plant physiology and the nature of fire. Alexander Fraser found an "unexpectedness of genius" in the work, at once "curious and profound." [44] *Siris,* with its synthesis of vital powers, fire, light, and divine influence, argues for a cosmic interrelatedness similar to that of Newton's *Opticks,* even if from another point of view. Would it be misleading to observe that Berkeley had "divinized" Newton's ether by associating it with the divine will, and "vitalized" it by substituting universal fire for subtle fluids? In so doing he perpetuated pre-Newtonian mystical speculations. We might cast a glance at the hylarchic principle of Henry More (1614–87), described in 1659 as

> a substance incorporeal, but without sense and animadversion, pervading the whole matter of the universe, and exercising a plastical power therein . . . raising such phenomena in the world, by directing the parts of the matter and their motion, as cannot be resolved into mere mechanical powers.[45]

In a letter to Henry Oldenburg (1615?–77) in 1676 Newton had spoken of a similar plastic principle impressing divinely conceived forms upon condensing ether:

> Various contextures of some certain ethereal spirits or vapors [have been] condensed as it were by precipitation . . . wrought into various forms, at first by the immediate hand of the Creator, and ever since by the power of nature, who by virtue of the command, "Increase and multiply," became a complete imitator of the copies set her by the Protoplast. Thus perhaps may all things be originated from ether.[46]

A. O. Lovejoy's *The Great Chain of Being* (1936) discusses the principle of plenitude involved in the phrase "increase and multiply" as a persistent element in seventeenth-century thought, particularly in Leibniz (1646–1746). The hypothesis of the ether, whether Newton's

44. Editor's preface to *Siris . . . , The Works of George Berkeley . . . , 3* (Oxford: Clarendon Press, 1901), 117.

45. More, *The Immortality of the Soul . . .* (London: J. Flesher for William Morden of Cambridge, 1659), Bk. 3, chap. 12, p. 450.

46. Letter of 25 January 1676,N.S. H. W. Turnbull, ed., *The Correspondence of Isaac Newton, 1* (1959), 414. See Gillispie, *The Edge of Objectivity* (1960), pp. 128–31. Also More, *Isaac Newton* (1934), pp. 610–11. Snow, *Matter and Gravity in Newton's Physical Philosophy* (1926), pp. 104–68, deals with the question of whether Newton's ether was altogether a physical agent. For a system of conjectures midway between those of Newton and Berkeley see Samuel Pike, *Philosophia Sacra: or, the Principles of Natural Philosophy. . . .* (London: for the author, 1753), pp. 79–105; Pike spoke of "A mixture of light and spirit in continual commotion and struggle," p. 92.

or Berkeley's, was associated with notions leading far beyond the limits of science as traditionally accepted. We must not discount the possibility that the ether, in the guise of a scientific hypothesis, permitted some of these notions to survive far into the eighteenth century. In expressions of the idea that electricity was the spirit of life, performing the functions of Berkeley's fire after the manner of Newton's ether, we shall encounter extravagances of speculation which suggest such a survival.

2

Electricity: The Soul of the Universe

i. Electricity and the Idea of Immanence

Seventeenth-century mechanists denied that electricity, by which they meant the attracting and repelling power of rubbed glass or amber, was an "occult" quality; "it may rather be the effect of a material effluvium, issuing from and returning to the electrical body." [1] Newton explained the phenomena in the same way: "Electric effluvia seem to instruct us, that there is something of an ethereal nature condensed in bodies." [2] The effluvia were not part "of the main body of phlegmatic ether" but a different kind of subtle fluid, as the fluids of gravity and magnetism probably were.[3] Sparks from rubbed glass represented "electric vapor . . . put into such an agitation as to emit light." [4] He drew an analogy between the hand rubbing a glass and "ferment in the heart"; each "raises" a subtle fluid and sets it into motion.[5] Newton added nothing to Boyle's physical description of the effluvia but he related them by analogy to vital energy and by coincidence of appearance to light. Speculators were long to satisfy themselves with such loose associations of forces.

1. Boyle, "Experiments and Notes About the Mechanical Origin of Electricity" (1675), p. 345; he cited Digby, Descartes, and Cabaeus.
2. Second paper on light and colors (1675), Cohen, ed., *Newton's Papers and Letters,* p. 180.
3. Ibid., p. 181.
4. Newton, *Opticks* (1952), p. 341. Qu. 8 (1704).
5. Second paper on light and colors, p. 181.

As early as 1708 a writer in the *Philosophical Transactions* remarked that the "large crackling" of sparks seemed "in some degree, to represent thunder and lightning." [6] Francis Hauksbee (d. 1713?) declared that electrical experiments "afford us a sort of representation of the great phenomena of the universe." [7] Stephen Hales supposed that, in states of sufficient vibration, the circulating fluid responsible for muscular motion became "a vibrating electrical virtue [which] can be conveyed and freely act with considerable energy along the surface of animal fibers, and therefore on the nerves." [8] Even though this analogy did not imply identity, the more analogies that were proposed between electricity, ether, and life, the easier it became to speculate on their identity. We may observe this association of ideas in a letter written by Peter Collinson (1694–1768) in 1745:

> The surprising phenomena of the polypus entertained the curious for a year or two but now the virtuosi of Europe are taken up in electrical experiments . . .
>
> Electricity seems to furnish an inexhaustible fund for inquiry, and sure and certain phenomena so various and wonderful that can only arise from causes very general and extensive and such as must have been designed by the almighty Author of nature for the production of very great effects and such as are of very great moment no doubt to the system of the universe—which by degrees may lead to higher truths, in particular to discover the nature of that subtle elastic and ethereal medium, which Sir Isaac Newton queries on at the end of his *Opticks*—had these discoveries happened in that great man's time, his illuminated mind would have applied them to wonderful purposes.[9]

Bryan Robinson sought to explain muscular motion on the supposition that electricity vaporized liquids in the blood to cause "a sudden and strong vibrating motion in the ether in the nerves and membranes of the muscles." [10] Benjamin Martin (1704–82) held that fire, light, and electricity were peculiar vibrating motions in the ether. Electric vibrations were "of a similar nature to lightning," [11] and

6. Wall, "Luminous Qualities of Amber," p. 71.

7. *Physico-Mechanical Experiments on Various Subjects. Containing an Account of Several Surprizing Phenomena Touching Light and Electricity. . . .* (London: R. Brugis for the author, 1709), p. 53.

8. *Statical Essays, 2* (1733), 59; also 93–97 for attempts to generate electric sparks by shaking blood. Hales supposed that "pure serene air" and sulphureous vapors, separated by clouds, exploded to form lightning (p. 288).

9. Letter of 30 March 1745 to Cadwallader Colden: *Colden Papers, 3* (1920), 109–11.

10. *An Appendix to an Essay on Aether* (1746), p. 141.

11. *An Essay on Electricity* (1746), p. 17.

"Sir Isaac Newton has plainly shown that this ethereal matter is the common subject of all kinds of light and fire as well as that of electricity." [12]

The identity of electricity and lightning followed easily upon Newton's synthesis of physical forces. For convenience in referring to assumptions that interrelated subtle fluids caused all physical and vital phenomena, we style this belief "the idea of immanence." To those of a speculative turn of mind, discoveries of electric fish and atmospheric electricity would seem to confirm what had been suspected concerning the importance of electricity in the economy of nature. The apparent realization of the idea of immanence provided a warrant for speculations on electricity and imparted a momentum that carried them remarkably far into the realm of pure surmise.

In 1746 Benjamin Wilson (1721–88) declared "the electric matter and the ether to be universally the same thing." [13] Wilson had read Newton and Robinson, and then "framed an hypothesis which I confirmed every day more and more . . . [and now] have matter enough to prove." [14] Wilson's proof consisted in arguing from similarity of effect to identity of cause:

> Thus have we gone through the most interesting of the electrical experiments, and from the various appearances they afford it appears that the electrical fluid is as universal and powerful an agent at or near the surface of the earth as that fluid which Sir Isaac Newton in his *Opticks* calls ether; that it is as subtle and elastic in its nature as ether is, and as ether does, that it pervades the pores of all bodies whatever that we are conversant with, is dispersed throughout whatever vacuum it is in our power to produce by art, and from the natural phenomena of thunder, lightning, etc. seems to be extended to very great distances in the air.[15]

The most prolific advocate of the idea of immanence was Richard Lovett (1692–1780), lay clerk of Worcester Cathedral. Between 1756

12. Martin, *A Supplement* (1746), p. 34.

13. *An Essay Towards an Explication of the Phaenomena of Electricity, Deduced from the Aether of Sir Isaac Newton,* p. 86.

14. Ibid., p. ix.

15. Wilson and Hoadly, *Observations* (1756), p. 68. Wilson argued that no one could read the general scholium to the second edition of the *Principia* and not agree (p. 71). For other statements of the identity between electricity and ether, see [Thomas Kirkpatrick] "Sir Isaac Newton's Aether Realized," *Monthly Review, 20* (April, 1759), 302. Also William Kenrick, *A Lecture on the Perpetual Motion* (London: for the author, 1771), p. 16.

and 1774 he published five books maintaining the identity of electricity and ether.

> I have not only taken Sir Isaac Newton as my guide, whenever it was consistent with what I was explaining, but have also taken for granted whatever he has delivered on the subject of a universal ether . . . and where experiments could not be fairly produced, have endeavored to account for it by the most rational arguments alone.[16]

The "rational arguments" were analogies and loose inferences from Newton's synthesis of forces. "It is my humble opinion that [electricity] ought to be esteemed as sacred, i.e. delegated by the wise Author of nature to be the principal, if not the only instrument which he has appointed." [17]

> The electrical fluid . . . appears to be a universal agent in the strictest sense, so as to occupy and fill all space, not only all free and open spaces, but the minutest vacuities and interstices or pores of the most compact and solid bodies . . . This grand principle is the primary or first, and indeed, sole cause of all other secondary causes whatsoever.—That it is indefinitely elastic, and acts by pressure or an impelling force; the mechanical cause that we breathe, live, and move; the efficient cause of all motion; the physical cause of gravitation, cohesion, magnetism, the ebbing and flowing of the sea, and of all other the most abstruse phenomena of nature.[18]

We may characterize this statement as a use of the idea of immanence to satisfy ambitions for total explanation. Lovett wrote that before the discovery that electricity and ether were the same it had been necessary to experiment in order to pursue scientific inquiry, "to explain the phenomena of nature . . . by first endeavoring to investigate the laws by which they acted." But now that the universal cause was discovered it was no longer necessary to limit explanation. With contented effrontery Lovett wrote,

16. "To the Reader," *The Subtil Medium Prov'd: or, That Wonderful Power of Nature, So Long Conjectur'd by the Most Ancient and Remarkable Philosophers, Which They Called Sometimes Aether, but Oftener Elementary Fire, Verify'd.* (1756).

17. *The Electrical Philosopher* (1774), p. 19.

18. Ibid., pp. 18–19.

> We now, with much greater readiness, account not only for the laws, but the cause of such phenomena, consequently our reasoning is now a priori. Fire, the grand desideratum, being discovered, we can with equal propriety proceed from the cause to the effect, which is such an advantage as was not attainable before.[19]

One of Lovett's books (1758) bore the title, *Sir Isaac Newton's Aether Realized . . . Whereby the Electeral Fluid, and the Subtil Aetherial Fluid of Philosophers Are, from the Newtonian Principles, Clearly Demonstrated to Be the Same Thing*. Had Newton "lived to see his subtle elastic medium evidently discovered," he would not have "sat for twenty years supinely," but would have derived all natural phenomena by a priori deductions from the subtlety and power of electric matter.[20]

Other speculators sought to explain electricity in terms reminiscent of Berkeley's subtle fire. John Freke (1688–1756) declared that electricity was a species of vital fire with which the air was everywhere impregnated.[21]

> I think it is a great pity that the word electricity should ever have been given to so wonderful a phenomenon, which might properly be considered as the first principle in nature. Perhaps the word vivacity might not have been an improper one.[22]

In 1746 an anonymous writer supposed that the "proximate cause" of electricity was the release of the "matter of heat and light" from ordinary matter: "The changing of bodies into light, and light into bodies, is very conformable to the course of nature." [23] This writer scorned the "skeptical dispositions" of empiricists. "There are some axioms which must ever be granted." Undeniably, electricity was a "very subtle ethereal agent." B. Rackstrow thought "ethereal or electrical fire" was the "vivifying spirit" supporting animal life: [24] "I believe if Sir Isaac Newton was alive to see the experiments we now

19. Ibid., p. 43.

20. *Philosophical Essays* (1766), p. 142.

21. *Essay to Shew the Cause of Electricity* (1746), pp. 3–5.

22. "Appendix" (1746), p. 59.

23. *A Philosophical Enquiry into the Properties of Electricity* (1746), p. 22. Cf. *Opticks* [1704], Qu. 8. The writer identified electricity with both ether and Berkeley's fire.

24. *Miscellaneous Observations* (1748), p. 25.

make in electricity, he would allow of elementary fire himself."[25] Rackstrow pointed out a number of analogies between electrical fire and lightning. Francis Penrose (1718–98) supposed that "flakes of fire" in storms at sea, the "great quantities of fire . . . seen passing swiftly over the hills" during a storm in 1703, the luminescence of the wakes of ships in tropical waters, St. Elmo's fire, and other phenomena proved that air, if violently agitated by fire, became light.[26]

John Wesley (1703–91) wrote in 1759 that Newton and Berkeley shared an identical belief in a universal fire pervading the universe.[27]

> From a thousand experiments it appears that there is a fluid far more subtle than air, which is everywhere diffused through all space, which surrounds the earth and pervades every part of it. And such is the extreme fineness, velocity, and expansiveness of this active principle, that all other matter seems to be only the body, and this the soul of the universe. . . .
>
> It is highly probable this is the general instrument of all the motion in the universe; from this pure fire (which is properly so called) the vulgar culinary fire is kindled. For in truth there is but one kind of fire in nature, which exists in all places and in all bodies. And this is subtle and active enough, not only to be, under the Great Cause, the secondary cause of motion, but to produce and sustain life throughout all nature, as well in animals as in vegetables.[28]

Another aspect of the idea of immanence, although not unrelated to electricity, was the notion of phlogiston, a subtle fluid exhausted in oxidation or released from bodies as the fluid of heat. The powers attributed to this supposed fluid by Priestley and others satisfied chemists and resulted in a virtual suspension of inquiry among those who

25. Ibid., p. 56. See the speech that Lovett put into the mouth of Berkeley, to the effect that his subtle fire had been "discovered": *Philosophical Essays* (1766), pp. 207–08.

26. *A Treatise on Electricity* (1752), p. 6.

27. *The Desideratum* (1760), p. 12. See Emanuel Swedenborg (1689–1722) on ether and electricity related as vital fire: *The Principia; or, the First Principles of Natural Things . . .* [1734], trans. A. Clissold, 2 (London: W. Newbery, 1846), 273–300, 311–29. Also Rev. William Jones, *An Essay on the First Principles* (1762), pp. 25–26 for speculation "if Newton had lived." Also Eusebius Valli, *Experiments on Animal Electricity* (1793), p. 244, for the substitution of electricity for ether. Also Pownall, "On the Ether Suggested by Sir Isaac Newton Compared with the Supposed Newly Discovered Principle of Galvanism" (1804), p.156. William Henly and Tiberius Cavallo thought electricity was fire, but not ether: Cavallo, *A Complete Treatise of Electricity* (1777), p. 117.

28. *Desideratum,* p. 9.

accepted it. Some time after he published *Observations on Different Kinds of Air* in 1772 Priestley came to believe that the fluid, with the aid of a few assumptions, could be made to account for oxidation, combustion, and the reactions of acids. He was led to this extremity of total explanation by speculations on subtle matter and electricity. By 1775 he "venture[d] to speak of [his] hypothesis with a little less diffidence." [29] Priestley had discharged sparks through air over solutions of blue turnsole (litmus), which had turned red. He assumed that air released the acid principle of phlogiston into the water. "From these experiments it pretty clearly follows that the electric matter either is or contains phlogiston; since it does the very same thing that phlogiston does." [30]

In an essay maintaining the identity of light, electricity, and fire, Rev. John Lyon (1734–1817) wrote,

> There is diffused within the substance, and on the surface of all bodies, whether animal, vegetable, or mineral, a certain fluid, which some have called ether, some phlogiston, others the sulphureous principle, the inflammable substance, the electric fluid, or the elementary fire.[31]

The "gravitating fire," as Erasmus Darwin called electricity, was believed to perform all the functions Newton had assigned to the ether. Henry Eeles credited it with causing the reflection and refraction of light.[32] John Freke suggested in 1746 that electricity caused planetary motion; John Lacy advanced a similar suggestion in 1779.[33] In the latter part of the century electricity was usually considered a fluid sui generis—analogous to other forces but less frequently identified with them. Many attributed great and general powers to elec-

29. *Experiments and Observations on Different Kinds of Air, 1* (London: J. Johnson), 177.

30. Ibid., p. 186.

31. *Experiments and Observations* (1780), p. 195. See [Archibald Maclaine], *Monthly Review, 53* (Aug. 1775), 171–72 for a hostile review of Dom Robert Hickman, *Dissertations sur le mécanisme électrique universel de la nature, relativement à la physique, à la métaphysique, à la politique, & à la morale.* Maclaine attacked the elevation of electricity from a curiosity to "become the plastic nature revived, and the great law of universal motion and agency, inanimate, animal, intellectual, moral, and political." Also Anon., *Franklin's Pretensions* (1777). I have not seen Louis Elisabeth, comte de LaVergne de Tressan, *Essai sur le fluide électrique, considéré comme agent universel* (Paris: 1786).

32. Letter of 1760 in *Philosophical Essays* (1771), pp. 159–66.

33. *The Universal System,* pp. iv–v. Also Knight, *An Attempt to Demonstrate, That All Phenomena in Nature May Be Explained* (1748), p. 95. These two works are more truly representative of the general idea of immanence than of its electrical applications alone.

tricity nevertheless. Later speculations will be easier to understand if we bear in mind the powers with which electricity had been associated by virtue of the idea of immanence.

ii. The Leyden Jar

After the invention of the Leyden jar in 1745–46 (see Plate 2) large condensers were used to accumulate the charges of electrostatic generators. On July 14, 1747, Sir William Watson (1715–87) discharged a Leyden jar across the Thames at Westminster. On August 14 a shock was sent through two miles of wire and two miles of the ground: "a distance which, without trial, as they justly observed, was too great to be credited." [1] Abbé Jean-Antoine Nollet (1700–70) displayed a Gallic talent for showmanship by convulsing one hundred and eighty guardsmen in an instant. Turbervill Needham saw a shock administered to the entire Carthusian convent in Paris, a spectacle prepared for Louis XV. Holding iron rods the monks formed a conducting chain said to have been 1.1 miles long. When the battery of Leyden jars was discharged all "gave a sudden spring." [2] Peter Collinson wrote to Benjamin Franklin in 1747 that the power of the Leyden jar was "amazing"; in Germany an ox was knocked down, as was a "lusty strong" Irish bishop in London.[3] Richard Lovett recalled that his interest in electricity dated from the discovery of the Leyden jar, when "a flood of light broke in upon us . . . and effectively convinced us that all matter was not . . . inactive." [4] Priestley wrote that the "astonishing" discovery "gave éclat to electricity. From this time it became the subject of general conversation." [5] Tiberius Cavallo (1749–1809) recalled, "Then, and not till then, the study of electricity became general, surprised every beholder." [6] So far as they go, these remarks accurately express the importance of the Leyden jar. The jar was to become a model for expressing electrical theories, as a fundamental analogue for the action of electricity in nature. Turbervill Needham had written from Paris in 1746 describing the confusion about electricity and its many "unaccountable phenomena." Buffon (1707–88)

1. Priestley, *History of Electricity* (1767), p. 107.
2. N.[eedham], *A Letter from Paris* (1746), p. 7. Also Benjamin Franklin's plans for an electrical "party of pleasure" in America: Cohen, ed., *Franklin's Experiments* (1941), pp. 199–200.
3. Letter of 12 April 1747: *Colden Papers, 3* (1920) 371. Also a similar description by Wesley: *Desideratum*, pp. 21–22.
4. *Electrical Philosopher*, p. 33.
5. *History of Electricity*, p. 84.
6. *Complete Treatise of Electricity*, p. vii.

had told him that the subject was "very far from being yet sufficiently ripe for the establishment of a course of laws, or indeed of any certain one, fixed and determined in all its appearances." [7] Soon thereafter the Leyden jar introduced apparent simplicity into electrical demonstrations. The definable path followed by its discharge and the jar's appearance of being "full" when charged, with an "overflow" of sparks to earthed points, seemed to indicate that a fluid entered the jar.

Between 1750 and 1757 Benjamin Franklin (1706–90) developed his theory of electricity, accounting for its principal appearances and providing an explanation of the Leyden jar. He postulated a fluid of electricity, consisting "of particles extremely mobile, since it can permeate common matter, even the densest metals, with ease and freedom." [8] Franklin believed, with Freke, Rackstrow, and Penrose, that electricity might be a vital fire existing in a quiescent state in bodies before it was "brought forth to action and to view." [9] He postulated a "natural quantity" of electric fluid diffused throughout "this globe of earth and water, with its plants, animals, and buildings." Bodies were charged positively or negatively as they held more or less than the natural quantity. He explained that equal and opposite charges were built up on the two surfaces of the Leyden jar, offsetting the natural equilibrium. The concept of equilibrium encouraged the quantification of electrical theories and their experimental investigation. While we do not find such a volume of speculation on the nature of electricity after Franklin as before, speculation continued as to the mode of electricity's action in nature. What Franklin took from the speculators with his insistence on experiment, he gave back with his dramatic disclosure that clouds acted like Leyden jars, storing the charges released as lightning during electrical storms.

The Leyden jar offered many convincing analogies to lightning discharges. William Watson wrote, "No one could think seriously upon this analogy but since the discovery of the experiment of Leyden." [10] Abbé Nollet wrote,

> We every day see more and more the perfect analogy (to compare great things with small) between the highly electrified glass jar,

7. *Letter from Paris,* p. 6.

8. *Franklin's Experiments* (1941), p. 213 (1750).

9. Ibid., p. 371 (1762). Cf. Lovett, *Philosophical Essays,* pp. v–vi. Priestley, *A Familiar Introduction to the Study of Electricity* (1768) is a clear contemporary summary of the Franklinian theory. Benjamin Wilson repeated the theory in *A Short View of Electricity* (1780).

10. "An Account of a Treatise" (1753), p. 210.

in the experiment of Leyden, and a cloud replete with the matter of thunder.[11]

Franklin did not content himself with listing analogies between lightning and the discharge of Leyden jars. He suggested experiments performed in 1752 by correspondents in France and England and by himself in America. The most exciting of these, and perhaps the earliest, was Franklin's kite experiment.

> At this key the phial may be charged, and from electric fire thus obtained spirits may be kindled and all the other electric experiments be performed which are usually done by the help of a rubbed glass or tube, and thereby the sameness of the electric matter with that of lightning completely demonstrated.[12]

Priestley acclaimed this as a "capital discovery . . . the greatest, perhaps, that has been made in the whole compass of philosophy, since the time of Sir Isaac Newton." [13]

Franklin supposed that electricity might be concentrated by wind and evaporation into highly charged clouds which stood above the earth like the opposing surface of a Leyden jar. Although he grew more doubtful about the notion, he wondered if the luminosity of tropical seas (resulting from large quantities of luminous dinoflagellates) might not be proof that friction among water particles generated the electrostatic charges of the clouds.[14] Franklin invented the lightning rod, providing a degree of protection from electrical storms and seeming to promise their eventual control.[15] The Royal Society

11. Ibid., p. 215. Cohen has discussed Nollet's analogies (1748) in *Franklin's Experiments,* pp. 108–09. For those of Johann Heinrich Winkler (1746), see pp. 107–08. For those of Franklin in 1747 and 1749, see p. 111.

12. *Franklin's Experiments,* p. 266. Letter of Oct. 1752.

13. *History of Electricity,* pp. 179–80.

14. *Franklin's Experiments,* p. 317 (1752). Cohen cites a letter to Franklin from James Bowdoin (1726–90), 12 Nov. 1753, asserting that the light arose from "little animals" (p. 329). For an example of the doubt which long prevailed over this subject see John Canton (1718–72), "Experiments to Prove That the Luminousness of the Sea Arises from the Putrefaction of Mineral Substances," *Phil. Trans., 59* (1769), 446–52. John Ellis, who conveyed an inquiry to Canton from Linnaeus, wrote on 1 Jan. 1770 that "millions of insects" caused the light: *2, Canton MSS,* 84.

15. See B. J. F. Schonland, "The Work of Benjamin Franklin" (1952). Much of interest has been written about opposition to the introduction of lightning rods: Schonland, *The Flight of Thunderbolts* (1950), pp. 1–33. Also Harris, *On the Nature of Thunderstorms* (1843). Also Andrew D. White, *A History of the Warfare of Science with Theology in Christendom, 1* (New York: Appleton, 1896), 364–72. Unnoticed by this literature is a letter certainly influenced by Franklin, which bears one of his pseudonyms—from "Americanus" to the *Gentleman's Mag., 34* (June 1764), 284. The

awarded Franklin the Copley Medal in 1753. The esteem in which he was held in France as a result of his experiments was to be a tangible factor in the diplomacy of the American war for independence (Plate 1).

The study of atmospheric electricity enrolled a celebrated martyr on August 6, 1753, when George Wilhelm Richmann of the Imperial Academy of Sciences at St. Petersburg was killed by a lightning bolt unwisely introduced into his home by experimental apparatus.[16]

> We are come at last to touch the celestial fire, which, if through our ignorance, we make too free with, as it is fabled Prometheus did of old, like him we may be brought too late to repent of our temerity.[17]

The discovery of atmospheric electricity inspired speculation that all kinds of natural phenomena were caused by electricity: "the aurora borealis, australis, all kinds of coruscation, meteors, lightning, thunder, [and] fire-balls." [18]

> May not the void space above the clouds be always occupied with an electricity opposite to that of the earth? And may not thunder, earthquakes, etc. be occasioned by the rushing of the electric fluid between them whenever the redundancy of ether is excessive? Is not the aurora borealis and other electrical meteors, which are remarkably bright and frequent before earthquakes, some evidence of this?
>
> Is not the earth in a constant state of moderate electrification

---

letter deplores the absence of a lightning rod from St. Bride's and its consequent damage on 18 June 1764. The letter as published could not have been written by Franklin, who was in America in June of 1764. The detailed description of lightning rods, the use of the pseudonym, and a tweak at George III under the guise "Divine Majesty" are very suggestive of him. Cf. his letter of 22 Aug. 1766 to the *Public Advertiser:* Vernon W. Crane, ed., *Benjamin Franklin's Letters to the Press 1758–1775* (Univ. of North Carolina Press, 1950), pp. 77–78 and xxx on the pseudonym "Americanus." Cf. Cohen, "Prejudice Against the Introduction of Lightning Rods" (1952), p. 412, for similar sentiments expressed by Franklin in 1762. Perhaps John Fothergill (1712–80) or Watson, with whom Franklin was in correspondence at the time, adapted a letter of Franklin's and sent it to the *Gentleman's Mag.* under his pseudonym.

16. Watson, "Death of Professor Richmann" (1754). Also Priestley, *History of Electricity* (1767), pp. 358–59. Note Dr. William Bewley's sardonic suggestion in the *Monthly Review, 37* (Aug. 1767), 102, that an "honorable place in the electrical martyrology" awaited the first man to fall by "pure, artificial electricity."

17. Anon., "Death of Professor Richmann" (1755), pp. 312–13.

18. Stukeley, "The Philosophy of Earthquakes" (1750), p. 748.

and is not this the cause of vegetation, exhalation, and other the most important [*sic*] processes in nature? These are promoted by increased electrification. And is it not probable that earthquakes, hurricanes, etc. as well as lightning, are the consequence of a too powerful electricity in the earth? [19]

In 1784 Sir Charles Blagden (1748–1820) gave an account "of some late fiery meteors," carefully providing observational data on their direction and duration of appearance. He was unable to "quit this subject, without some reflections about the cause." "The only agent" capable of accounting for the appearances was electricity. He had not a shred of evidence that it caused shooting stars but managed to argue from "the most remarkable analogy." [20] Giovanni Battista Beccaria (1716–81) of the University of Turin proved that the atmosphere was the residuum of small electrical charges in serene weather. He fired skyrockets into fogs, stretched wires along mountains, and flew kites, meticulously entering his observations in a journal. With a long "exploring wire" he discovered a daily cycle of positive electricity, intensifying until noon and declining until sunset.[21] John Read of Knightsbridge kept a similar journal from 1790 to 1792 and believed he had proved the existence of Franklin's "natural quantity" of electricity.[22] The disposition of electricity during thunderstorms "in the earth and atmosphere [is] similar to the experiment of a charged Leyden bottle." [23]

After the London earthquakes of February 18 and March 8, 1749, the *Philosophical Transactions* issued a special supplement of fifty-

19. Priestley, *History of Electricity,* p. 498.

20. "An Account of Some Late Fiery Meteors," p. 222. Also Dr. Ebeneezer Macfait, "Observations on Thunder and Electricity" (1754), p. 216. Also a letter of Alexander Garden (c. 1730–91) to Cadwallader Colden, 14 Jan. 1755, *Colden Papers, 5* (1923), 3, for another example of the Leyden jar analogy. Also Abbé Pierre Bertholon, *De l'électricité des météores, 2* (1787), Pl. 2, 3, 6, for exaggerated representations of electric phenomena in nature. Cavallo, *Complete Treatise of Electricity,* p. 74, added whirlwinds and waterspouts. Charles Stanhope explained in *Principles of Electricity* (1779) how a return stroke might be fatal some distance from the lightning bolt which neutralized the charge in a column of a cloud directly overhead. A sensational example was described by Patrick Brydone in "An Account of a Thunder-Storm in Scotland . . ." *Phil. Trans.,* 77 (1787), 61–70, which Stanhope interpreted with a menacing engraving in "Remarks on Mr. Brydone's Account . . ." ibid., pp. 130–50.

21. *An Essay on the Mild and Slow Electricity Which Prevails in the Atmosphere During Serene Weather* (1776), p. 423–49. Cf. Darwin, "The Economy of Vegetation" (1791), n. to Canto I, line 553; also Bennet, *New Experiments on Electricity* (1789).

22. *Summary View of Spontaneous Electricity* (1793), p. 40.

23. Ibid., p. 42. *Gentleman's Mag.* published over one hundred articles on lightning between 1731 and 1786. S. Ayscough, *General Index to . . . the Gentleman's Magazine, 1* (London: Nichols, Son, and Bentley, 1818), 268–69.

seven articles. The most extravagant of these was William Stukeley's "The Philosophy of Earthquakes." With perfect confidence Stukeley (1687–1765) reasoned from the cycles of earthquakes since a great quake in Asia Minor in 17 A.D. to conjectural cycles of terrestrial electricity.[24] Joseph Priestley constructed an earthquake machine in which, across a board for the earth and water for the sea, a Leyden jar discharge toppled model houses—illustrating by analogy the origin of earthquakes.[25] Priestley's was only one of a number of naive experimental models constructed to support hopeful intuitions of electricity in nature; experiments alone did not guarantee the use of limited explanations. During an eruption of Vesuvius in 1767 the English Resident in Naples, Sir William Hamilton (1730–1803), thought he found evidence that terrestrial electricity caused volcanic action in the "ferilli" or lightnings due to ionization in the smoke column:

> Continual flashes of forked or zig-zag lightning shot from this black column, the thunder of which was heard in the neighborhood of the mountain, but not at Naples; there were no clouds in the sky at this time, except those of smoke issuing from the crater of Vesuvius. I was much pleased with this phenomenon, which I had not seen before in that perfection.[26]

The agreeable eloquence of descriptions of electricity by Wesley, Priestley, Cavallo, and others derived from the fact that these investigators had presided over its development from a parlor curiosity into the greatest force in the cosmos. There had been the objectively true discoveries of Franklin, Stanhope (1753–1816), Read, Beccaria,

24. See the following articles on the debate in Boston in 1755 as to whether the placing of lightning rods had attracted electricity and caused an earthquake felt in the city. Cohen, "Prejudice Against the Introduction of Lightning Rods" (1952), pp. 425–35. Eleanor Tilton, "Lightning Rods and the Earthquake of 1755," *New England Quart., 13* (1940), 85–97. Also Vivenzio, *Istoria e teoria de'tremuoti* (1783). In a letter to Dr. James Lind (1736–1812) 10 July 1784, Tiberius Cavallo praised Vivenzio and recommended earthquake rods "fixed very deep into the ground" to dissipate subterranean charges: *1, Cavallo MSS,* f. 21.

25. *History of Electricity,* pp. 689–90. While he erred in failing to see what kind of evidence, if any, this model gave, Priestley's device pointed toward such later geological models as Sir Humphry Davy's chemical volcano and tar models for glacial flow devised by James David Forbes (1809–68).

26. *Observations on Mount Vesuvius* . . . (1772), pp. 37–38. Matthew Maty (1718–76) wrote Hamilton on 26 July 1770 that his account had "been prodigiously received" at the Royal Society: *Hamilton and Greville Papers, 1* (BM ADD MSS 42,069), f. 81. See his plate of a towering black cloud bristling with electricity in "An account of the late eruption of Mt. Vesuvius . . ." (1795), Pl. 7.

and Bennet (1750–99). Earthquakes, volcanoes, fireballs, the aurora borealis, gravity, whirlwinds, and the phosphorescence of the sea were included as surmise gathered momentum. Perhaps we cannot be certain that these speculations would not have been advanced had electrical discoveries not been preceded by the idea of immanence, or had the Leyden jar not been conceived as a model for electrical action. Still, there were many who drew the obvious conclusions from the general ideas in advancing the individual speculations and their uncritical excesses demonstrate the persistence of ambitions for total explanation.

iii. Electricity and Vital Energy

The dramatic electrical experiments of the 1740s soon aroused speculation on electricity's role in organic life. When it was discovered that a capillary tube would sometimes emit water at a faster rate when electrified (and glow in the dark like an illuminated fountain) Abbé Nollet hastened to apply the discovery to organisms:

> I considered all bodies as assemblages of capillary tubes, filled with a fluid that tends to run through them and often to issue out of them. In consequence of this idea I imagined that the electrical virtue might possibly communicate some motion to the sap of vegetables and also augment the insensible perspiration of animals.[1]

He electrified fruits, plants, and moist sponges; within hours they became "remarkably lighter." He electrified a cat, a pigeon, and a finch for five hours and found them respectively 65–70 grains, 35–38 grains, and 6–7 grains lighter than control specimens chosen for similarity of weight. He then electrified the control specimens and they became lighter.[2] Germinating seeds seemed to advance three days over control specimens when electrified. Stephen Demainbray (1710–82), who was to become George III's tutor in natural science, carried out a similar series of experiments in Edinburgh in 1746 and 1747. He electrified a myrtle tree throughout the month of December 1746, and found that it put forth shoots sooner than an unelectrified tree. He supposed the shoots appeared "by electrification." Demainbray repeated the experiment in 1747:

1. "Part of a Letter" (1748), p. 189.
2. Ibid., p. 190 (7,000 grains = one pound).

On the 17th of January last, Mr. Boutcher favoured me with two myrtles of the greatest equality of growth, vigour, etc. and allowed them each an equal quantity of water.

On electrifying one of them, it hath produced several shoots full three inches.

The other shrub (which I did not electrify) hath not shown any alteration since I first had it.[3]

Similar experiments were performed by G. M. Bose (1710–61) in Wittemberg, Jean Jallabert (1712–68) in Geneva, and Abbé Menon of the College of Beuil at Angers. Erasmus Darwin wrote in 1791,

The influence of electricity in forwarding the germination of plants and their growth seems to be pretty well established. . . .

Mr. d'Ormoy not only found various seeds to vegetate sooner, and to grow taller which were put upon his insulated table and supplied with electricity, but also that silkworms began to spin much sooner which were kept electrified than those of the same hatch which were kept in the same place and manner, except that they were not electrified." [4]

Abbé Pierre Bertholon (1742–1800) maintained that plants inspired a universal electric fluid just as animals respired atmospheric air. The "active, penetrating fluid, analogous to fire" might someday be gathered by an "électro-végéto-mètre" to promote plant growth in gardens.[5] These beliefs rested upon a slight experimental foundation.

3. "Experiments," p. 93.

4. "The Economy of Vegetation," Canto I, line 463 n. The use of control specimens by Nollet, Demainbray, and Abbé d'Ormoy indicates some sophistication in experimental method. It is possible that in some of these cases they observed acceleration of growth actually promoted by electricity. Cf. V. H. Blackman, A. T. Legg, and F. G. Gregory, "The Effect of a Direct Electric Current of Very Low Intensity on the Rate of Growth of the Coleoptile of Barley," *Proc. Roy. Soc. B.*, *95* (1923), 214–28. Also Blackman and Legg, "Pot Culture Experiments With an Electric Charge," *J. Agr. Sci.*, *14* (1924), 268–87. Also A. R. Schrank, "Electronasty and Electrotropism," *Encyclopedia of Plant Physiology*, *17* (Berlin, Göttingen, and Heidelberg: Springer-Verlag, 1959), part 1, 148–63 incl. bibliog. See d'Ormoy, "De l'influence de l'électricité sur la végétation" (1789), pp. 175–76 for the silkworm experiment, or Ritterbush, note in *J. Lepid. Soc.*, *17*, No. 4 (1964).

5. *De l'électricité des végétaux* (1783), pp. 21, 393. Cf. Pl. 1; Pl. 2 depicted the use of electrified water-sprinkling devices. See pp. 6–18 on analogies with animals, 115–28 for conjectural physiology, and 334–43 for illuminated flowers. Also Carl Heinrich Koestlin, *Dissertatio Physica Experimentalis de Effectibus Electricitatis in Quaedam Corpora Organica* . . . (Tübingen: Sigismund, 1775), for the belief that negative electricity retarded plant growth. Also Robertson, *A General View of the Natural History of the Atmosphere*, *2* (1808), 303, for an account of Bertholon's "heavenly manure." Also Bennet, *Experiments on Electricity* (1789), p. 56, for the belief that

An altogether unjustifiable inference was that especially lively organisms had more electric fluid than others. They were repeatedly tested with pith-ball electrometers, but no trace of electricity was ever detected. Several dogged speculators nevertheless contrived to overcome their lack of evidence.

The first organic faculty specifically ascribed to electricity was the movement of the leaves of *Mimosa pudica,* the object of widespread curiosity in the eighteenth century. Matthew Prior (1664–1721) asked in his poem, "Solomon on the Vanity of the World," (1719)

> Whence does it happen, that the plant which well
> We name the sensitive should move and feel?
> Whence know her leaves to answer her command,
> And with quick horror fly the neighbouring hand? [6]

John Freke assumed that "the nature of the sensitive plant is to have more of this [electric] fluid in it than there is in any other plant or thing." He observed the leaves of the plant collapse at a touch like the divergent balls of a charged pith-ball electrometer. He electrified a willow tree and found that its leaves expanded, and that they would droop when touched. He concluded that the sensitive plant functioned in the same way. It lost its electricity at a touch, whereupon the leaves would hang "in a languid state" until more electricity flowed back into the plant.[7] He thought the reactions of the electrified willow tree "as great a proof of the truth of my conjecture as the nature of the thing can admit of." [8] Robert Turner of Worcester placed a feather on the prime conductor of an electrostatic generator; the plumes expanded when charged and drooped when earthed:

> Just so acts the sensitive plant, which, as being endued with this virtue naturally, will, at the approach of a hand or a finger . . . immediately shut up, as having lost all its electric virtue, and will remain so till it has again received a quantity of this virtue sufficient to distend the leaves as before.[9]

"fairy rings" of mushrooms arose from the electric effects of lightning. Erasmus Darwin concurred in Add. Note 13 of "The Economy of Vegetation." Also Bywater, *An Essay on the History, Practice, and Theory of Electricity* (1810), p. 127. Also K. P. Sprengel and deCandolle, *Elements of the Philosophy of Plants* (1821), p. 243.

6. Reginald B. Johnson, ed., *The Poetical Works of Matthew Prior,* 2 (London: Bell and Sons, 1892), 90, lines 86–89.

7. *Essay to Shew the Cause of Electricity,* p. 40.

8. Ibid., p. 41.

9. *Electricology* (1746), p. 26. The prime conductor was a cylindrical conducting surface used to accumulate the charges of electrostatic generators. Cf. Pl. 2, below.

Several Continental speculators convinced themselves that the plant would not contract its leaves if struck with a nonconductor. Simple experiments could have disproved this hypothesis. These speculators were not seeking accuracy; they knew exactly what they wanted to prove.

> Now suppose this plant to contain more electric fire than any other plant or animal. It must of course communicate that fire to any other that touches it. And if so, its leaves and branches must be in a languid state, till they have recovered their natural quantity. To illustrate this, set any small tree in a pot on a cake of [insulating] brimstone. Electrify it and it grows extremely turgid, so as to erect its leaves. But the moment you touch one of them the whole tree droops and hangs all its leaves and branches.[10]

John Freke further supposed that electricity guided pollen to nearby flowers:

> Now if there was not some very attracting influence to guide it, it would but seldom happen, I think, that they could come together by chance. —If therefore you suppose, that both the matrix and the farina abound with more of this fire than is in any other part of the plant or flower, this great wonder is at an end; for, by the natural attraction there might be in each, from the fire supposed to be in them, they would fly together and be closely connected, as they are constantly found to be in their proper season.[11]

Freke considered no experiments with pollen grains and charged surfaces. The conjecture was so pleasing as to require no further support from facts.

In 1762 Linnaeus's daughter observed flashes of light about Indian cress (nasturtium) at dusk, and assumed they were electrical.[12] Haggren observed similar phenomena in marigold, the red lily, French marigold, and tournefoil in 1783. The light appeared as "un

10. [Wesley], *Desideratum,* pp. 30–31. Also Browning, "The Effect of Electricity on Vegetables" (1747), p. 374.

11. *Essay to Shew Cause of Electricity,* pp. 40–41. While he might have meant wind-blown pollen, the agency of insects in pollination was not then generally appreciated.

12. Linnaea, "Om Indianska Krassens Blickande" (1762), pp. 284–87. The explanation for this surprising report lies in the way a colored image at dusk may be fleetingly focused on the macula of the retina, causing a sensation of bright light apparently located on the image of the flower. See Thomas, *Das Elisabeth Linné-Phänomen* (1914).

foible éclair" most easily seen at dusk on yellow petals. The light seemed restricted to the petals and was not observed on the pollen. It might be possible, Haggren observed, for bursting pollen to cause the "electric light." A manuscript note in Joseph Banks's copy of this article reads as follows: "July 14th, 1797. Mr. F. E. [?] Forster saw this phenomenon in the Calendula officinalis, in his Garden at Hackney." [13]

Erasmus Darwin described the electric nasturtium in verse and was led to conjecture,

> It may be a mode of defense, by which it harasses or destroys the night-flying insects which infest it; and probably it may emit the same sparks during the day, which must be then invisible.[14]

Richard Pulteney (1730–1801), who had been a serious student of botany for some forty years, displayed a characteristic susceptibility to notions about electricity in organisms.

> It may be conjectured, that after a perfect elaboration of the juices in the antherae and stigmata, some species of attraction takes place between them, perhaps of the electrical kind, somewhat like this having been manifested in the flashings observable in some flowers in the evenings. . . . And, as in the universe at large, the phenomena of electricity are sensibly manifested to us by particular modifications of the principle occasionally excited, although unquestionably ever active, so, possibly, the same principle may prevail throughout the whole vegetable creation in the process above mentioned, though unobserved hitherto, except in these instances.[15]

Linnaeus wrote in 1767 that leaves inspired "luce electricum" on their upper surfaces and exhaled dew below.[16] He believed that animal bodies consisted of fine capillary tubes sustained by "vestal fire with ethereo-electric flames." [17] The medullary part of an animal body might be supposed to take its vitality from an electrical principle inhaled by the lungs: [18]

13. "Mémoire sur des fleurs donnant des éclairs; traduction de Suédois de M. Haggren, lecteur d'histoire naturelle, par M. Gevalin," [Rozier's] *Observations sur la physique*, . . . , *33* (1788), 111. The Banks copy is at the British Museum (BM: 432, f. 16). Edward Forster (1765–1849), an active member of the Linnaean Society, lived at Hackney.

14. "The Loves of the Plants" (1789), n. to IV, 45.

15. *Historical and Biographical Sketches of the Progress of Botany, 1* (1790), 345–46.

16. *Systema Naturae* . . . , Tom. 2, [*3*] (12th ed. Stockholm: Lars Salvius, 1767), 8.

17. Ibid., Tom. 1, [*1*] (1766), 15; also 16–17.

18. *Genera Morborum* (1763), p. 31.

> The object of respiration, [I] thought, is to extract the electric fluid from the air by the lungs, and thus to transmit it to the medulla, becoming the spiritus animalis, as it were; and hence that the chief office of the lungs is not to accelerate the motion of the blood. Some foreigner has considered this as an hypothesis only, but Linnaeus as an axiom.[19]

The idea of electrical vital processes grew naturally from the subtle fluid physiology, with which David Hartley found electricity to be "connected in various ways."[20] William Stukeley believed that "All life is owing to the subtle, electric fire pervading the macrocosm; & operating in divers proportions."[21]

> Come we to the animal world, we must needs assert, that all motion, voluntary and involuntary, generation, even life itself, all the operations of the vegetable kingdom, and an infinity more of nature's works, are owing to the activity of this electric fire, the very soul of the material world.[22]

Marmaduke Berdoe, a physician at Bath who had been educated in France, published *An Enquiry into the Influence of the Electric Fluid in the Structure and Formation of Animated Beings* in 1771. He speculated about an electrical life force residing near the heart whose influence was transmitted throughout the body by a mucus or Ur-fleisch. He explained the stinging effect of "the species of zoophytes which mariners call the sting-cup" by supposing that the creature acted as a Leyden jar:

> When taken out of the sea [it] is a round transparent globule of limpid mucus, without any perceptible degree of organization, but so full of the electric fluid, that if it meets with bodies less electric than itself, it shocks them very severely.[23]

The bot fly could not attain its reputed speeds of hundreds of miles per hour were it not for "the prodigious quantity of the electric fluid concentrated within and acting upon the mucus of which they are composed."[24] He credited electricity with the development of the embryo and its progress through a succession of primitive forms be-

19. Linnaeus, autobiographical sketch, in Pulteney, *A General View of the Writings of Linnaeus* (2d ed. 1805), p. 553.
20. *Observations on Man, 1,* 28.
21. MS, Letter of 13 May 1752 to Peter Collinson, p. 15.
22. Stukeley, "Philosophy of Earthquakes," p. 748.
23. P. 108.
24. Ibid., p. 157.

fore birth, sexual reproduction, heredity, vegetable growth and, according to the amount of electricity it contained, the station of an animal on the scale of beings.[25]

> It seems then, that the more abundantly this electric influence is shed in animal bodies, they become more perfect, and less susceptible of perishing from the various changes of the elementary fire. Some species of zoophytes and plants have this property nearly in the same degree, hence their analogy; but the class of animals possess a more abundant portion of it, so as to give them a locomotive power. For without those quick irritations of this ether through the structure of animals they would become fixed to the spot from which they received their existence, and like the imperfect zoophyte [e.g. a sponge], obey the moving impulse of any foreign agent which should act against it.[26]

He imagined that electricity was the agent "by which nature passes from the most inconsiderable to the most difficult task of organization." The luminescence of the sea suggested that it was a primordial residuum of electricity giving rise to life:

> Let the curious spectator . . . trace the progress of the semi-formed glow-worm just rising from the ocean, and crawling from its shores with the first principle, the electric fire, still acting on its constituent matter. Semi-marine in its nature, it still shines with that astonishing luster, which is the chief privilege of its original parent [the sea].[27]

Domenico Cotugno (1736–1822), professor of anatomy at Naples, wrote to Giovanni Vivenzio on October 2, 1784, claiming that he had received a severe shock while dissecting a small mouse. "I had no idea that such an animal was electrical; but in this I had the positive proof of experience."[28] Stukeley, Linnaeus, Berdoe, and others did

25. See Chapters 3 and 4, below, for the scale of beings and analogies between plants and animals. Berdoe fully anticipated electrical theories of evolution proposed by Lamarck and Robert Chambers.

26. Berdoe, *Enquiry,* p. 61.

27. Ibid., p. xiii.

28. Cavallo, "An Account of Animal Electricity" (1795), pp. 6–8. See George Gregory's contention that electricity passes through living bodies, but only over the surface of dead ones: *The Economy of Nature Explained, 1* (2d ed. 1798), 360. Réaumur had supposed in 1749 that artificial incubators hastened the hatching of eggs because the subtle fluid of heat agitated the developing embryo. Cf. attempts by Bonnet and Achard to employ electricity for the same purpose: Needham, *A History of Embryology* (2d ed. 1959), p. 203.

not speculate in order to account for otherwise inexplicable experiments. They seized eagerly upon every example within reach, supporting the idea of immanence and satisfying ambitions for total explanation.

iv. Animated Phials

In the mid-eighteenth century much was made of the electric torpedo of the Atlantic and Mediterranean, the electric eel of the Guianas (*Electrophorus electricus*), and the African electric catfish (*Malapterurus electrophorus*). The torpedo had been known since classical times and was investigated by members of the Accademia del Cimento in Florence in the 1670s, but its effects were not identified as electrical. Stefano Lorenzini's *Osservazioni intorno alle torpedini* (1678) was translated into English in 1705. He thought material effluvia caused the "stupefying quality" and traced the effects produced by the fish to "two hooked bodies or muscles."[1] Alfonso Borelli and Claude Perrault (1613–88) had also speculated about material effluvia. Réaumur (1683–1757) wrote in 1714 that the numbing effects were due to a contraction of the torpedo's muscles, dealing a sharp blow which could be transmitted through solid bodies, but not through liquids.[2] A refusal to countenance "pain at a distance" was one common characteristic of the mechanist accounts.[3] The fifth edition of Chamber's *Cyclopaedia* (1743) supposed that Réaumur had "cleared the point" of the torpedo's discharge.[4]

In 1746 Robert Turner concocted an analogy to persuade his readers that the torpedo was electric. His account anticipated by twenty years any other claim that the torpedo was an electric fish and is of great interest because he never even saw a torpedo, simply choosing its effect as a phenomenon likely to yield an electrical interpretation. His notion arose solely from the idea of immanence yet it is hard not to credit him with a brilliant conjecture. He could not find a torpedo to observe, so he made do with a flounder. He placed it on the prime conductor of an electrostatic generator, charged

1. *Curious and Accurate Observations on the Dissections of the Cramp-Fish* (1705), p. 72.

2. "Des effets que produit le poisson appellé en françois torpille, . . . et de la cause dont ils dépendent," p. 357.

3. Lorenzini, *Cramp Fish* (1705), p. 72. For the history of the torpedo up to the time of Réaumur, see Kellaway, "The Part Played by the Electric Fish" (1946). Also Oppian's *Halieuticks* (1722), Bk. 3, lines 201–12 and Bk. 2, lines 109–52.

4. 2, no. 154.

the creature, and obtained shocks by touching it. "It becomes an artificial torpedo and acts in every respect as a natural one does." [5] The "electrified flounder" did indeed cause "something like a numbness." The shocks were transmitted by conducting substances but could not be felt when the fish was touched with nonconductors.

> The parallel might be carried further, but this I hope is sufficient to clear up this surprising phenomenon, and to set the matter of the torpedo's being an electrified fish by nature . . . beyond all further dispute . . .
>
> As the ether is continually pervading the pores of all bodies, it may from their particular textures and juices be retained in them (like as it is in the electrified phial) till some body be brought near them, at which time the virtue will be discharged upon it.[6]

Like Priestley's earthquake machine or Freke's electrified willow, Turner's flounder yielded no real evidence. He was convinced of the truth of his hypothesis by his ability to make the Leyden jar serve as a model for the fish's action. Turner, as other speculators, supposed that the fish was a passive mechanism collecting electricity from "continually pervading" ether and storing it for eventual release. Volta would be the first to suppose that the fish might create the electricity itself.

Experimental demonstrations of the Leyden jar analogy were performed with the electric eel, known to the eighteenth-century naturalists as the "Gymnotus electricus." J. N. S. Allamand (1713–87) wrote to the governor of the Dutch colony at Essequibo asking for an explanation of the "engourdissement douloureux" which the fish was alleged to produce.[7] The governor was Laurens Storm van s'Gravesande (1704–75), nephew of the famous Dutch physicist William Jacob s'Gravesande. He replied in a letter dated November 22, 1754, that the fish "produces the same effect as the electricity, which I felt when I was with you, when holding in the hand a [Leyden] bottle fastened to the electrified tube [prime conductor] by an iron wire." [8] Two of

5. *Electricology,* p. 28.
6. Ibid., p. 28.
7. See Walker, "Animal Electricity Before Galvani" (1937), pp. 87–90, for an account of the discoveries relating to the Gymnotus and torpedo. He cites an observation by Jean Richer in 1671: "Observations astronomiques" (1729), pp. 325–26. Also de LaCondamine, *Relation abrégée d'un voyage* (1745), p. 158.
8. Allamand, "Kort verhaal van de uitwerkzelen" (1758), p. 374. Michel Adanson (1727–1806) remarked an analogy between the Leyden jar "which I have felt many times" and the electric catfish in 1751: "Voyage au Sénégal" (1757), p. 135.

the electric eels had been taken to Barbados, where several people were cured of gout by the shocks. The governor noted that the Gymnotus did not produce sparks as the Leyden jar might, although its shocks resembled electricity in most respects. He promised to send a Gymnotus to Europe; if it retained the properties it had in America, it might be useful in curing gout. Its effects were "probably the same as the electricity, which has sometimes been used with good result in the cure of this disease." [9]

Frans van der Lott performed the definitive experiments on electric eels in 1761. Its effects were similar to those he recalled from electrical experiments he had performed in 1750 at Middleburg in the Netherlands. He wrote that the power of the fish resembled electricity but could not be made to jump a gap. Another difference was the fish's ability to collect electricity under water, while most electrostatic effects required dry weather.[10] When van der Lott touched a Gymnotus in a tub of water with an iron rod it gave him a shock. When he held the rod in a dry cloth he felt no shock until the cloth was moistened (disproving Réaumur's contention that water did not transmit the shock).[11] The shock was transmitted by some, but not all, copper objects. "Good English pewter" carried the shock well, but its effects were diminished if the pewter contained too much lead. With gold the shock was felt right through the body, somewhat less with silver. "With lead, tin, baked earth, bone, sealing wax, [and] beeswax it has no effect; the same with dried wood." "The nearer the head, the stronger the shock; below the throat the shock is tremendous." [12] In the presence of the governor, five persons joined hands. The first touched the submerged eel with a silver-hilted sword. This was a variation of the common experiment wherein those who wished to feel the shock of the Leyden jar joined hands. It was observed that each man felt the shock in the arm leading to the fish and only up to the shoulder; in the arm leading away from the fish to the next man, no one felt the shock.[13]

Another observation was made on behalf of his patron Adriaan

9. Ibid., p. 378. The torpedo releases pulses of 50 amps at 50 to 60 volts; *Malapterurus,* up to 350 volts; and *Electrophorus,* more than 500 volts: Harry Grundfest, "Electric Fishes," *Sci. American, 203* (Oct. 1960), 115–24.

10. This objection was raised a number of times. One wonders why the moisture of thunderclouds was overlooked by those who tried to make this point about the fish.

11. "Kort bericht von der Conger-aal, ofte drilvisch" (1761), p. 89.

12. Ibid., p. 90.

13. Ibid., p. 91.

Spoors, counsel to the governor, who feared to touch the fish yet wished to feel the shock. Van der Lott placed an electric eel in one end of a vessel twenty-six feet long and several feet wide. At a distance of twenty feet from the eel Spoor placed his hand in the water, "not believing that the shock would travel so far." When the fish was disturbed he "admitted having felt the shock in a very considerable way." Even air bubbles rising from the fish displayed electrical effects. An editor's note to this passage remarked that van der Lott's experiments seemed to prove "that this fish is equal in its effects to electricity." [14]

Many curative properties were ascribed to the shocks. Chickens with their claws curled back against the tarsi were dying because they could not walk. They were held to the eel's back. Each "chicken was shocked in such a way that it began to squawk most horribly. When this was repeated a second time the chicken was completely cured." [15] A freshly caught eel was thrown three times against the paralyzed knees of a native. "This poor man, who had been carried from his plantation, went back without any crutches, completely recovered." [16] An eight-year-old negro child with his arms and legs bent almost double was also cured:

> Abraham van Doorn . . . threw the boy daily into a tub of water in which a large eel of the black variety was swimming, by which the boy was very strongly shocked and crept out on his hands and feet, but sometimes if he wasn't capable of that he had to be helped . . . The result was a complete cure of the nervous disease, although his thighs remain somewhat swollen as before.[17]

The same method cured slaves of fevers and headaches.[18]

Pieter van Muschenbroek (1692–1761) inferred from these experiments that the European torpedo was electric as well. He was not sure how a difference of potential could be maintained in a conducting medium, but believed that the effects of the fish and the Leyden jar were similar in most other respects.[19] In a review of Priestley's

14. Ibid., p. 92.
15. Ibid., p. 93.
16. Ibid., pp. 93–94.
17. Ibid., p. 94.
18. Ibid., pp. 94–95. Also see Philippe Fermin, *Description générale, historique, géographique et physique de la Colonie de Surinam . . .* , 2 (Amsterdam: E. van Harrevelt, 1769), 260–63.
19. *Cours de physique experimentale et mathematique* (1762?), trans. Sigaud de la Fond, *1* (Leyden: Samuel and Jean Luchtmanns, 1769,) 393, par. 909.

History of Electricity in 1767, Dr. William Bewley (1726–83) chided him for failing to describe the "remarkable (supposed) electrical phenomenon" which the Dutch had noticed. Bewley refused to credit the accounts and preferred the old theory, so "plausibly," "satisfactorily and circumstantially ascertained by the experiments of Réaumur."[20]

> We shall do no injustice to this piscine electricity, if we venture to rank it among the deliramenta of electricians, in company with Mr. Grey's planetarium, the Italian medicated tubes and globes, and the beatification of Professor Bose.

Thomas Pennant (1726–98) called the torpedo a "cramp ray" in the first edition of *British Zoology* and added that its power had been "prettily explained by M. Réaumur."[21]

The American naturalist Edward Bancroft (1744–1821), who joined the circle of Franklin and Priestley in England after six years in Guiana, described the electrical effects of the Gymnotus in 1769.[22] Bancroft met John Walsh (1725?–95), M.P. for Worcester, who had been elected to the Royal Society in 1770, and probably suggested to him that he try experiments on the European torpedo. Benjamin Franklin conceived several experiments that might demonstrate the analogy with the Leyden jar. He suggested that Walsh and others join hands to feel the shock, and touch the fish with various conductors and nonconductors. Leyden jars might be introduced into the circuit to show "if the back and belly of the fish are at the time of the stroke in different states of electricity."[23]

Walsh pursued the line of inquiry suggested by Franklin at La Rochelle near the Isle of Ré, where torpedoes were commonly caught by commercial fishermen. Walsh arranged five persons in a circle with bowls of water intervening; shocks were transmitted around the entire chain, from each man through the water to the next, further disproving Réaumur's assertion that liquids could not transmit the shock.[24] Walsh triumphantly called the torpedo an "animate phial," and took great pains to establish the analogy between the torpedo and the Leyden jar: "The Leyden phial contains all his magic powers."[25] He addressed his paper on the torpedo to Franklin: "You will please

20. *Monthly Review*, 37 (Dec. 1767), 454.
21. "Cramp Ray" (1769), pp. 67–69.
22. *Natural History of Guiana*, pp. 192–96.
23. Letter of 12 Aug. 1772, in the Library of The American Philosophical Society: Cohen, *Franklin and Newton*, pp. 353–54.
24. Walsh, "Electric Property of the Torpedo" (1773), pp. 467–68.
25. "Of Torpedos Found on the Coast of England" (1774), p. 473.

to acquaint Dr. Bancroft of our having thus satisfied his suspicion concerning the torpedo."[26]

> I rejoice in addressing these communications to you. He, who predicted and showed that electricity wings the formidable bolt of the atmosphere, will hear with attention, that in the deep it speeds an humbler bolt, silent and invisible. He, who analyzed the electrified phial, will hear with pleasure that its laws prevail in animate phials. He, who by reason became an electrician, will hear with reverence of an instinctive electrician, gifted in his birth with a wonderful apparatus, and with the skill to use it.[27]

Walsh did notice one new fact with regard to the torpedo's discharges. He observed that the fish signaled the shocks with its eyes, indicating that they were given at its will. The *Monthly Review* "retracted our former suspicions."[28] Thomas Pennant acknowledged Walsh's discovery by calling the torpedo an "electric ray."[29]

Walsh supposed that the fish bore different charges on its surfaces "in an opposition of a plus and a minus state, like that of a Leyden phial."[30] The analogy between the torpedo and the Leyden jar puzzled some, who wondered why a spark did not show. Walsh explained that the charge would not jump a gap because the electricity was not sufficiently "dense." The "quantity" of electricity which might jump a gap from a small phial could be diffused over several large phials so that the gap could no longer be jumped:

> [The charge] will, thus dilated, yield all the negative phenomena, if I may so call them, of the torpedo; it will not now pass the hundredth part of that inch of air, which in its condensed state it sprung through with ease; it will now refuse the minute intersection in the strip of tinfoil; the spark and its attendant sound, even the attraction or repulsion of light bodies, will now be wanting.[31]

26. "Electric Property of the Torpedo," p. 464.
27. Ibid., pp. 476–77.
28. [Archibald Maclaine], *Monthly Review, 52* (1775), 578; also [William Bewley] ibid., *51* (1774), 219.
29. "Electric Ray" (1776), pp. 79–80. Linnaeus named the eel Gymnotus electricus in 1767, citing van s'Gravesande's letter of 1754. *Systema Naturae . . .*, 13th ed. [same as 12th ed. Stockholm] Tom 1. [*1*] (Vienna: Johann Thomas de Trattner, 1767), 427–28. Raja torpedo (listed among the amphibians, not the fishes) was held to administer a physical blow; Réaumur was cited, p. 395.
30. "Electric Property of Torpedo," p. 472.
31. Ibid., pp. 475–76.

The discovery of electrostatic capacity, or capacitance, was an unexpected result of the effort to save the analogy between the Leyden jar and the torpedo. Henry Cavendish (1731–1810) presumably worked out the relationship for Walsh. In 1776 Cavendish published a paper demonstrating that capacitance varied inversely with the area charged. He suggested, on the basis of John Hunter's dissections of the torpedo and Gymnotus, that a Gymnotus dissipated and weakened its charge over a tissue surface which might be estimated at 3,700 square inches, many times larger than that of a small Leyden jar which could easily "force" a comparable charge across a gap.[32] In 1797 William Nicholson (1753–1815) calculated the area of a torpedo's charged surface as 4,500 square inches, observing that a charge dissipated over so large an area could not be made to jump even a narrow spark gap.[33] This explanation did not convince those who were unwilling to follow Cavendish's reasoning. John Hunter, who had at first concurred with Walsh, "avoided the word electrical" in a paper read to the Royal Society in 1775, "not thinking he was sufficiently warranted by any experiments that had been made to use it." [34] Walsh's critics, Ronayne, Henly, and Canton, denied that the torpedo was truly analogous to the Leyden jar.[35] In 1774 Hugh Williamson succeeded in bridging a gap "the thickness of double-post paper" with the charge of a Gymnotus, but was "not so fortunate as to render the spark generally visible." [36] In 1776 Walsh succeeded in producing from a Gymnotus a "small but vivid spark, plainly visible in a dark room." [37]

To strengthen its analogy with the torpedo Cavendish proved that a Leyden jar might be discharged under water. He devised an artificial torpedo of wood, leather, and wire. A metal plate on the upper surface was connected to the knob of a Leyden jar; another plate below, to the outside surface of the jar. The plates were separated by an insulating body of leather. Cavendish submerged the device and felt shocks by placing one hand in the water as the circuit was

32. "An Account of Some Attempts to Imitate the Effects of the Torpedo by Electricity," p. 220.

33. "Observations on the Electrophore, Tending to Explain the Means by Which the Torpedo and Other Fish Communicate the Electric Shock," pp. 355–59.

34. May 11, 1775. *Journal Book of the Royal Society* [copy], *27*, 249.

35. Walker, "Animal Electricity Before Galvani," pp. 93–95.

36. "Experiments and Observations on the Gymnotus" (1775), p. 100. He could, of course, detect the charge even without a visible spark.

37. Cavallo, "Of the Electric Properties of the Torpedo" (1786), p. 309. He wrote to Dr. James Lind on 3 March 1792 to describe "sparks produced by the electric eel to be so vivid as to illuminate a whole apartment," *2*, *Cavallo MSS*, f. 6.

closed. He even buried the model under wet sand and walked over it in his bare feet, noting with satisfaction that, so far as their transmission through water was concerned, "the effects of this artificial torpedo agree very well with those of the natural one." [38] The Leyden jar, which had served as a model for thunderclouds and earthquakes, was successfully applied to electric fish. Its application by Galvani to all living things was to climax eighteenth-century speculation on electricity in nature.

We might take notice of the ease with which a layman could be misled by the search for electricity in fish. In 1786 a British officer on the way to India reported a new electric fish from the Comoro Islands near Madagascar, and sent a drawing of it to the *Philosophical Transactions.* The fish was a "toby"—*Canthigaster janthinopterus,* Bleeker. James Leonard Brierly Smith, professor of ichthyology at Rhodes University, has handled hundreds of these fish and denies that the toby possesses any electric properties. "There has never been any other report that suggests such a thing."

> These fishes have a curious habit, which could easily give a person not well acquainted with the effects of the electric current, but who had only heard of them, the impression that he was receiving an electric shock. When taken alive from the water these fishes grit their teeth and vibrate their fins in short bursts with such rapidity, as not only to produce a whirring noise, but of such power and high frequency as to cause the same effect as if one were to hold a small vibrator in the hand.[39]

The officer had taken the fish from a tidal pool and dropped it, supposing he had received an electric shock. The incident was character-

38. "Account of Some Attempts," p. 216.

39. Private letter, 10 Oct. 1959. Paterson, "A New Electric Fish" (1786). Also *Gentleman's Mag., 66* (1786), 1007 and plate. Also Cavallo, "Discoveries Concerning Muscular Motion" (1795), pp. 4–5. Also Darwin, "Economy of Vegetation" (1791), n. to I, 202. On the toby, see Smith, "The Fishes of Aldabra, Part X," *Ann. Mag. Nat. Hist.*, ser. 13, *1* (1958), 60 and Pl. 1, Fig. A. Or P. Bleeker, *Atlas ichthyologique des Indes Orientales Nééerlandaises, 5* (Amsterdam: Fréderic Muller, 1865), 80 and Pl. 213, Fig. 7.

For an account of how the charge of electric fish is generated on differentially permeable membranes, see J. A. Colin Nicol, *The Biology of Marine Animals* (London: Pitman & Sons, 1960), pp. 395–400, esp. Fig. 9.18. Also R. T. Cox, "Electric Fish," *Amer. J. Physics, 11* (1943), 13–22. For genus *Torpedo,* synonymy and many excellent references, see Henry G. Bigelow and William C. Schroeder, *Fishes of the Western North Atlantic,* Memoir no. 1 of the Sears Foundation for Marine Research (Yale Univ. 1953), pp. 80–131. Also Broussonet, "Mémoire sur le trembleur" (1782) [*Malapterurus*].

istic of the willingness to ascribe any inexplicable effect to the action of electricity.

v. The Sovereign Remedy

The belief that electric fish had curative powers, shared by van s'Gravesande and van der Lott, was not entirely a speculative indulgence. It seems inevitable that the curative powers ascribed to the subtle fire-substance of Berkeley's tar-water should have been transferred to the electric fluid. Berkeley himself wrote in 1752 that "certain electrical experiments . . . seem not a little to confirm what had before been suggested in *Siris*."[1] While prior speculation on the medicinal value of subtle fluids was incorporated into the notion that electricity had curative powers, the enthusiastic use of electricity in eighteenth-century medicine cannot be accounted for on these grounds alone. Medical knowledge was slight and not able to solve the public health problems attending the growth of cities. Bacteriology, physiology, and organic chemistry had barely begun. The popularity of Berkeley's tar-water and John Hill's herbal preparations testified sadly to the weakness of medical science.[2] We should expect a remedy effective in any way to have been enthusiastically received.

Electric shocks are of undoubted value in the treatment of paralysis induced by hysteria. A Roman physician, Scribonius Largus, used the shocks of torpedoes to cure gout; Galen recommended them for headaches. Job Ludolf (1624–1704) reported that the Abyssinians used the electric catfish to cure malaria:

> The patient is first to be bound hard to a table, after which the fish being applied to his joints, causeth a most cruel pain over all his members; which being done, the fit never returns again.[3]

A genuine cure of group hysteria was effected by electricity at a Lancashire cotton workshop in 1787. A woman threw a fit as the result of a practical joke; as a rumor spread about cotton poisoning, twenty-four persons were affected within four days: "Dr. St. Clare had taken with him a portable electrical machine, and by electric shocks

1. "Further Thoughts on Tar-Water," *A Miscellany, Containing Several Tracts on Various Subjects* (Dublin: George Faulkner, 1752), p. 28.
2. Fulton, "Medicine in the Eighteenth Century" (1950).
3. *A New History of Ethiopia* . . . (London: Samuel Smith, 1682), p. 62. Cf. Peter Kellaway, "The Part Played by the Electric Fish in the Early History of [Medicine]" (1946).

the patients were universally relieved without exception." [4] No doubt a number of the cures reported by practitioners of medical electricity had psychological rather than somatic foundations. And the credulity which attaches to any new remedy probably induced a number of cures.

If we are to assess the influence of general ideas on the electrical theory of medicine we must disregard the claims of quacks. James Graham (1745–94) erected a Temple of Health on the Royal Terrace at Adelphi. His establishment became fashionable and soon featured enormous pyramids and cylinders of electrical apparatus, giant footmen, music, perfume, and a growing pile of discarded crutches.[5] He claimed to have cured over five hundred patients with electricity alone, as did Henry Eeles.[6] The reports of interested persons such as manufacturers of electrical equipment or physicians who advertised their cures need not be taken as examples of speculation. Francis Lowndes claimed to find electricity effective in curing nervous headaches, hysteric complaints, palsy, hemiplegia, tetanus, lockjaw, St. Vitus' dance, tremors, wry neck, epilepsy, gout, sciatica, rheumatism, ophthalmia, chilblains, toothache, amaurosis, opacity of the aqueous humor, hoarseness, sprains and bruises, deafness, ulcers, lumbar abscess, tapeworms, morbid discharges, cutaneous eruptions, amenorrhea, obstruction of urine, constipation, jaundice, induration of the prostate, fistula of the tear ducts, dysphagia, dropsy, hydrocele, and cancer.[7] It is unlikely that he believed his own claims.

We might also discount the cures claimed by John Wesley, who hailed electricity as "the noblest medicine yet known in the world" and a "sovereign remedy." He seems to have been motivated as much by eager benevolence as by general theories of electrical action.

> It seems therefore to be the grand desideratum in physick, from which we may expect relief when all other relief fails, even in many of the most painful and stubborn disorders to which the human frame is liable.[8]

Wesley drew sparks from the eyes of a man who had been blind for twenty-four years. "He told us he could see Sidgate, which he had

4. J. F. C. Hecker, *The Epidemics of the Middle Ages,* trans. B. G. Babington (London: Sydenham Soc., 1844), p. 140. Cf. William Sargant, *The Battle for the Mind: A Physiology of Conversion and Brainwashing* (London: Heinemann, 1957), pp. 124–25.

5. "Description of Dr. Graham's Medical Apparatus" (1780), p. 18.

6. Graham, *Short Extract* (1782?). Also Eeles, *Philosophical Essays* (1771), p. xii.

7. *Observations on Medical Electricity* (1787), pp. vii–viii.

8. *Desideratum,* pp. 72, 70, 43.

not seen for many years before. He could also distinguish objects in the room and was able to walk home without a guide." [9] A plasterer who had fallen from his scaffold lay in pain for several days until he was carried in to be electrified. "After a few minutes he walked home alone, and on Monday next went to work." [10]

It is possible to find accounts untouched by the motives of quacks, interested persons, or enthusiasts. A letter from a doctor at the county hospital in Shrewsbury displayed caution and a sincere desire to discover any useful properties electricity might possess. His patient was a woman whose arm had been paralyzed for years. After five weeks of shocks, "She had got some little strength in her arm, could open and shut her fingers, and lift it half-way to her head." The woman regarded the treatment as too painful and chose "to remain paralytic [rather] than undergo such operations any more." "I wish indeed she had tried it a while longer, as it bid fair to do her service; and this was the only case, which gave us reasonable hopes from its use." [11]

Tiberius Cavallo appraised the subject of medical electricity with commendable detachment:

> The power of electricity is neither that admirable panacea, as it was considered by some fanatical and interested persons, nor so useless an application as others have asserted; but that, when properly managed, it is an harmless remedy, which sometimes relieves, and often perfectly cures various disorders, some of which could not be removed by the utmost endeavors of physicians and surgeons.[12]

9. Ibid., p. 44.

10. Ibid., pp. 46–47.

11. Hart, "Part of a Letter" (1754), pp. 786–87. He also cited a case wherein shocks increased the degree of paralysis. Also see Watson, *Observations Upon the Effects of Electricity Applied to a Tetanus of Four Months' Continuance* (1764).

12. *An Essay on the Theory and Practice of Medical Electricity* (1780), p. 3. In 1774 the Royal Humane Society was founded to encourage the practice of artificial respiration and other means of recovering persons supposedly dead. Electricity was used with apparent sucess several times. Cf. Giovanni Aldini, *General Views on the Application of Galvanism to Medical Purposes; Principally in Cases of Suspended Animation* (1819), pp. 47–48. Also *Reports of the Society Instituted in the Year 1774, for the Recovery of Persons . . .* (London: Humane Soc., 1776), pp. 75–78. Also [Tilloch?], "Galvanic Experiments Made by Mr. Carpue on the Body of Michael Carney" (1804). In the preface to *Frankenstein* Mrs. Shelley observed that the central event of the story had been supposed not unlikely by Erasmus Darwin and other physiological writers. In December of 1960 in Birkenhead an unfortunate and deluded man removed the body of his mother from her grave and attempted revival with house current: *Guardian* (22 Dec. 1960), p. 5.

If this were a complete account of eighteenth-century medical electricity we should conclude that its use in medicine might have developed independently of the idea of immanence. Even if this proved to be so the reported cures would have given weight to the more general idea that electricity was of prime importance in forwarding life. In the absence of a sound appreciation of physiology or any understanding of the actual effects of electric shocks it was only too easy to yield to a sense of mystery and ascribe too much significance to dramatic cures. We may, however, detect the influence of certain familiar beliefs about the importance of electricity and its mode of action.

One of the advantages of the subtle spirit of evergreens, according to Berkeley, was its ability to penetrate animal bodies. Before the introduction of hypodermic injections in 1853 medicines were introduced into the bloodstream through wounds or blisters.[13] Electricity, by direct analogy to Berkeley's belief, was thought capable of vaporizing medicines and carrying them deep into the body. Giovanni Pivati of Venice, Verati of Bologna, Bianchi of Turin, and Winkler of Leipzig all tried to develop such a technique. Henry Baker wrote in 1748,

> A gentleman [in Rome] covered the internal surface of a cylinder of glass . . . with a purgative medicine; and . . . a man, electrified therewith, found on the spot the same effects as if he had swallowed the medicine.[14]

John Hill, Baker's persistent critic, was moved to vigorous reproach by this assertion.[15]

Electricity itself, even without vaporized medicines, was supposed to have curative properties. Francis Penrose described it as a "volatile and penetrating" medicine, of greatest use where "nerves are obstructed." [16] Its effectiveness was supposed to consist "either in producing a tremulous, vibratory motion throughout the solids and fluids in general, and thereby accelerating the circulation of the

13. Samuel J. Zakon, "The Centenary of the Hypodermic Syringe 1853–1953," *A.M.A. Arch. Dermatol. and Syphilol., 68* (1953), 591. See Alexander Wood, "New Method of Treating Neuralgia by Direct Application of Opiates to the Painful Parts," *Edinburgh Med. and Surg. J., 82* (1855), 275–81. This date may be incorrect for the first medical use of injected fluids. John Hunter, who performed many experimental injections, may have tried them in treating his patients. "Lectures on the Principles of Surgery" [1786–87], *Works, 1* (1835), 347–50.

14. "Medical Experiments of Electricity," p. 274.

15. *The Inspector* (1753), no. 70, *1*, 296–300; no. 72, *1*, 306–09.

16. *Treatise on Electricity,* p. 40.

latter; or . . . by actually pervading the finer channels of the fluids, by which means those passages may be opened."[17] Tiberius Cavallo supposed that sparks from a small Leyden jar were effective in cases of paralysis and hysteria. Infected areas and swellings might be treated by drawing sparks from them. Delicate persons and mild disorders were best treated with point discharges—gentle baths in the electric fluid. John Birch (1745?–1815), who founded an electrical department at St. Thomas' Hospital, employed shocks as "deobstruents," sparks as stimulants, and point discharges as sedatives[18] (Plate 2). On one occasion, when Birch had cured a swollen knee, "Mr. Else [a surgeon] was so satisfied of the effects of electricity as to declare he would never amputate another limb for this complaint till [electricity] had been properly tried."[19]

Behind many claims for the effectiveness of electricity in curing disease lay the belief that it was the cause of life. This notion had always been part of the idea of immanence. John Freke, who had identified the "vis vitae" with electricity, supposed that cures might be effected by replacing lost electrical energy.

> From thence may proceed the danger of lodging old people with young children; who, by long experience have been found to draw from young children their natural strength; the old people having in them a less proportion of this fire than the young ones seem to have.[20]

Richard Lovett argued in 1756 that as electricity and ether are "the very same identical substance, . . . then electrical ether must necessarily, as you observe, discover a natural tendency to heal."[21] Marmaduke Berdoe attributed the continued growth of hair and nails after death to residual electricity remaining in the body.[22] Eusebius Valli tried to starve dogs in some experiments. They lived five or six weeks longer than he had expected. He supposed they had been receiving electricity from the atmosphere.[23] George Adams (1750–95) argued that as electricity "probably forms the most important part of our constitution," disease might be explained as a

17. Becket, *An Essay on Electricity* (1773), p. 54.
18. "Letter on Medical Electricity" (1792), p. 509.
19. Ibid., p. 536. An exhibit of eighteenth-century electrical equipment, prepared by Margaret Rowbottom, may be seen at the Wellcome Historical Medical Museum.
20. *Essay to Shew the Cause,* pp. 43–44.
21. *Subtil Medium Prov'd,* p. 73.
22. *Enquiry* (1771), pp. 77–80.
23. *Experiments on Animal Electricity,* pp. 109–10.

disturbance in electrical equilibrium which the physician must restore.[24] "We may find that what we call sensibility of nerves and many other diseases . . . are owing to the body's being possessed of too large or too small a quantity of this subtle fluid." [25] John Read supposed that a lack of electricity led to weak health and found evidence for his belief in the fact that certain winds injurious to crops were found lacking in electricity: "And I conjecture that the energy of the brain and nerves depends on a proper intensity of electricity; as the act of respiring healthfully depends on a proper intensity of air." [26]

In medicine, as in all other subjects of electrical speculation, true discoveries and inherited ideas combined to produce enthusiastic and uncritical statements. The electricity of lightning, the electric fish, and some of the cures effected by electricity were true discoveries. The electricity of earthquakes, the electric toby, or the argument that electricity must be a curative agent were inferences from these discoveries. We contend that such inferences were encouraged by the idea of immanence and ambitions for total explanation, and would have been less frequent had it not been for the influence of inherited speculation. The Leyden jar analogy, avidly applied to the torpedo, the jellyfish, the sensitive plant, earthquakes, and thunderstorms, reflected the idea of universal subtle fluids collected by organisms and satisfied desires for comprehensive explanations wherein a single device might explain a great diversity of phenomena. The inheritance of a harmonious system of forces was made to order for electrical speculation. This relationship between the speculative framework and the newly discovered cosmic force accounts for the extravagance of belief described in this chapter.

vi. The Climax of Speculation

Before discussing the influence of the Leyden jar analogy on the work of Galvani, we must note the approach to the subject of nervous action in the eighteenth century. According to the modern chemical mediation theory, a nerve impulse is a change of electric potential conveyed from synapse to synapse by the release of acetylcholine, a substance that induces a charge when oxidized. From the twenty-

24. *An Essay on Electricity* (2d ed. 1785), p. 312.
25. Ibid., p. 316.
26. *Summary View of Spontaneous Electricity* (1793), p. 69; also 24.

fourth query of the *Opticks* [1717], through the writings of physiologists who assumed the importance of subtle fluids, had grown the idea that nerves acted on the muscles by means of subtle fluids whose energies caused muscular contraction. Jan Swammerdam (1637–80) had demonstrated the dependence of muscular contraction on nervous stimulation in the seventeenth century.[1] Beccaria observed in 1753 that naked muscular fibers might be stimulated into contraction by direct electrical stimulation.[2] He did not attempt to stimulate the muscle by applying an electric shock to the nerve.

Albrecht von Haller's investigation of the nervous influence was a remarkable exercise in limited explanation. He was well acquainted with the agency of electricity as a stimulus to muscular contraction. He also believed in an invisible electric fluid, but he did not identify the nervous fluid with electricity:

> It is necessary to avoid placing too much emphasis on this superior irritating force of electricity, and not to conclude from it that electricity is the cause of the movement that it excites. . . . The superior exciting force of electricity consists only in the facility with which the spark penetrates the muscle.
>
> At this time one would be unable to decide on the identity of the electrical material and animal spirits.[3]

Haller (1708–77) thought the nervous fluid might be "more gross than fire, or ether, or electric or magnetic matter, since it can be contained in channels." [4]

In an essay on the role of speculation in medicine in 1772, James Maclurg offered a comment on the relationship between nervous action and electricity, which recalled Newton's use of limited explanation:

> For though it is by no means demonstrated that the nervous power is the same with that which occasions the phenomena of electricity; and the laws of this power are so independent on [sic] any such hypothesis as the laws of gravitation are upon the

1. *Biblia Naturae . . .* , 2 (Leyden: Isaak Severinus, Boudewyn van der Aa, and Pieter van der Aa, 1738), Pl. 49, Fig. 5–9.
2. *A Treatise Upon Artificial Electricity* (1776), p. 270.
3. *Mémoires sur les parties sensibles et irritables* (1760), quoted by Hoff: "Galvani and the Pre-Galvanian Electrophysiologists" (1936), pp. 163–67.
4. *Elementa Physiologiae* (1762), quoted by Sir Michael Foster, in *Lectures on the History of Physiology . . .* (Cambridge Univ. Press, 1901), p. 297.

> hypothesis of an ethereal fluid; yet the contemplation of such active and subtle energies has enlarged our views and drawn the attention from those principles of mechanics and chemistry, to which it was before too slavishly attached.[5]

John Hunter remarked, upon dissecting the torpedo, that its electrical organs were "liberally supplied with nerves."[6] Alexander Monro (1735–1817), who succeeded his father of the same name as professor of anatomy and surgery at Edinburgh, refused to infer from Hunter's observation that the nervous fluid was electric:

> All we can conclude from these facts is, that the nerves [in the fish] enable this machinery to perform its proper office of collecting the electrical fluid, but without directly furnishing to it any of that fluid.[7]

The most "just" and "becoming" conclusion was the assumption of "a living principle pervading the universe," acting in accordance with the divine will.[8] Most eighteenth-century physiologists believed that the source of vital power lay outside the organism. Many believed it was a physical entity: the subtle fluid of ether, heat, or electricity. A minority, including Berkeley, Whytt, and Monro, believed the external force was immaterial and associated with the divine will. Haller, an empiricist, had spoken of muscular contraction as a function of irritability and presupposed nothing whatsoever about its cause or place of origin.

Felix Fontana (1730–1805), professor of natural philosophy at Pisa and Rome, was led to consider nervous action by his investigation of the action of poisons. We may trace a weakening of the empirical attitude in his remarks on the cause of muscular motion. He, too, explained the phenomena by an external principle and was strongly tempted to identify it with electricity:

> En un mot, non seulement le mécanisme du mouvement musculaire est inconnu, mais nous ne pouvons même rien imaginer

5. *Experiments,* p. lxii. For Haller's empiricism see Howard Mumford Jones, "Albrecht von Haller and English Philosophy," *Publications, Modern Language Assn., 40* (1925), 103–27. Also Hochdoerfer, "The Conflict Between the Religious and Scientific Views of Albrecht von Haller (1708–1777)" (1932), pp. 78–80. He had a word, "Wirklichkeitssinn," for what Freud called "the reality principle" which lies at the heart of empiricism.

6. "Observations on the Torpedo" (1773), pp. 486–87; also his Croonian Lecture of 1776, in *Works, 4* (1837), 212.

7. *Observations on the Structure and Functions of the Nervous System* (1783), p. 75.

8. Ibid., p. 104.

qui puisse l'expliquer, et il semble que nous soyons forcés de recourir à quelque autre principe, si non à l'électricité ordinaire, à quelque chose du moins de fort analogue à l'électricité. Le Gymnote électrique et la torpille rendent la chose, si non probable, du moins possible, et l'on pourroit croire que ce principe suit les loix les plus ordinaires de l'électricité. Il peut être encore plus modifié dans le nerfs qu'il ne l'est dans la torpille, et dans les Gymnotes. Les nerfs seraient les organes destinés à conduire ce fluide, et peut être encore à l'exciter; mais tout reste encore à faire. Il faut auparavant s'assurer par des expériences certaines, si le principe électrique a vraiment lieu dans les muscles qui se contractent. Il faut fixer les lois qu'observe ce fluide dans le corps animal, et après tout cela il restera encore à savoir ce qui excite, et comment s'excite en nous ce principe. Que de choses incertaines pour la postérité.[9]

Luigi Galvani of Bologna (1737–98) succumbed altogether to the Leyden jar analogy and to ambitions for total explanation. He believed he had discovered the manner in which electricity caused muscular motion. He was misled by the desire to show analogies with the Leyden jar and to make of it a universal model for living things. Galvani's first experiments showed that a preparation of the muscles and nerves of a dead frog would undergo muscular contraction when exposed to atmospheric electricity. He did not suppose that the electricity acted as a stimulus to the nerves but that it insinuated itself into the animal, was collected there and suddenly discharged when the muscle overflowed, as in the Leyden jar.[10] Indeed, Galvani completely neglected the work of Haller and Monro and did not regard the electricity as a stimulus to nervous action. He moved his preparations indoors, where the contractions were not repeated unless he used an electrical machine or rubbed the brass hook connected to the spinal cord against an iron plate.[11] He was led to believe that the rubbing somehow released a residual electricity which had been collected within the animal. The torpedo and the Gymnotus would be mere special cases wherein the quantity of electricity was conspicuous beside this discovery that all animals stored electricity on their tissues.

Walsh had demonstrated the torpedo's analogy with the Leyden jar by forming a circle of experimenters which could be broken to inter-

9. *Traite sur le vénin de la vipere,* 2 (1781), 244–45.

10. De Viribus Electricitatis in Motu Musculari Commentarius [1791], trans. Foley, p. 59.

11. Ibid., pp. 59–60.

rupt the current. Galvani supposed that the muscles were organic Leyden jars discharged by the nerves. With "some metallic instrument" he rubbed the top of a silver box, permitting the feet of the lower half of a frog which he held by its nerves to touch the box. This disposition looked to Galvani like the conducting circuit in the usual Leyden jar experiments. When he closed the apparent circuit by rubbing the metal and silver (causing a change of potential to excite the nerve), "I saw the frog react in violent contractions." [12] He then tried extending the circuit to include another person. He invited his friend Rialpus to touch the metal plate while he held the nerve as before. When the friends touched hands the change of potential arising from the metallic probe and the silver plate was conveyed through Galvani's body to the hook attached to the nerve, which he held. Again it seemed to Galvani that the frog possessed a charge like a Leyden jar because it moved every time they touched hands. This experiment was judged "sufficient to indicate an electrical flowing-out, as it were, of the nerve fluid through the human chain." [13]

Galvani displayed an uncanny ability to extract results favorable to the Leyden jar analogy from falsely conceived experiments. Recalling Cavendish's submerged leads from a Leyden jar, he sought to show that the frog current also flowed under water. He submerged the preparation, unwittingly aiding the ionization of the metals, and observed the usual contractions. When he submerged the preparation in a nonconducting fluid (oil, which also stopped the electrochemical reaction) the contractions could not be excited. His principal proof of any influence remotely resembling electricity was the way an apparent circuit might be broken and remade. To Galvani these experiments seemed directly analogous to those performed on the torpedo by Walsh, although he did not say so. Galvani never even skirted the discovery that the metals had produced electricity because he was oblivious to the agency of nerves as conductors of stimuli and looked upon them merely as strands of conducting substance which permitted an "electrical flowing-out" from the muscles. He was not even able to offer a clear hypothesis, retreating into ambiguity as to the direction in which the current flowed. The "special characteristic" of animal electricity, he observed, "seems to be that it courses strongly from the muscles to the nerves, or rather from the latter to the former." [14] He

12. Ibid., p. 60.

13. Ibid., p. 60. Galvani omitted any mention of Rialpus' probe, but it may be seen in Pl. 4, Fig. 17, which illustrates the experiment.

14. Ibid., p. 75.

openly stated that the resemblance between his experiments and "the electric circuit which is completed in a Leyden jar strengthened this suspicion and our surprise."[15] By the argument of "causes and phenomena" (i.e. that similar effects imply similar causes) he was led to identify "our contractions" with "the streaming out of electric fluid from a Leyden jar."[16] It was the idea of immanence, through its model, the Leyden jar, which led Galvani into this singular error.

Eusebius Valli listed many analogies between genuine electrical effects and Galvani's observations: "We cannot avoid being convinced that the shock of the torpedo, and the shock and spark of the Gymnotus, are effects of the same cause which produces the movements in the frogs, fowls, cats, dogs, and horses made the subject of experiment."[17] George Cadogan Morgan (1754–98) wrote in 1794, "The knowledge of the electric fluid is leading us rapidly into a full investigation of the nervous influence and of all the mysteries connected with the sensations and motions of animal life." We might take note of his proviso: "provided Signor Galvani be right."[18] Alessandro Volta (1745–1827) remained under the spell of the idea until November of 1792.

> Le fluide électrique tend sans cesse à passer d'une partie à l'autre du corps organique vivant, et même des membres tronqués, tant qu'il y subsiste un reste de vitalité; qu'il tend à passer des nerfs aux muscles, ou vice versa, et que les mouvement musculaires sont dûs à une semblable transfusion, plus ou moins rapide. En vérité il semble qu'on ne peut rien opposer à cela, ni à la façon dont M. Galvani explique la chose, par une espèce de décharge semblable à celle de la bouteille de Leyde.[19]

Galvani had carried his experiments only far enough to support an ambiguously stated analogy with the Leyden jar. He was the first to see muscular contractions attend the electrical stimulation of the nerves, but this discovery had to be quarried out from his erroneous conclusions and viewed in different terms.

In 1793 Alexander Monro used Humboldt's technique of destroying nervous sensibility with opium, and found that contractions could not

15. Ibid., p. 60.
16. Ibid., p. 74.
17. *Experiments on Animal Electricity,* p. 113.
18. *Lectures on Electricity, I,* xxiii–iv.
19. "Account of Some Discoveries Made by Mr. Galvani of Bologna" (1793), pp. 18–19 (13 Sept. 1792). Note the words "vice versa," repeating the ambiguity of Galvani's formulation.

then be excited with the metals. He produced contractions by direct stimulation of the nerve, without bringing the muscle into the circuit at all. He disproved Galvani's belief that the current was directed from the brain by showing that contractions could not be excited if the stimulus were applied above the sixth vertebra of the spinal column. "This [electric] fluid acts merely as a stimulus to the nervous fluid or energy." Galvani's "experiments have merely shown a new mode of exciting the nervous fluid or energy, without throwing any further or direct light on the nature of this [nervous] fluid." [20] "I have, I apprehend, refuted the theory of Doctors Galvani, Valli, and others, which supposes that the nerve is electrified plus and the muscle minus, resembling the Leyden phial." [21]

Richard Fowler (1765–1863) also traced the stimulus to the two metals and denied that the animals possessed any electricity themselves.[22] William Charles Wells 1757–1817), later well known for his *Essay on Dew* (1814), reported that bodies charged by friction could excite the contractions if applied to the nerves. "The theory advanced by M. Galvani . . . is erroneous [and] . . . the influence, whatever its nature may be, by which [the motions] are excited, does not exist in a disengaged state in the muscles and nerves previously to the application of metals." [23]

In 1794 Galvani published an anonymous tract describing how a single metal or the mere connection of the muscle with a severed nerve might excite the contractions.[24] Monro, Cavallo, and Fowler agreed that, particularly in the period immediately following the frog's death, one metal and sometimes an injury of the nerve alone would be sufficient to excite contractions.[25] Swammerdam had noticed such contractions, which depend on injury currents, in the seventeenth century. In the years following Galvani's discovery it became increasingly clear that, with this exception, two metals were required and that the electricity arose from reactions between them.

20. *Experiments on the Nervous System,* pp. 42–43.

21. Ibid., p. 41.

22. *Experiments and Observations* (1793).

23. "Observations on the Influence, Which Incites the Muscles of Animals to Contract in Mr. Galvani's Experiments" (1795), p. 248.

24. *Dell'uso e dell'attività dell'arco conduttore nelle contrazione dei muscoli.* Cf. Fulton and Cushing, "A Bibliographical Study of the Galvani and Aldini Writings" (1936), pp. 260–61.

25. Cavallo, "An Account of the Discoveries Concerning Muscular Motion" (1795). pp. 25–26. Fowler, *Experiments and Observations,* pp. 66–67. Also "Galvanism," *Supplement to the Third Edition of the Encyclopaedia Britannica, 1* (Edinburgh: Thomas Bonar, 1801), 677–78, n.B, and 679 n.C. Galvani was not discredited because two metals were invariably necessary to excite contractions, but because his Leyden jar analogy was untrue.

Galvani's most convinced disciples resisted the suggestion that two metals gave rise to electricity which stimulated the nerve. Eusebius Valli separated a nerve from the leg of a horse, cut it, coated one end of the nerve with tinfoil, and ostensibly restored the circuit with a silver shilling piece. "Now Dr. Valli thinks, that Mr. Volta's hypothesis is ridiculous, because, says he, how is it possible for a single shilling to contain electricity sufficient to move the leg of a horse?"[26] In 1793 John Robison (1739–1805) constructed the first multiple voltaic cell from "a number of pieces of zinc made of the size of a shilling, and made . . . up into a rouleau, with as many shillings."[27] Before Volta's more famous electrochemical cells were devised, Robison proved that electrochemical electricity could be used to excite the contractions.

Notions about electrostatic animal electricity lost their appeal to most natural scientists once Volta found his range and trained the full force of his arguments upon the Leyden jar model. He was able to measure the current created by the contact of two small metal bodies such as those used by Galvani by generating it to a detectable size with his "doubler" of electricity. He held that the multiple voltaic cell was a much better model for the electric organs of the torpedo and the electric eel than the Leyden jar. He insisted that organic tissues "cannot be compared either to the electrophore ["doubler"] or condenser, or to the Leyden flask, or any machine excitable by friction or by any other means capable of electrifying insulating bodies, which before my discovery were always believed to be the only ones originally electric."[28]

It had become apparent that the Leyden jar was inapplicable to muscular motion. Galvani's statement that animals accumulated electricity in their own tissues was shown to be without foundation. After the discovery of electrochemical electricity it became necessary to believe that the electricity of the torpedo and Gymnotus must be created by the animals themselves by processes of which no one had a clear understanding, for the electricity did not resemble that collected from external sources.[29] Yet another disclosure, and a more fundamental one, was that electricity might arise from perfectly ordinary chemical reactions. At a stroke electricity was dethroned from its position as

26. Letter of 23 Nov. 1792 from Tiberius Cavallo to Dr. James Lind: *2, Cavallo MSS,* ff. 25–26.

27. Letter of 28 May 1793 to Richard Fowler; quoted by Fowler, *Experiments and Observations* (1793), p. 173. Cf. Cavallo, "Account of Discoveries," p. 53.

28. "On the Electricity Excited by the Mere Contact of Conducting Substances of Different Kinds" (1800), trans. Tilloch, p. 311.

29. Ibid., p. 290.

master of the cosmos and shown to be a property of common matter. This difference of emphasis, as much as the specific errors disclosed in the theory of life, destroyed the idea of immanence upon which speculations on electricity had been based. If any further proof were required for the influence of antecedent speculation about subtle fluids on notions of electricity in organic life, it could be found in the suddenness with which these notions were discredited once the special nature of electricity was disproved. Converts had been won to the belief that electricity was the prime agent in organic nature right up to the threshold of a more critical scientific age. The dissolution of this belief was swift and dramatic, and very much a revelation of the speculative foundations on which it had rested.

3

Clearing the Mysteries of Vegetation

A review of speculation on the role of electricity in the economy of nature has shown how broad speculative concepts came to supplant corpuscles and matter in motion in attempts to explain the vital principle that enlivens plants and animals. Of equal importance for our study are eighteenth-century suppositions about the relationship between the two great kingdoms of nature.

Modern science observes between plants and animals a wide evolutionary divergence and differences in the chemistry of organic process. The central nervous system of animals makes possible more elaborate responses to the environment, attaining in higher forms a capacity for discriminative reaction. We may note that these distinctions are blurred among lower forms, but this does not compromise our understanding that the plant kingdom differs significantly from animal groups.

Many eighteenth-century writers chose to dwell upon the similarities between plants and animals until the recital of analogies became an end in itself. Drawing analogies throughout nature gave rise to the satisfaction of creating comprehensive explanations, rewarding those who overlooked the differences between plants and animals in order to dwell upon their similarities.

Francis Bacon (1561–1626) emphasized the differences between plants and animals. The heart of animals was a "cell or seat" of life which plants lacked, and their body heat led Bacon to suppose that they "hold more of flame than the spirits of plants do." Bacon called these "radical differences" and enumerated eight secondary differences such as the immobility of plants, nutrition by roots rather than mouths, random growth of limbs, internal simplicity, and their lack of "sense" and voluntary motion.[1] He quoted with approval the classical phrase, "Homo est planta inversa," to denote a radical difference in morphological orientation: "for the root in plants is as the head in living creatures." Plutarch had written, "Plato, Anaxagoras, and Democritus believe plants to be terrestrial animals," foraging in the soil for food.[2] Although he believed that plants could choose one kind of food over another in the soil, through a power of selective nutrition, Plato did not doubt that plants were fundamentally different from animals.[3]

Aristotle was less inclined than Plato to arrange the creatures of nature into separate ideal categories. For Aristotle the differentiation of plants and animals was contingent upon differences in function. He did not insist upon an essential distinction and wrote of zoophytes or apparently intermediate marine forms. We may attribute this difference in emphasis to a conceptual scheme giving rise to an emphasis upon the similarity of plants to animals: the notion of a hierarchical chain of being or ladder of organic forms.

Under the concept of a chain of being, organisms were arranged not only according to their structural complexity but by their complexity of function as well. The ascent of the scale was marked by "a graduated differentiation in amount of vitality and capacity for motion."[4] The parallelism between organization and capacity immensely increased the persuasiveness of the idea and made it the greatest synthetic scheme in pre-Darwinian biology.

Within this all-embracing system the different capacities of plants and animals could be accounted for by their relative standing on the scale of forms:

> Next after lifeless things in the upward scale comes the plant, and of plants one will differ from another as to its amount of apparent

1. *Sylva Sylvarum* (1626), Cent. VII, cap. 607, pp. 154–55.

2. "Quaestiones Naturales," in J. F. Dübner, ed., *Plutarch Scripta Moralia*, 2 (Paris: Institut de France, 1877), 1114.

3. F. M. Cornford, *Plato's Cosmology: The Timaeus of Plato Translated with a Running Commentary* (2d ed. London: Routledge and Kegan Paul, 1948), pp. 302–03. Also Charles Daremberg, ed., *Fragments du commentaire de Galien sur le Timée de Platon* . . . (Paris: Victor Masson, and Leipzig: Michelsen, 1848), p. 13.

4. *Historia Animalium* viii. 1.

> vitality; and, in a word, the whole genus of plants, whilst it is devoid of life as compared with an animal, is endowed with life as compared with other corporeal entities.[5]

Theophrastus used the scale of beings to support analogies between plants and animals. Both had veins of sorts; plant fibers resembled muscular tissue; both conserved moisture and warmth and were sometimes adapted for aquatic life. One might better understand plants by drawing analogies to nearby forms on the scale of beings, "for instance, an analogy presented by animals."

> In that case we must of course make the closest resemblances and the most perfectly developed examples our standard; and, finally, the ways in which the parts of plants are affected must be compared to the corresponding effects in the case of animals, so far as one can in any given case find an analogy for comparison.[6]

We shall find that analogies with mineral formations were also maintained. It was also possible, of course, to entertain the idea of a scale of beings without drawing analogies at all.[7]

There was a reciprocal relationship between analogies and imputed proximity of place on the scale. The discovery of certain properties which plants shared with animals lent encouragement to the belief that they were close to animals upon the scale of beings and that consequently any number of analogies might pertain between them. We refer to the belief that plentiful analogies between plants and other forms derived from their proximity on the scale of beings as "the idea of botanical analogy."

Aristotle and the pseudo-Aristotelian Nicholas of Damascus in the first century B.C. used the scale of functions as an argument for the proposition that plants could not practice selective nutrition or perform any other exercise of sensory powers.

> In plants we do not find sensation nor any organ of sensation, nor any semblance of it, nor any definite form or capacity to pursue objects, nor movement nor means of approach to any object perceived, nor any token whereby we may judge that they

5. Ibid.
6. *De Plantis* I. i. 5.
7. We use the phrase "chain of being" to denote the complex of ideas described by Lovejoy in *The Great Chain of Being: A Study in the History of an Idea* (1936), and "scale of beings" to refer to the sequence of organisms independent of any other beliefs. "Scale of functions" refers to the parallel series of capacities.

> possess sense-perception corresponding to the tokens by which we know that they receive nutriment and grow.[8]

We shall have occasion to refer to the belief that plant function must in all cases be lower than that of any animal as "the orthodoxy of graded function." Many eighteenth-century writers were to argue on precisely these grounds against the attribution of sexuality to plants.

A more poetic frame of reference for analogies, which became unfashionable before the time of the seventeenth-century mechanists, was the concept of microcosm and macrocosm.[9] William Gilbert (1540–1603) dwelt upon an analogy between magnetic polarity in the earth and a polarity in vegetable grafts.[10] He also noted an analogy between the way minerals "take from universal nature the forms by which they are perfected" and the mode of growth of animal embryos "in the warm uterine cavity." [11] It was perhaps this broad principle of analogy that motivated Bishop Thomas Sprat's complacent advice to members of the Royal Society in 1667. His words might equally well be applied to the relation of organisms on the scale of beings:

> There is nothing of all the works of nature so inconsiderable, so remote, or so fully known, but by being made to reflect on other things, it will at once enlighten them and show itself the clearer. Such is the dependence amongst all the orders of creatures, the inanimate, the sensitive, the rational, the natural, the artificial; that the apprehension of one of them is a good step towards the understanding of the rest. And this is the highest pitch of humane reason, to follow all the links of this chain till all their secrets are open to our minds, and their works advanced, or imitated

8. [Nicholas Damascenus] *De Plantis* i. l; also i. 2. Also Aristotle *De Somno et Vigilia* i. The debate about selective nutrition was reflected in Jethro Tull's criticisms of John Woodward in 1731.

9. See John Clarke, *Physical Science in the Time of Nero: Being a Translation of the Quaestiones Naturales of Seneca . . .* (London: Macmillan, 1910), p. 126. Also Phineas Fletcher's didactic poem, "The Purple Island; or, the Isle of Man" (1633). Also Thomas Robinson, *The Anatomy of the Earth* (London: J. Newton, 1694). Also Agnes Arber, "Analogy in the History of Science" (1948), p. 227.

10. Jane M. Oppenheimer, "William Gilbert: Plant Grafting and the Grand Analogy" (1953), pp. 165–76. If a magnet AD was cut into AB and CD, it would not realign AB-DC or DC-AB; a plant branch AD cut into AB and CD would not resume growth if grafted AB-DC or DC-AB onto the original stock. Also see Athanasius Kircher, "De Magnetica Facultate Plantarum," *Magnes sive de Arte Magnetica Opus Tripartitum . . .* (Rome: Ludovico Grignano, 1641), pp. 698–750.

11. Gilbert, *De Magnete, Magnetisque Corporibus, et de Magno Magnete Tellure; Physiologa Nova, Plurimis & Argumentis, & Experimentis Demonstrata* (London: Peter Short, 1600), p. 20.

> by our hands. This is truly to command the world, to rank all the varieties and degrees of things so orderly one upon one another that standing on top of them we may perfectly behold all that are below and . . . look the nearer into heaven.[12]

This exhortation alerts us to the possibility that a man who referred to such analogies would generally do so only to confirm what he already supposed he knew. And that was likely to be the existence of a scale of beings, the framework within which analogies between plants and animal forms were almost always employed.

i. Analogy As an Aid to Understanding

The pursuit of cabinet specimens, a mark of the amateur in more recent times, was the chief activity of eighteenth-century naturalists. Newtonianism, whether in its experimental or speculative aspect, barely figured in the thought of naturalists before 1730. A statement of their program is instead to be found in Francis Bacon's injunction to study nature fact by fact. Part of the vision of his *New Atlantis* [1624] was an army of collectors ranging the earth, seeking specimens for the cabinet of a central repository where they would be sorted and arranged. Bacon did not yield to desires for total explanation. He believed that naturalists should forsake conjecture until, as would invariably happen, correct generalizations emerged from the assembled data:

> In our method axioms are raised up in gradual succession and step by step, so that we do not arrive at the most general statement until the last stage, and these general statements come out, not notional, but well-defined and such as nature may acknowledge to be really well-known to her, and which shall cleave to the very marrow of things.[1]

12. *The History of the Royal-Society* (1667), p. 110.

1. "Distributio Operis" [1620], Thomas W. Moffett, ed., *Selections from the Works of Lord Bacon . . .* (Dublin Univ. Press, 1847), p. 119. The lives of modern biologists frequently recapitulate the history of biology by beginning with collecting. See Marston Bates, *The Nature of Natural History* (London: Chapman and Hart, 1951) for a description of modern naturalists. A typical collector's letter about bringing "the whole creation into the light of day" is quoted by Colin Matheson in "Thomas Pennant and the Morris Brothers," *Annals of Sci., 10* (1954), 262. The letter was written by William Morris to Richard Morris, 23 Aug. 1755. On Baconian induction, see F. H. Anderson, *The Philosophy of Francis Bacon* (Univ. of Chicago Press, 1948), pp. 181–89, 290–91. Also Kentish, *Method of Studying Natural History* (1787).

The eighteenth-century naturalists accepted this principle for a time and set out on what Bacon called "this labor, investigation, and personal survey of the world." [2] The goal was a giant catalogue setting forth all knowledge of nature in a rational system. The naturalists went about collecting as though systematic knowledge would arise by itself, a naive method which could not satisfy their desires for explanation. Cabinets filled with concretions or petrefactions did not give rise to sound knowledge. Worse still, collecting specimens was very easy. A world-wide collection apparatus, without central direction or a system of priorities, began to pour forth torrents of shells, fossils, insects, dried plants, and other curiosities. In 1710 Addison's *Tatler* essays described Sir Nicholas Gimcrack, the standard comic figure of a virtuoso. In 1728 Swift published *Gulliver's Travels* with its satire on witless scientific investigation. Pope's *New Dunciad* (1742) criticized the latter-day virtuosi as "A tribe, with weeds and shells fantastic crown'd" who saw "Nature in some partial narrow shape." [3]

Even though John Hill (1716–75), a copious writer on natural history, had disgraced himself with hasty and ill-considered compilations, he was able to attack the *Philosophical Transactions* for many trivial and foolish articles.[4] The *Monthly Review's* writer thought Hill's attack would "be attended with considerable advantages to the public" by making the Royal Society more cautious about "what kind of papers they admit into their future publications." [5] The attack drew the attention of the London literary world and led almost at once to changes of policy announced by the Royal Society in March of 1752. Responsibility for the *Philosophical Transactions* was taken from the secretary and assumed by the society as a whole. A committee was appointed to "reconsider" and "select" the papers "most proper for publication." [6] George Reuben Potter recognized how much Hill's attack helped to expose the weaknesses of eighteenth-

2. Ibid., p. 123. Cf. Priestley's plan for scientific societies to achieve "the complete discovery of the face of the earth," *History of Electricity* (1767), p. xvii.

3. Lines 398, 455. James Jurin, in the dedication to the *Philosophical Transactions*, no. 392 (1726), made it out to be Newton's opinion that natural history was at best a "humble handmaid to philosophy."

4. Hill, *A Review of the Works of the Royal Society* (1751). His remarks in the *Monthly Review* show common sense and a lively desire to make natural history a useful study: *2* (1749–50), 134–38, 466–75; *3* (1750), 196–212, 437–44; *4* (1750), 52–62, 111–22, and 241–55. On the uselessness of collections, see *The Inspector, 1* (1753), no. 68, 287–88; *2*, no. 132, 235–38.

5. [John Ward], *Monthly Review, 4* (1751), 280. Also Clark Emery, "'Sir' John Hill versus the Royal Society" (1942).

6. "Advertisement," *Phil. Trans., 47* (1751–52).

century natural history.[7] Hill was unable to suggest a way to meet the real problem, which was how to direct the activities of naturalists toward experiment and the development of sound theory.

Goldsmith (1728–74) attacked "the labors of some of the learned" in 1762:

> They view all nature bit by bit; now the proboscis, now the antennae, now the pinnae of—a flea. . . . Thus they proceed, laborious in trifles, constant in experiment, without one single abstraction, by which alone knowledge may be properly said to increase; till at last their ideas, ever employed upon minute things, contract to the size of the diminutive object and a single mite shall fill their whole mind's capacity.[8]

Frustrated in experiment by the subtle fluid physiology, the naturalists were to turn, as Goldsmith suggested, to an abstract idea of nature. The principle of limited explanation was not to be observed; sound observational techniques were not developed.

One indication of the weakness of physiology was the revival of the empiric–dogmatic dispute in medicine which set practical and theoretical doctors at odds over questions of method. The attacks of the empiricists were aimed at the excesses of seventeenth-century mechanism. The dogmatics accused the others of undue contempt for reason.[9] Robert Whytt wrote in 1760,

7. Potter, "John Hill's *Review*" (1943). Hill had some promise as a naturalist. His *Essays in Natural History* (1752) were detailed and original studies of insects, after the manner of Réaumur. *The Construction of Timber* (1770) was an admirable monograph. *A General Natural History, 2* (1751) contained the first description of the Linnaean sexual system published in England, with a comment that its author "deserves infinite praise" (page v). The next description, sometimes referred to as the first, was an anonymous review of the *Species Plantarum* (1753) by William Watson in *Gentleman's Mag., 24* (Dec. 1754), 555–58. Hill's system of vegetable generation, published in 1758, was wildly conjectural, but innocent of speculation about subtle fluids. Hill was extremely vain and produced enormous compilations for profit. See attacks by [William Rose], *Monthly Review, 23* (1760), 407; John Ellis, in Smith, ed., *Correspondence of Linnaeus, 1* (1821), 232; and Peter Ascanius, *2,* 483; also *1,* 83, 254; and *2,* 5–7, 46. Also Sir John Hawkins, *The Life of Samuel Johnson* (London: J. Buckland, J. Rivington and Sons, 1787), p. 213. Also Isaac D'Israeli "Sir John Hill" (1814). Also T. G. Hill, "Sir John Hill 1716–1775" (1913). Also W. T. Stearn, "The Reception of the *Species Plantarum* in England . . . ," in Linnaeus, *Species Plantarum . . . , 1* (London: Ray Society, 1957), 79–80.

8. *The Citizen of the World . . .* (London: J. Newbery, 1762), p. 103. John Baker, *Abraham Trembley* (1952), cited this and a similar passage from Goldsmith's essay, "On the Instability of Worldly Grandeur," *The Bee . . .* (London: J. Wilkie, 1759), p. 185.

9. See Thomas Percival, "The Empiric, or Man of Experience, Being Arguments against the Use of Theory and Reasoning in Physick," *Essays Medical and Experi-*

> I find that many of the London physicians begin to despise reasoning too much, and to trust to what they call experience and observation alone: but it is most certain that in medicine as well as philosophy, neither reasoning nor experiment will do alone; *sed alterum alterius auxilio egit.*[10]

Uncertainties in physiology also greatly retarded the development of scientific agriculture.[11] John Dove observed that agricultural philosophers could neither kill weeds nor enrich the land: "A philosophy deficient in both these ought to be hissed out of the world." [12] Adam Dickson's *Treatise of Agriculture* (1762) castigated writers who held that water alone, or air, or oils, or salt, or earth was the undoubted food of plants.[13] Lord Kames (1696–1782) laid the blame on the backward state of plant physiology:

> After much labor is bestowed on botany, and many volumes composed on that subject, it appears very little advanced above infancy; no other science has made so slow a progress . . . [The study of botany] has been mostly confined to giving names to plants, and to distribute them into classes, not by distinguishing their powers and properties, but by certain visible marks. This is an excellent preparation for composing a dictionary, but it leaves us in the dark as to the higher parts of the science.[14]

We might think of the naturalists as becoming ever more eager to narrow the gap between the primitive state of physiology and the bland certainty of so much moral and social dogma or the enviable science of celestial mechanics. Writers in medicine, physiology, agriculture, and the manifold pursuits of natural history consciously

---

mental (London: J. Johnson, 1767), pp. 9–42; also "The Dogmatic, or Rationalist; Being Arguments for the use of Theory and Reasoning in Physick," ibid., pp. 45–58. Also John Aikin, "The Hill of Science, a Vision," *Miscellaneous Pieces in Prose* (Belfast: James Magee, 1774); Maclurg, *Experiments* (1772), pp. xix–xxi; John Gregory, *Lectures* [1770], pp. 103–50; John Abernethy, *The Hunterian Oration for the Year 1819*, pp. 8–10.

10. Letter of 20 Oct. 1760 to Cadwallader Colden: *Colden Papers, 5* (1923), 356. Also James Gregory, *Memorial to the Managers of the Royal Infirmary* (2d ed. Edinburgh: William Creech, 1803), pp. 408–27.

11. On contemporary theories see Arthur Young, *A Course of Experimental Agriculture . . . 1* (London: J. Dodsley, 1770), vii–xvi.

12. *Strictures on Agriculture* (1770), p. 16.

13. Pp. 5–46.

14. Henry Home, Lord Kames, *The Gentleman Farmer* (1776), pp. 393–94; also "Of the Laws of Motion" [1754], p. 3.

sought a comprehensive abstract scheme which would assure investigators that they were proceeding toward lasting explanations. Empirical restraints took little hold among naturalists in Britain who wanted, in Hartley's words, to solve the cypher of nature.[15]

The resort to analogies to escape the implications of empiricism began in theology. In *Christianity Not Mysterious* (1696) John Toland (1670–1722) interpreted Lockeian empiricism as meaning that theologians should renounce uncertain claims to knowledge of the divine. The deists generally advocated a retreat to a sound core of empirically verifiable statements. Toland defined evidence as "the exact conformity of our ideas or thoughts with their objects, or the things we think upon." [16] Peter Browne (1663?–1735), then a fellow of Trinity College, Dublin, agreed with Toland that human faculties were too weak to supply clear and adequate ideas of the spiritual world; he skirted this empirical barrier by asserting that such ideas might be attained "by analogy with the things of this world." [17]

> The constant method of arguing in divine things is this: from the things whereof we have clear and distinct ideas we infer the existence of those things whereof we have no idea at all.[18]

William King (1650–1729), Archbishop of Dublin, preached a sermon at the opening of the Irish parliament in 1709 in which he asserted that man might reason by analogy from human to divine attributes.

> This analogical evidence of God's nature and attributes is all of which we are capable at present, and we must either be contented to know him thus or sit down with an entire ignorance and neglect of God.[19]

Browne, who had become bishop of Cork and Ross in 1710, returned to the question at great length in 1728. "For want of any simple and

15. Continental naturalists seem to have succumbed less readily to the appeal of abstract ideas. One thinks of the voluminous works of Réaumur, the careful observations of Trembley, or the meticulous dissections by Lyonnet (1707?–89).

16. P. 16. Toland said at one point that he knew plants performed complicated processes "analogous to those of animals" even though he did not "clearly comprehend how all these operations are performed" (p. 76). John Harris, speaking from the very pulpit of orthodoxy in his 1698 Boyle Lectures, admitted the fallibility of notions of gravity, light, sound, magnetism, and electricity and then stated that God was just as difficult to know: *The Atheistical Objections* (1698), lecture 2.

17. *Answering Letter* (1697), p. 45.

18. Ibid., p. 50. Cf. Locke, *An Essay Concerning Humane Understanding* (London: Thomas Basset, 1690), Bk. 2, chap. 23, p. 140.

19. King, *Divine Predestination and Fore-Knowledg* (1709), p. 14.

direct idea of [God], we . . . form to ourselves an indirect, analogous, and very complex idea of him." [20] Browne defined analogy as the association of ideas of things by comparison of their attributes, "as when the idea of a tree and that of a horse are compared in respect of their vegetative and animal life, in respect of the circulation of the sap in one and of the blood and spirits in the other." [21] Despite the "mediate" and "improper" process of reasoning from ideas rather than the things themselves, Browne stated, "Analogy is founded in the very nature of things on both sides of the comparison." [22] This uncritical inference depended upon the belief that God had created man in his own image and the world according to a uniform divine plan. We have already seen how analogies were drawn from one kind of energy to another within the harmonious universe of interrelated forces. The resort to such analogies constituted a clear challenge to the epistemological caution of empiricists.[23]

Richard Barton drew analogies between the tendency of matter toward a common center and the attraction of human love by the divine being; "universal ether or elemental fire" caused the first, and the Holy Ghost caused the second. One section of Barton's *Analogy of Divine Wisdom* (1750) bore the title, "The analogy of divine wisdom, between material light, and spiritual knowledge. Between the general law of spiritual beings, and the general law of material things. Between the divine influence upon spirit by grace, and the divine influence upon matter by attraction. Between the universal aether and the infinite divine spirit."

20. *Procedure, Extent, and Limits of Human Understanding,* p. 82.

21. Ibid., p. 181.

22. Ibid., p. 82.

23. Seventeenth-century writers generally regarded analogies as indications of the underlying mechanical regularity of the world but not as substitutes for sound mechanical knowledge. See *Pseudodoxia Epidemica . . .* in Charles Sayle, ed., *The Works of Sir Thomas Browne, 1* (Edinburgh: John Grant, 1912), 291. Cf. Aquinas's belief that the attributes of God were present, but imperfect, in man: *Summa Theologica . . . ,* trans. Fathers of the English Dominican Province (London: R. and T. Washbourne, 1911), part 1, no. 1, p. 180 (Qu. 14, art. i). Berkeley took a similar position in *Alciphron* (1732). Browne regarded Berkeley's grudging concessions as an invitation to lengthy argument in *Things Divine and Supernatural Conceived by Analogy with Things Natural and Human* (1733), pp. 374–554. Joseph Butler, *The Analogy of Religion* (1736), held that imperfections in sense knowledge and revelation required the use of analogical knowledge, "a confirmation of all facts to which it can be applied as it is the only proof of most" (p. 288). He dismissed the analogy between plants and animals (p. 28). Also Soame Jenyns, "On the Analogy between things Material and Intellectual" (1782), p. 75. Also Thomas Reid, *Essays on the Intellectual Powers of Man* (Edinburgh: John Bell, and G., G., and J. Robinson of London, 1785), pp. 52–56; also *An Inquiry into the Human Mind, on the Principles of Common Sense* (Edinburgh: A. Kincaid and J. Bell, and A. Millar of London, 1764), pp. 502–24.

Arguments from analogy conformed to the bias of eighteenth-century thinkers, which was their faith in nature's simple plan. The universe displayed consistent uniformities because its creator had acted upon a preconceived plan which might someday be fully cleared. Newton commended the process of reasoning from like effects to like causes and did so in the case of his celebrated inference, from the flammability of substances with high refractive indices, that water and diamond must have combustible ingredients.[24] Speculative Newtonian natural philosophers were wont to infer identity of cause from the slightest similarity of property or relation. The synthesis of physical forces encouraged analogies because, as John Stuart Mill put it, an analogy "is put out of court" if the attributes of the compared entities are not related.[25] It was in this way that the Leyden jar and life forms were compared within the general framework of the idea of immanence.

The notion of a scale of being provided the basis for analogies between plants and animals. David Hartley suggested that such analogies might be arrived at by the association of ideas:

> The whole superstructure of ideas and associations observable in human life may, by proceeding upwards according to analysis and downwards according to synthesis, be built upon as small a foundation as we please.[26]

Hartley represented the scale of beings as a series of entities A, B, C, D . . . M, N, O, P . . . to which functions or properties might be applied by analogical argument.

> Animals are also analogous to vegetables in many things, and vegetables to minerals; so that there seems to be a perfect thread of analogy continued from the most perfect animal to the most imperfect mineral, even till we come to elementary bodies themselves.[27]

"Contiguous species" such as A and B were "more analogous" than A and C, although "this deficiency may be supplied in some things" from adjacent species, "so that M can have no part, property, etc. but what shall have something quite analogous to it in some species, near or remote, above it or below it, and even in several species." "For

24. *Opticks* [1704], p. 274.
25. *A System of Logic, 2* (1843), 98.
26. *Observations on Man, 1* (1749), 71.
27. Ibid., *1,* 294. Cf. Mill (n. 25 above, p. 104) on "adjacent cases." Also [John Gregory], *A Comparative View of the State and Faculties of Man with Those of the Animal World* (London: J. Dodsley, 1765), pp. 8–9.

the more anyone looks into the external natural world, the more analogies, general or particular, perfect or imperfect, will he find everywhere." [28]

Turbervill Needham correctly observed that "mere analogy" founded upon a few facts could provide hypotheses only. He criticized the many observers who had used analogies to escape "painful uncertainty."

> The most obvious and easy method is to class, if it admits it, and reduce [a novel appearance] to some other known phenomena; possibly we are as yet no nearer the physical cause, because that of both is unknown. We have still, however, the satisfaction to have diminished the surprise it gives, by taking from its singularity, and rest in some measure contented with this little deceit.[29]

Many naturalists were to seek contentment of the kind Needham described. The use of analogies to escape empirical restraints plainly appears in an argument offered by George Bell in 1777: plants contained "parts of such a degree of minuteness that they elude the human sight. The nature of these must therefore be inferred from analogy only." [30] Tiberius Cavallo observed in 1777 that a discovery in any part of nature quickly became general because a similarity in natural phenomena depended upon interrelated causes. "From the simplest to the most complicated of her objects an analogy is observable." [31]

Thomas Percival wrote in 1785 that "very slight evidence" sometimes "amounts to credibility" because "uncertainty is painful to the understanding." "This every philosopher experiences in his researches into nature." [32] A great many speculators who did not care to apply the principle of limited explanation would instead rely upon analogy, perpetuating the ambitions for total explanation which were so conspicuous a part of seventeenth-century mechanism.

The naturalists whom Pope had criticized for triviality and pettiness adopted as a metaphysical warrant the scale of beings which he had described in *An Essay on Man* (1733–34). We may detect Pope's influence in the "poetical effusion" written by Benjamin Stillingfleet (1702–

28. Ibid., *1*, 295.

29. "A Summary of Some Late Observations" (1748) pp. [617–18].

30. *De Physiologia Plantarum* [1777], p. 395.

31. *A Complete Treatise of Electricity* (1777), p. 75. Also Jean Senebier, "De l'analogie," in *L'art observer,* 2 (Geneva: Cl. Philibert and Bart. Chirol, 1775), 82–96.

32. "Speculations on the Perceptive Power of Vegetables," pp. 114–15. Cf. Gregory, *Lectures* [1770], pp. 119–20.

71) as the conclusion to his translation of Linnaeus's essay on the economy of nature:

> each moss,
> Each shell, each crawling insect holds a rank
> Important in the plan of Him, who fram'd
> This scale of beings; holds a rank, which lost
> Wou'd break the chain, and leave behind a gap
> Which nature's self would rue.[33]

Richard Bradley, who described the scale of beings with enthusiasm in 1721, used it to support analogies among minerals, plants, and animals. In 1764 Charles Bonnet (1720–93) published his *Contemplation de la nature* in which the scale of beings was set forth in elaborate completeness (see Table 1). Bonnet blamed the sterility of natural history on the absence of speculations such as his own:

> Ban the art of conjecture from physical science altogether and you reduce it to pure observation, and what good are observations if we derive nothing of consequence from them? We ceaselessly amass materials but never build anything with them. We endlessly confound means and ends.[34]

Bonnet had despaired of physical explanations for organisms when he became aware of the intricacy of organisms revealed in Pierre Lyonet's *Traité anatomique de la chenille* (1762). Relying upon the apparent closeness of plants and animals in the march of nature he instead drew plentiful analogies between them in his long essay, "Parallel of Plants and Animals." The ancients had styled plants "vegetating animals" but it might equally well be said that animals were "vagabond plants." [35]

> Neither from the relative simplicity of organization, nor the manner of birth, nutrition, growth, or multiplying (by buds), nor the faculty of locomotion may one obtain sufficient characters to distinguish the two orders of beings.[36]

33. Stillingfleet, *Miscellaneous Tracts* [1759], p. 128. Also W. Coxe, ed., *Literary Life and Select Works of Benjamin Stillingfleet . . .* , 2 (London: Longman, Hurst, Rees, Orme, and Brown, 1811), part 1, 45–47. Cf. Pope, *An Essay on Man*, Epistle 1 (1733), lines 207–46.

34. *1*, xi.

35. Ibid., *2*, 51. For "Parallel of Plants and Animals" see pp. 1–77. Also Bazin (d. 1754), *Les plantes et leur analogie avec les insectes* (1741).

36. Ibid., *1*, 38.

Bonnet proposed the rhetorical question, "Is it then in vain that we search for a proper character to distinguish the vegetable from the animal?" [37]

The purpose of our narrative will be to portray the historical background of such extreme statements about the analogy between plants and animals. The general trends herein described did much to promote reliance upon botanical analogy in resolving significant new problems that confronted eighteenth-century naturalists.

ii. Plant Nutrition and Growth 1660–1727

Robert Hooke (1635–1703) wrote in 1665 that plants grew by "mechanical principles" similar to those which produced stalactites, "without the least show or probability of any other seminal formatrix." [1] His hopes for scientific explanation were brave indeed.

> As far as I have been able to look into the nature of this primary of life and vegetation, I cannot find the least probable argument to persuade me there is any other concurrent cause than such as is purely mechanical, and that the effects or productions are as necessary upon the concurrence of these causes as that a ship, when the sails are hoist up, and the rudder is set to such a position should, when the wind blows, be moved in such a way or course.[2]

Hooke chose a most interesting way to represent the ideal of comprehensiveness in explanation. He described the scale of functions accompanying the scale of beings and argued that science should start with the simplest functions as manifested by the simplest organisms and progress step by step until the most complex were explained:

> Nor do I imagine that the skips from the one [function] to another will be found very great, if beginning from fluidity, or body without any form, we descend [sic] gradually, till we arrive at the highest form of a brute animal's soul, making the steps or foundations of our inquiry fluidity, orbiculation, fixation, angulization or crystallization, germination or ebullition, vegetation, plantanimation, animation, sensation, imagination.[3]

37. Ibid., 2, 69.
1. *Micrographia* (1665), p. 130; cf. pp. 88–92.
2. Ibid., p. 130.
3. Ibid., p. 127; cf. his remarks on the ascent of the "Scalam intellectus," p. 93. "Plantanimation" refers to the sensitive plant.

TABLE 1. *Idée d'une échelle des êtres naturelles* *

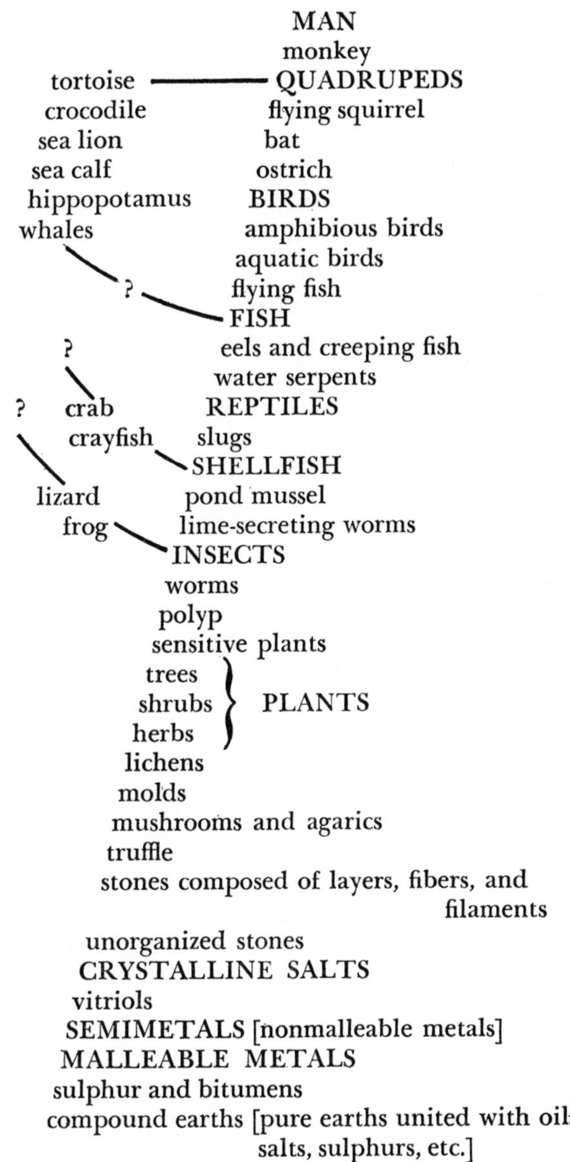

PURE EARTH

WATER

AIR

ETHEREAL MATTER

* From Charles Bonnet, *Contemplation de la nature, I* (1764), 33–69.

Mechanistic interpretations of nature proceeded upward along the scale of being and sought to interpret any one form by means of lower ones; any function manifested, by lower ones. The eighteenth-century naturalists were to use higher animal forms to explain the life of plants, a tendency which illustrates very well their rejection of seventeenth-century mechanism. For some reason expressions of the scale of functions such as that quoted above are much rarer than descriptions of the scale of beings. August Thienemann discovered a manuscript thesis on the relation of natural history to the chain of being, written in Thuringia in 1780. The writer listed thirty-three steps in the ascent from earth through plants and animals to God, and described the attendant scale of functions in the following words:

> Von der Erde zum Kiesel
> Vom Kiesel zur Bewegung,
> Von der Bewegung zur Reizbarkeit,
> Von der Reizbarkeit zur Empfindung,
> Von der Empfindung zur Vernunft.[4]

Between 1665 and 1722 there were several attempts to explain plant growth as a process closely similar to the growth of minerals, a plausible comparison for early chemists who did not distinguish organic from inorganic substance. Hooke was persuaded that the *arbor Dianae* of dendritic silver was a perfect model for plant growth. Joseph Needham cites this analogy as "perhaps the first occasion on which a non-living phenomenon has been appealed to as an illustration of what went on in [a] living body." [5] Daniel Coxe reported in 1674 that a salt obtained from fern ashes would, if dissolved in a volatile solvent, deposit plant forms as the fluid evaporated. He obtained "forty branches which, abating the color, did most exactly resemble that sort of fern which is single like Polypody and not branched. . . . I preserved these artificial, regenerated, or resuscitated vegetables many weeks." All who saw them remarked their resemblance to ferns and Coxe resolved to display them to the Royal Society. Unhappily, during the rough coach journey to London they were "resolved into the confused chaos out of which they were educed." He grew from ammonium carbonate "a forest in perspective, so admirably delineated,

4. Anon., *Entwurf einer nach der mutmasslichen Stufen-Folge eingerichteten allgemeinen Naturgeschichte 1780*, p. 190. "Kiesel" in this passage may be taken to mean any crystalline substance.

5. Needham, *A History of Embryology* (2d ed. 1959), p. 219. He cites Maupertuis, *Vénus physique* [1744], not mentioning similar descriptions by Hooke, Coxe, and Beaumont.

as not to be excelled, if imitated, by the pencil of the greatest masters in painting. They were all . . . shadows, rudiments, adumbrations, or representations of firs, pines, and another sort of tree." [6] Coxe asserted that all substances were chemically similar, a belief he shared with Nehemiah Grew, in reaction against the claims made for herb remedies by empiric physicians.[7]

In 1676 John Beaumont (d. 1731) created a stir by announcing that plants must grow after the fashion of minerals because his "diligence" in searching mines in the Mendip Hills had been rewarded by the discovery of an "entire plant, though small, growing up after the side of a stone."

> Nor can it be said but those stone-plants have true life and growth; for since in the curiosity of their make they may contend with the greatest part of the vegetable kingdom, having parts to assimilate nourishment by attraction, retention, concoction, and expulsion, I know not why they may not be allowed as proper a vegetation as any plant whatsoever.

Snowflakes, fossil plants in coal, and moss agates seemed to indicate that "nature can and does work the shapes of plants and animals without the help of a vegetative soul." With Beaumont we again encounter the dualism which underlay seventeenth-century mechanistic physiology. Organic functions could be explained in terms of matter in motion only by admitting the agency of an immaterial external force influencing the particles. Beaumont resorted to a "seminal root" in the mineral, acting by "a strong internal light . . . which imprints them in the matter." "It seems difficult to conceive how the matter should come to have such a determinate weight to run into such figures, without a specifical rector to intend and dispose it." [8]

The direct analogy from minerals to plants was an extreme tenet of mechanistic physiology. The more usual belief was that plants added particles of matter by concretion after their "intussusception" through the roots. Sir Kenelm Digby (1603–65) read a discourse on the growth of plants to the future Royal Society several years before it was chartered. Digby maintained that stems were formed by "hot, moist, airy, and consequently green and tender" streams of sun-seeking

6. "Vegetable Salts Perfectly Resembling Plants," pp. 175–76.

7. "That Salts Do Not Differ from Each Other" (1674), p. 155.

8. "Rock Plants and Their Growth" (1676). Also Tournefort, "Description du Labirinth de Candie, avec quelques observations sur l'accroissement & sur la generation des pierres," *Mém. Acad. Roy. des Sci.* (for 1702), pp. 224–41. The analogy was criticized [by de Vallemont], *Curiosities of Nature and Art* (1707), p. 302.

particles; roots, by "more dry, cold, earthy" particles with unexplained tendencies toward the earth.[9] The radicle of an inverted seed would grow toward the ground because it had absorbed drier, earthier, and colder particles. A seedling was forced to grow because the kernel had absorbed particles which it could no longer contain. Again we notice that the celebrated particulate view of matter was little more than an etiological myth attributing to small particles all of the mysterious forces formerly attributed to the organism as a whole. The spiritus rector and archaeus against which Bacon had argued merely took refuge beyond the range of the microscope, there to exercise their strange "vivifick" and "pulsive" powers.

Nehemiah Grew (1628–1712), the celebrated microscopist, postulated four basic shapes for salt crystals, whose simple combinations were thought to produce the shapes of natural things by magnification of their irregularities of surface. Lignous fibers in plants were extended columns of cubes whose smooth faces adhered.[10] Spiral and circular vessels were traced to complex groupings of slender isosceles triangles. Branching structures reflected the beveled corners of tiny polygonal prisms composing them. This modular theory of construction was held to explain numerical regularity in flower parts. Grew included drawings to show how all leaf outlines might be resolved into the circle. From these hypothetical foundations arose an ungainly theory of plant physiology. "A mixture of particles" passed into the spongy cortical substance of the roots with ground water and, undergoing "easy fermentation" in the bark, became sap.[11] Grew compared the bark to the coating of a cheese or the "skin" formed "over divers liquors." Only the largest particles remained in the spongy cortex to become bark. The smaller ones rose by a weird series of detours whose description seemed to Grew to constitute a mechanical explanation. "And so they all now grow." [12] Grew published these conjectures in 1672 and ten years later incorporated them without change into *The Anatomy of Plants.* In the dedication of a discourse on the anatomy of trunks in 1675 Grew addressed Charles II:

> That by all these means, the ascent of the sap, the distribution of the air, the confection of several sorts of liquors, as lymphs, milks, oils, balsams; with other acts of vegetation, are all con-

9. "A Discourse Concerning the Vegetation of Plants" [written in the 1640s, read in 1660] (1669), p. 214.
10. *Anatomy of Plants* (1682), p. 159; cf. Pl. 53.
11. *Anatomy of Vegetables Begun* (1672), pp. "49"–52 [sigs. E2–E2v].
12. Ibid., p. "52" [sig. E3v].

> trived and brought about in a mechanical way. In sum, your Majesty will find, that we are come ashore into a new world, whereof we see no end.[13]

Grew justified; he did not investigate. He sought to establish the possibility of mechanical physiology but did not achieve a sound theory himself. In the preface to the treatise he wrote in 1673 to "propound" the "idea of a phytological history," he admitted to believing in immaterial causes. Grew said he was determined to be "silent" on such causes:

> I do not find they do so well answer the scope whereto I am more obliged: for the investigation of the nature of any other secondary causes than such as are material, cannot be so useful to one that is considering the nature of a disease, or compounding or applying a remedy thereunto.[14]

The strained assertiveness of Grew's mechanistic physiology was a consequence of his realization that the movements of particles explained very little unless it was made clear why they moved. The new world he laid before Charles II was a world of vain surmise, wherein a plant "bleeds" because its parenchyma had "a continual conatus to dilate itself." [15] The "nitro-aerial salt" which caused water to freeze in patterns and minerals to assume regular crystalline shapes, formed fluids into plant substance "as the mould of a button to which the other principles, as its attire, do all conform." [16] Grew devoted much of his argument in *Cosmologia Sacra* (1701) to a description of "a vital or directive principle [which] seemeth of necessity to be assistant to the corporeal." [17] Grew had never escaped the necessity for such a principle as the directing force in the welter of his particulate plant physiology.

Explanations based upon subtle fluids, equally comprehensive but not predicated upon the influence of immaterial agencies, were shortly to become popular. Such explanations were not to indicate an empirical attitude. Their introduction did represent considerable progress in the refinement of explanatory texture from the level of gross particles. The belief that tissues were finer and more complex more accu-

13. *Comparative Anatomy of Trunks*, sig. A3ᵛ–A4.
14. *An Idea of a Phytological History Propounded* (1673), sig. A6–A6ᵛ.
15. *Comparative Anatomy of Trunks*, p. 45.
16. *Anatomy of Plants*, p. 158.
17. P. 35; see 31–84. For dualistic mechanism also see [de Vallemont], *Curiosities of Nature and Art*. Also N. Dedu, *De l'ame des plantes* (1685), pp. 249–58.

rately represented the true texture of organic bodies. Inevitably, the recognition of the intricacy of plant bodies suggested analogies with animals, as Grew himself had observed.

> Your Majesty will here see that there are those things which are little less admirable within a plant than within an animal. That a plant, as well as an animal, is constituted of several organical parts . . . That every plant hath bowels of divers kinds, containing divers kinds of liquors. That even a plant lives partly upon air, for the reception whereof it hath peculiar organs. So that a plant is, as it were, an animal in queers [quires], even as an animal is a plant, or rather, several plants, bound up into one volume.[18]

Several of my correspondents in the field of plant physiology have argued that the search for analogies between plants and animals has been one of the curses of botany. Perhaps our study will confirm this opinion. But whatever one might think about analogies between plants and animals, analogies between plants and minerals were a curse several times over. Grew's studies of plant anatomy showed in plants a level of complexity which accreting salts simply could not be used to explain. Gross corpuscles were abandoned as explanatory devices because they did not accord with observed tissues and because, in using them, it had been necessary to rely on extrascientific immaterial causes.

Another extreme belief in mechanistic physiology, shortly to be overthrown, was that water, under the mysterious influence which Grew called the nitro-aerial salt, might be transformed directly into plant substance. Van Helmont (1577–1644) had grown a willow tree in a tub for five years. The tree multiplied its weight by a factor of thirty-three (not counting the weight of leaves lost every autumn) while the soil lost weight hardly at all. He had used distilled water or rain water only and ascribed the tree's growth to the water's accretion into plant substance.[19] John Woodward (1665–1728), a speculative geologist and professor of physick at Gresham College, objected that the water must have contained minerals in solution. He found that mineral substances, which he supposed to be the "food" of plants, settled out of river water in sealed flasks. As similar flasks containing growing plants showed no sediment, the plants must have absorbed

18. *Comparative Anatomy of Trunks*, sig. A2^{v}–A3.

19. *Opera Omnia* . . . (Frankfurt: J. J. Erythropili, 1682), pp. 104–05. Also Bacon, *Sylva Sylvarum* (1626), Cent. V, cap. 411, p. 112. Also John Houghton, *A Collection for Improvement of Husbandry and Trade*, no. 8 (4 May 1692).

it in the process of growth. He performed a variety of experiments "with due care and exactness" in 1691 and 1692 which showed that plants grown in river water grew to twice the size of those grown in rain water.[20] Woodward was impressed with the regularity of nature, which he traced to the universal action of heat as a physical cause. He thought heat raised water in plants by capillarity because in autumn, leaves fell first from the taller plants and then, as temperatures fell, from shrubs and lower bushes. "There's a procedure in every part of nature that is perfectly regular and geometrical if we can but find it out."[21] He enunciated the first mathematical law in plant physiology:

> The plant is more or less nourished and augmented, in proportion as the water in which it stands contains a greater or smaller quantity of proper terrestrial matter in it.[22]

For every gram that plants gained in weight they were observed to absorb between fifty and two hundred grams of water. The larger the plant, the more water it imbibed. Woodward was thus the first to measure the absorption of fluids by plants. The early physiologists did not know that the bulk of living plants is formed in the process of photosynthesis whereby water and carbon dioxide are transformed into hydrocarbons in the leaves.

Woodward tried to explain why wheat exhausted the soil so that only corn would grow, which had in turn to be succeeded by legumes in the sequence of crop rotation. He supposed that each plant exhausted a different kind of food in its growth, which would account for differences among plants and their associations on different kinds of soil. This notion was characteristic of mechanist physiology and it bears an interesting similarity to Plato's notion of selective nutrition. Woodward's contributions to the experimental method in plant physiology helped to guarantee that gas interchange would someday be discovered, although that discovery was to owe a good deal to eighteenth-century concepts of subtle fluids. Until the 1770s it would be believed that plants imbibed "food," whether gross or subtle, from the soil. Woodward was led to assume the existence of a universally diffused vegetable matter after he observed algae appear in sealed tubes of water and sand; he regarded the algae as a kind of nutrient

20. "Some Thoughts and Experiments Concerning Vegetation" (1699), p. 200; experiments A, B, and C of 1691.

21. Ibid., p. 227.

22. Ibid., p. 213.

substance contained by water. In *An Essay toward a Natural History of the Earth* (1695) he called vegetable matter "the standing fund and promptuary out of which is derived the matter of all animal and vegetable bodies and whereinto, at the dissolution of those bodies, that matter is restored . . . for the constitution and formation of others." [23] His notion of vegetable matter was an explanatory device rather than a discovered physical substance, but we may observe that it anticipated ideas about a similarly diffused, subtle nutrient fluid in the eighteenth century.

The mechanistic theory of nutrition led to the celebrated agricultural philosophy of Jethro Tull (1674–1741), who recommended that a field be plowed four to eight times to reduce soil particles to a size that could be absorbed by the roots. Crop rotation, justified by Woodward's assumption that different crops took different kinds of particles from the soil, was not necessary if the land were plowed often enough. Crop rotation was necessary not because different plants depleted different kinds of food, but because they "foraged" at different depths.

> Certainly no mortal, except Dr. Woodward, can pretend to distinguish the particles of vegetable matter by any characters, hieroglyphics, or other manner whatever, so as to determine to what species or class of plants they [belong].

He was motivated in this attack by the orthodoxy of graded function. Roots were not analogous to mouths which could select their food, but to the mesenteric lacteals of intestines; roots "have no need to be guarded by senses":

> These spongy superficies of animal guts, and vegetable roots, have no more taste or power of refusing whatever comes in contact with them, the one than the other.

Plants were held to grow by the automatic assimilation of small particles, which might be created artificially by protracted tillage, "in proportion to which the food will be produced." It was foolish to believe that plants used different foods; such a belief would imply "that a horse, by feeding in a certain pasture, will degenerate into a bull, and in other pasture revert to a horse again." [24]

The first analogy suggested to relate plants with animals was that of circulation. William Harvey (1578–1657) published his discovery

23. P. 79.

24. [Tull], *The New Horse-Houghing Husbandry* (1731), pp. 46, 55, 54, 64, 81. Cf. Nicholas Damascenus, *De Plantis,* i. 1, 2.

of a continuous circulation of blood in animals in 1628. Some years were to pass before the idea of a comparable circulation occurred to plant physiologists, not only because the orthodoxy of graded function enforced a limit on the functions to be ascribed to plants, but because the motion of fluids in plants does not depend upon a conspicuous vascular system. Mechanistic physiologists held that plants absorbed water by capillarity and that the rise of sap was owing to the action of heat. In 1665 Johann David Major (1639–93) argued that plant nutrition could not be performed without the same organs that animals employed. He believed that nutritive substances were brought to growing parts and excretions carried away exactly as in animal bodies—by the circulation of body fluids. Plants could not grow, he argued, "if the motion of the sap were only from bottom to top, that is from the root to the top of the stalk, and if it never returned by nervous or fibrous channels analogous to the veins of animals." "This circulation of the succi nutriti undoubtedly enables plants to live for a certain time . . ." and, if we are to believe Major, had "never before specifically [been] published by anyone." [25] In 1669 John Ray (1627–1705) and Francis Willughby (1635–72) found that cut sections of trees oozed sap at either end, which would not have happened had capillarity been the chief cause of fluid movement.[26] They also found that sap flowed copiously on the north side of trees, not heated by the rays of the sun, and that a cold spell stopped the flow only in a few of the trees observed. In 1670 Willughby wrote that the flow of sap in walnut trees was sometimes more conspicuous during periods of cold weather.[27]

Martin Lister (1638?–1712) made similar observations at York in the winter of 1670–71. He praised Ray and Willughby for what he took to be their discovery of fluid movements in plants the year round. Lister was encouraged to believe that plant and animal circulation depended on similar vascular systems but did not say so at first, calling instead for further study of plant anatomy. "We shall have but dark and imperfect notions of the motion of the juices in vegetables until their true texture be better discovered." [28] Nehemiah Grew had denied that plants had veins, arguing that fluids sometimes circulated through the solid parts of plant tissue. The tracheids and vessel elements of

25. *Dissertatio Botanica* (1665), sig. C3, C2^v.

26. Ray and Willughby, "Concerning the Motion of the Sap in Trees," p. 963. In this article injured plants were for the first time said to "bleed." The O.E.D. cites Grew's use of the word in 1675.

27. "Letter to the Royal Society," pp. 1166–67.

28. Letter of 25 Jan. 1671, *Phil. Trans.*, no. 68 (1671 N.S.), p. 2064.

woody plants have only the smallest openings for fluids; there is no vascular system for plant circulation. The lack of evidence did not deter Martin Lister, who announced in 1672 that sap rose in a "few determinate and set places," where one might find "vessels analogous to our human veins and not mere pores"; their purpose was "to carry the succus nutritus of plants." [29] Lister found veins in all and "lacteal vessels" in some of the plants he examined. In a third article in 1673 he insisted on a total analogy of circulation because nature "make[s] against the general opinion of one only [sic] sap loosely pervading the whole plant like water in a sponge." [30] Part of his argument was directed against mechanistic plant physiology and might thus be interpreted as a plea for appreciation of the complexity of plant tissue. Nevertheless, Martin Lister was of a speculative temperament, and the idea of botanical analogy meant more to him than modest insights into plant anatomy.

> These juices move by far a different contrivance of parts from that of animals; not yet here discovering any uniting of veins into one common trunk, no pulsation, no sensible stop by ligature, no difference in veins, etc. All which difficulties notwithstanding may, I hope, in time be happily overcome; and the analogy betwixt plants and animals be in all things else, as well as the motion of their juice, fully cleared.[31]

Members of the Royal Society asked Nehemiah Grew "to endeavor whether he can discover any such thing as a peristaltic motion in plants." [32] John Beale (1603–83?) recognized such notions as excesses of speculation. He believed that sap was converted into plant substance as it coursed upward and that plants lacked a continuous vascular system. One Richard Reed attacked Beale, "thinking it an heresy in husbandry, obstinately to deny the descent of the sap . . . [because] the graft hath influence . . . to alter and change the very way of the growing of the root in the earth, which I cannot see how it should

29. "A Letter Containing an Ingenious Account of Veins, by Him Observ'd in Plants, Analogous to Human Veins" (1672), pp. 3053–55. Kurt Sprengel, *Historia Rei Herbariae,* 2 (1808), 11, spoke of "Analogia seductus Mart. Lister."

30. "A Further Account Concerning the Existence of Veins in All Kinds of Plants," p. 5132.

31. Ibid., pp. 5136–37.

32. Letter of 6 July 1672 from Henry Oldenburg to John Ray, in William Derham, ed., *Philosophical Letters between the Late Learned Mr. Ray and Several of His Ingenious Correspondents, Natives and Foreigners* . . . (London: William and John Innys, 1718), p. 110.

do but by sending down its sap thither."[33] Beale conceded that some "efficacy" passed down the trunk from a graft but would not credit a total analogy of circulation between plants and animals. "The main quantity of the sap" moved upward only.[34] While the notion of continuous circulation was incorrect, the fluid movements and other growth mechanisms of plants were indeed more complex than the crystallization of minerals. Once this point had been made the vascular analogy fell into disfavor, except among speculators who cared but little for the truth. For a time at least, the analogy of circulation helped to draw attention to a neglected problem and, from the standpoint of the eventual development of true knowledge, served to good effect.

Another step toward the identification of circulating nutrients with subtle fluids was taken by Richard Bradley (1688–1732), a speculative plant physiologist who became professor of botany at Cambridge in 1724. He wrote in 1716 that gross fluids could not circulate in plants because their vessels were too fine for "anything more gross than vapor" to move through them.[35] Bradley had much in common with earlier mechanists. He supposed, with Coxe and Grew, that "the salts . . . in flesh, fruit, and herbs are the same, only differing in the proportions of their quantities," a belief he supported with the irrelevant observation that both herbivores and carnivores would feed on fruit.[36] Bradley gave favorable mention to analogies with minerals in *A Philosophical Account of the Works of Nature* (1721), the most elaborate speculative work on natural history written in the first half of the eighteenth century. Plant tissues were said to strain juices as "the several strata of earth do to minerals . . . as the different juices passing through the several veins or beds of earth are altered by a

33. "Descent of Sap" (1671), p. 2130.

34. "In What Sense Sap Descends and Circulates" (1671), p. 2145. Continental writings on plant physiology showed a similar development. Claude Perrault resembled Grew in many ways. He held that the movement of plants by the wind forced the movement of fluids: "De la circulation de la seve des plantes," *Essais de physique* (1680), p. 178. Note his illustration of cells, p. 157. Edme Mariotte (ob. 1684) followed Lister in accepting the vascular analogy. He thought roots were analogous to the mesenteric lacteals of animals: "De la vegetation des plantes" [1676], pp. 129–33. Marcello Malpighi (1628–94), motivated chiefly by his discoveries about the intricacy of plant tissues, proposed many analogies. Lamettrie called him the Harvey of botany: "L'Homme-plante," 2, *Œuvres* (1764), 14–15. Malpighi thought spiral vessels were analogous to the excretory tubules of insects and the gills of fish. Cf. A. R. Hall, *The Scientific Revolution* (1954), pp. 287–88.

35. "Observations and Experiments Relating to the Motion of the Sap in Vegetables," pp. 488–90.

36. *New Improvements* (1717), part 1, p. 29.

sort of filtration." [37]Crystals grew "by a cause nearly the same of [sic] that which gives us different colors in the leaves and flowers of vegetables, [by] the several strainers or vessels which compose plants." [38] In 1727 he listed three examples in support of his concept of circulation: an inverted tree whose branches were planted and roots exposed to sunlight continued its growth in the reversed position; an old pear tree sawed through and raised from its stump on wedges lived when its branches were grafted to four young trees growing nearby; a bud of yellow jasmine tinged the leaves of a white jasmine onto which it was grafted. Bradley compared this effect to an inoculation spreading through the human body.[39] He supposed that arterial vessels in the trunk transported the vapor upward and that veins in the bark carried it down. He drew analogies between minerals and plants, as well as between animals and plants. The vascular analogy between plants and animals could only be saved by making out the circulating fluids to be very fine and attenuated.

Patrick Blair (d. 1728) attacked Bradley's notion of circulating vapors several times between 1720 and 1724. Blair was a conventional mechanist and believed in the circulation of gross fluids.[40] "Prying and inquisitive persons" would still be ignorant of the circulation of the sap had it not been for Harvey's discovery of the circulation of the blood. "The great obstacle I suppose for finding out the same in plants too must be the want of a due consideration of this analogy, the inconveniency of detecting the succiferous vessels in plants, and the sap being of the same color with the vessels." Malpighi and Grew, he charged, "were still deficient in a right notion of the motion of the sap." [41] Blair thought to distinguish arterial and venous fluids in the wood and bark and, although he did not discover vegetable capillaries connecting the two, prided himself on the suggestion that "there must be such a communication betwixt their tubuli at the extremities as there is betwixt the arteries and veins in animal bodies." [42]

37. P. 13.

38. Ibid. See J. F. Henkel, *Flore saturnisans* [1722] for mechanistic physiology and analogies with minerals. Also Henry Baker, "Concerning the Vegetation of Metals," in *Employment for the Microscope* (1753), pp. 191–208; also "Of the Resuscitation of Plants," pp. 208–12. Baker regarded dendritic mineral growths as curiosities with no real bearing on plant growth and nutrition.

39. *Ten Practical Discourses*, pp. 70–71.

40. When the heat of the earth "dilates it pores" the root admits "nutritive particles" "crowded in by subsequent ones of the same configuration." Blair's copy of a letter he wrote to John Martyn in 1724: *Rawlinson MS*, p. [27].

41. Blair, *Botanick Essays* (1720), pp. 331–32.

42. Ibid., p. 389.

> Thus I hope I have proved the circulation of the sap in plants to be the same with that of the blood in animals, in so natural, plain, and intelligible a manner that after its being so fully discovered the vegetation of plants needs be no longer a mystery.[43]

Bishop Richard Rawlinson gave the Bodleian Library a copy of Bradley's *Philosophical Account of the Works of Nature* bound up with a number of copied Blair letters dating from 1723 and 1724, and a preface of twenty-eight quarto pages for a treatise which does not seem to have been completed. In the preface Blair insisted on the circulation analogy although he reproved a certain "theoretical" Dr. Chambers, who apparently believed in "a Systole and Diastole" in plant circulation.[44] Blair's belief in gross circulating fluids blinded him to the importance of transpiration, which he tried to measure with commendable experiments. He found that a tobacco plant weighing 6.25 pounds lost 2.5 pounds by evaporation in the three days after it was uprooted:

> There is an insensible transpiration in plants as well as animals; that the pores of some plants are more open, and others more shut, and that some plants have a more volatile sap than others. . . . The insensible transpiration is more regular in plants than in animals.[45]

"There may be a juster calculation of the vegetation by the staticks in plants than in animals." [46] Blair praised the attempts of Santorio Santorio (1561–1636) to measure weight loss from excretion and perspiration in the human body, and thought similar attempts might be made with plants: "They might be of moment." [47] Such experiments were eventually to lead to the abandonment of the notion of a continuous circulation of palpable fluids, after the investigations of Stephen Hales.

Stephen Hales (1679–1761) is known as the founder of experimental plant physiology.[48] His quantitative observations, which re-

43. Ibid., p. 408.

44. Pp. [99–105]. The reference to Chambers occurs in Blair's copy of a letter of 14 Dec. 1724 to John Martyn: *Rawlinson MS,* p. [69]. The accusation might apply to Claude Perrault's intermittent pulses but not to Ephraim Chambers (1680?–1740), if his "Circulation of the Sap" (1728) is a fair indication of his opinions in 1724.

45. *Botanick Essays* (1720), p. 362.

46. Ibid., p. 364.

47. Ibid., p. 362.

48. A. E. Clark-Kennedy, *Stephen Hales* (1929). Hales displayed the same benevolent temperament we have encountered in Berkeley and Wesley, which he described

duced different processes in plants to numerical ratios, bespoke a staunch experimental attitude. "Nature in all her operations acts conformably to those mechanic laws which were established at her first institution."[49]

> It is impossible for the most sagacious and penetrating genius to pry into ["the wonderful and secret operations of nature"] unless he will be at the pains of analyzing nature by a numerous and regular series of experiments.[50]

Experiments wherein he had measured animal "staticks" led him to hope "that in [plants] also, by the same method of inquiry, considerable discoveries may in time be made, there being, in many respects, a great analogy between plants and animals."[51] Hales did not object to hypothetical analogies, but he knew they could be rendered less seductive by resolving always "to number, weigh, and measure."[52]

Hales's most important discovery in plant physiology was the agency of leaves in promoting transpiration.[53] He argued that as the surface area of a sunflower's leaves was 2.5 times that of its roots, the roots must absorb water 2.5 times as fast as the leaves transpired it.[54] Hales recognized, with John Beale, that in general fluids followed an upward course in plants; he described it as "only a progressive, and not a circulating motion, as in animals."[55] He cited the experience of

---

in a letter of 25 Nov. 1760 to James Bradley as "the pleasure of having done something for the benefit of mankind": *45 Bradley MSS* (Bodleian Western MS 16,541), f. 56.

49. *Vegetable Staticks* (1727), p. 156.

50. Ibid., p. vii.

51. Ibid., p. 3.

52. Ibid., p. 1.

53. Evaporation from leaf surfaces draws water at pressures which sometimes attain three hundred atmospheres. Hales's discovery is central to the currently held Dixon theory of fluid movements, although the modern theory also depends upon the concept of cohesion tension in continuous water columns.

54. Cohen notes Hales's supposition that plants were acted upon by fluids rather as the Leyden jar was by Franklin's fluid: *Franklin and Newton*, pp. 266–80. This is particularly true of Hales's assumption that the amount of water entering the plant's roots must equal the amount transpired, just as Franklin assumed that the amount of electric fluid entering a Leyden jar must equal the amount repelled from the outside. Hales's belief that thunderclouds built up chemical concentrations resembled Franklin's insight into the accumulation of electric charges. Both investigators had a gift for expressing descriptive propositions amenable to mathematical interpretation.

55. *Vegetable Staticks*, p. 14. Matthew Maty wrote in *Phil. Trans.*, "[Hales's] reasons have been thought so convincing, that the system of the circulation in plants has been ever since exploded in England": *63* (1773), 126 n. Bonnet's *Recherches sur l'usage des feuilles* (1754) was also cited, to the same effect. Cf. Henri Guerlac, "The

carpenters and nurserymen in opposition to Lister's contention that plants had veins and year-round circulation.[56]

One of his most sophisticated experiments was performed upon growing vine stems to show that equidistant marks would diverge during growth. Hales made similar marks on the leg of a young chicken. After two months the leg had grown longer but the marks were no farther apart. The bone had grown only at the extremities.[57] This may have been the first time in the history of biology that an analogy was tested and overthrown. Subjecting hypothetical analogies to experiment is the method of much experimental physiology today. The methods Hales used were so promising that one wonders why they did not lead to the foundation of an experimental tradition and a host of discoveries. While many conceptual tools had not yet come into use, comparable tissues might have been weighed at different times of the year, the difference between root pressure and transpiration pressure might have been investigated, rates of growth measured, and some of Hales's own inquiries extended by further experiments. In an article on experimental biology during this period H. Hamshaw Thomas admits to puzzlement on this point:

> I do not think we can account for the general cessation of experimental work on plants for some fifty years [in England] by saying that progress in plant biology had to wait for the fuller development of chemical knowledge. There were so many problems which might have been elucidated by careful experiment and observation. Some of the earlier workers had disclosed curious facts which had never been properly examined. But for some reason the urge to try experiments had faded.[58]

We must also try to explain why Hales's disproof of the circulation analogy did not altogether discredit analogies between plants and animals. The answer is to be found in Hales's book itself. *Vegetable Staticks* introduced into plant physiology not only Newton's experimental methods but the debilitating notion of subtle matter:

> There is diffused through all natural, mutually attracting bodies a large proportion of particles which, as the first great author of this important discovery, Sir Isaac Newton, observes, are ca-

---

Continental Reputation of Stephen Hales," *Arch. Internat. histoire des sci.,* 4th year (1951), pp. 393–404.

56. *Haemastaticks* (1731), p. 264.
57. *Vegetable Staticks,* p. 338; see Fig. 40–42.
58. "Experimental Plant Biology in Pre-Linnaean Times" (1955), p. 22.

pable of being thrown off from dense bodies by heat or fermentation into a vigorously elastic and permanently repelling state.[59]

Hales often cited the *Opticks,* particularly the later queries. Cohen finds that he transferred the authority of the *Principia* to these speculations and considered them as well-founded theories. We may notice the consequences in the debate over the circulation of sap. Hales disproved the vascular analogy for gross fluids but permitted equally speculative notions, based on the ether, to survive. Although sap usually rose straight up a tree's trunk, it might be diverted around a series of deep notches which left no vertical vessel intact. Hales concluded from this fact that plant tissue reduced the sap "almost to a vapor." In the subtle state it traveled through the lignous parts of a plant until attraction congealed it into leaves or branches: "We can discover no other cause of the sap's motion but the strong attraction of the capillary sap vessels, assisted by the brisk undulations and vibrations caused by the sun's warmth." [60] The subtle vapors might pass freely into the air or receive further powers from that "fine elastic fluid with particles of very different natures floating in it whereby it is admirably fitted by the great Author of nature to be the breath of life of vegetables as well as of animals." [61] Decay returned the subtle matter to the air by fermentation. The crude mechanism of Beaumont and Coxe, Hooke and Grew, was left behind, but ambitions for comprehensiveness and causal explanation were served by subtle substances obedient to Newtonian attraction—"that universal principle which is so operative in all the very different works of nature." [62]

Hales came very close indeed to a clear statement of the interchange of gases by plants. He confined mint plants under bell jars and noticed that the water rose. He concluded that plants had "fixed" one-seventh of the confined air and converted it into their own substance. The chemistry of gases was not yet well understood. No one seemed able to take advantage of Hales's observation. It is not unlikely that the ambiguity of a statement which described air as a mixture of subtle fluids and particles may have obscured the discovery. Hales thought part of the contraction observed in the volume of confined air might have been due to the loss of its repelling power.[63] Priestley's discoveries on gas interchange had to be disen-

59. Page v.
60. Ibid., p. 136; experiment 10.
61. Ibid., p. 148; also 284–86, 319.
62. Ibid., p. 96; also 313.
63. *Vegetable Staticks* (2d ed. 1731), pp. 318–31. Francis Home, in *The Principles*

tangled from subtle fluids before they could be properly understood. Linnaeus wrote that leaves were the lungs of plants but had no precise understanding of what it was they absorbed. No further studies of gas interchange were undertaken until the 1770s.

Hales also came very close to discovering the agency of light on green leaves but did not bring the question into focus because he thought light and ether might be the same thing:

> And may not light also, by freely entering the expanded surfaces of leaves and flowers contribute much to ennobling the principles of vegetables; for Sir Isaac Newton puts it as a very probable query, "Are not gross bodies and light convertible into one another?" [64]

The debate over circulation became pointless and disappeared into the universal solvent. Had it not been for the refinement of explanatory texture to include subtle fluids, the circulation analogy, disproved for gross fluids, would probably have lost its appeal. But who could tell whether subtle fluids rose and fell or rose only? Who could prove that subtle humors were not the principal food of plants, imbibed through the roots? Who could argue against the free motion of a universally penetrating effluvium? The flourishing school of plant physiology virtually disappeared at the time its most powerful instrument—the quantitative method developed by Woodward, Blair, and Hales—had been perfected.

We might characterize Hales as the last of the mechanistic physiologists. If he began an era it was a speculative rather than an experimental one, owing to the persuasive appeal of his statement of notions about subtle fluids:

> Our atmosphere is a *chaos,* consisting not only of elastic, but also of unelastic air particles . . .
>
> Since the air is found so manifestly to abound in almost all natural bodies; since we find it so operative and active a principle in every chemical operation . . . may we not with good reason adopt this now fixed, now volatile *Proteus* among our chemical principles? [65]

---

of Agriculture and Vegetation (1757), discussed Hales's demonstration that atmospheric air was "fixed" by plants but was unable to conclude anything from it and wrote that soil, perhaps through combination with air to produce nitrates, was the food of plants (pp. 107–56).

64. *Vegetable Staticks,* p. 327. He quoted Qu. 30 (1717) of the *Opticks.*

65. *Vegetable Staticks,* pp. 315–16. For an example of the stultifying effect of subtle

The physiology of subtle fluids received the approval of Linnaeus, who wrote,

> The food of plants comes from the earth in a very subtle state and is carried to their roots in water . . . When a plant is unable to attract to itself enough of these subtle humors it wilts and dies.[66]

Sir Hans Sloane (1660–1753), William Sherard (1659–1728), Philip Miller (1691–1771), and other prominent botanists showed little interest in plant physiology. Not until the days of Priestley, Ingenhousz, Sir Humphry Davy, and Thomas Knight were studies in experimental plant physiology to be resumed in England.

The conclusions we draw from this survey of the subject of plant nutrition between 1665 and 1727 bear on what follows concerning the idea of botanical analogy. The anatomical studies of Grew and Malpighi suggested a structual complexity in plants which advanced them toward animals on the scale of beings and permanently discouraged the prosecution of analogies with minerals. Corpuscularian physiology was succeeded by the physiology of subtle fluids. A flourishing experimental tradition came to an end as explanatory texture was modified to a level of coincidence with subtle fluids. We suggest that the suspension of serious inquiry into plant physiology was due largely to the introduction of subtle fluids. We must now confront the question which might be raised as to why the discredit of the vascular analogy did not lead to a repudiation of the more general idea of botanical analogy. Another area of physiology had been opened for those who wished to pursue analogies between plants and animals.

iii. Plant Generation 1676–1830

While circulation in plants was the first contribution to the belief that plants were analogous to animals, their sexuality was the most important contribution to this belief. This was so not just because

---

fluids on plant physiology see Francis Penrose, *A Physical Essay on the Animal Economy . . .* (London: W. Owen and S. Parker of Oxford, 1754), pp. 18–21. Also, for "hot and cold ether," Penrose, *Letters Philosophical and Astronomical, in Which the Following Operations of Nature Are Treated of and Explained, in the Most Simple and Natural Manner, According to Sir Isaac Newton's Opinions . . .* (Plymouth: M. Haydon, 1789), pp. 167–215.

66. "Sponsalia Plantarum" [1746], p. 66.

the addition of a shared attribute encouraged more complete statements of analogy. The discovery of sexuality revised ideas of the functional difference between plants and animals, seeming to bring them closer together on the scale of beings. In order to make this relationship plain we shall trace speculation on the mode of fertilization until the growth of the pollen tube was first understood. Some of the disputes over embryology and the orthodoxy of graded function were conducted with dismaying intricacy, which we seek to avoid.

The Aristotelian function gradient implied that plants, lacking the ability to move about in pursuit of mates, were not sexually differentiated.[1] Without a knowledge of their sexual anatomy, those who suspected the existence of sexes in plants could make little progress against so persuasive an idea. Upon his return from Assyria Herodotus wrote that date palms were of two sexes and described the artificial fertilization of the females wherein male branches were shaken nearby. Pliny thought the male date palm did "the part of a husband" "with his breathing and exhalations upon [the females], or else with a certain dust that passeth from him." [2] Plants had been described colloquially as male or female with regard to size, vigor, or domestication.[3] The use of analogies in plant generation did not, however, require the discovery of sexuality. Hippocrates likened the embryo developing in the uterus to a seed growing in the soil.[4] Andrea Cesalpino (1519–1603) thought the stalk of plants was similar to the animal reproductive system because each bore fruit.[5] Malpighi repeated the analogy between the fetus and the seedling. George Garden of Aberdeen (1649–1733) thought the immature seeds in the ovary bore a better analogy to the fetus than did a seedling growing apart from the parent. Each embryo in a plant seed "has all its members folded up according to their several joints and plicatures" like a fetus.[6] Leeuwenhoek (1632–1723) wrote in 1693,

1. *De Generatione Animalium* i. 1, 23; also ii. 4.

2. *Historia Naturalis* xiii. 4; trans. Holland (1601), p. 386; also 385, "even in the very herbs, there are both sexes."

3. Blair, *Botanick Essays,* p. 235, 247. Also Bacon, *Sylva Sylvarum,* Cent. VII, cap. 608, p. 155. Dioscorides gave the names "mas" and 'foemina" to different plants, which still bear them as specific names in genus *Mercurialis.* Also two ferns, *Filix mas* and *Filix femina,* now *Dryopteris filix-mas* and *Athyrium filix-femina:* Nordenskiold, *History of Biology,* p. 197.

4. *De Generationis* xxii. E. Littré, ed., *Œuvres completes d'Hippocrate . . . ,* 7 (Paris: J. B. Ballière, 1851), 514–49.

5. *De Plantis* (1583), p. 12. He did not trace fertilization to the flowers but did remark that there must be a "breath" flowing from the male plant to warm the seed (p. 15).

6. "Of Generation" (1691), p. 476.

> I say . . . we shall not find any other difference between plants and animals than that the first, wanting a locomotive power, cannot couple as animals do and therefore must contain in the same individual not only the origin of the future plants which I compared to the animalcule in the male sperm, but also the material nourishment sufficient for it till it is furnished with a root to provide for itself.[7]

"As plants are not male and female, nor have a matrix for the first reception and sustentation of the young, so the parent tree produces a perfect plant wrapped up in the seed." Despite his belief that plants were not of two sexes he insisted upon an analogy between the minute embryo plant in fertilized seeds and the mammalian embryo. He thought the mammalian embryo arose within the male and traveled to the uterus in the form of a swimming animalcule, which planted itself in the uterus to grow like a garden seedling. Andry, Hartsoeker, and Dalenpatius were to make this idea famous in their animalculist thesis, which asserted that the seminal animalcule was an exact miniature of the male parent. Because "plants receive a great alteration from the different soils in which the seeds are planted," the animalcule might be influenced by the womb in which it grew—a presumptive explanation of hybrids.[8] Leeuwenhoek drew no analogies between the seminal animalcule and the pollen of plants because he was ignorant of their sexual anatomy. This step would be taken in 1703 by Samuel Morland.

These extravagant suppositions are worth citing because they are further proof that what mattered most to these early speculators was the consistency of their claims with general ideas. A horrible example of such contentment with doctrine was an article published by the minor poet Henry Baker (1698–1774) in 1740. He displayed a perfect ignorance of everything written on plant sexuality after Leeuwenhoek's article of 1693 and showed the extent to which analogies might be carried without any notion of sexuality.

> A ripe seed falling to the earth is in the condition of the ovum of an animal getting loose from its ovary and dropping into the uterus, and, to go on with the analogy, the juices of the earth

7. "The Seeds of Plants," p. 704.

8. Ibid., p. 705. Leeuwenhoek's explanation of plant growth was mechanistic. His assertion about the growth of the fetus recalls Woodward. He based plant shapes on modular soil particles and explained the suspension of fluids within them by likening plants to columns of clay pellets which support water by cohesion.

> swell and extend the vessels of the seed as the juices of the uterus do those of the ovum, till the seminal leaves unfold and perform the office of a placenta to the infant included plant; which, imbibing suitable and sufficient moisture, gradually extends its parts, fixes its own root, shoots above the ground, and may be said to be born.[9]

Baker sought to develop a nonsexual system of preformed, enclosed individuals. He was then ready for his grand conception of plants with successive generations of offspring nested ever more minutely one inside the other. He closed his article with the relevant lines from his poem "The Universe" [1734].

> Each seed includes a Plant: that Plant, again,
> Has other Seeds, which other Plants contain:
> Those other Plants have All their Seeds, and Those
> More Plants again, successively, inclose.
> Thus ev'ry single Berry that we find,
> Has, really, in itself whole Forests of its Kind.[10]

So far we have traced the analogy between embryos and seeds without the addition of a sexual theory.

Nehemiah Grew supplied some of the missing anatomical knowledge in 1682.[11] He described the anthers as "so many little testicles . . . [containing] the vegetable sperm. Which, so soon as the penis [pistil] is exerted, or the testicles come to break, falls down upon the seed-case or womb and so touches it with a prolific virtue." On the basis of its shape he thought the female organ, the pistil, "does not unaptly resemble a small penis, with the sheath upon it as its praeputium." [12] This partial discovery of sexual anatomy may be seen, in part, as a consequence of the interest in such matters aroused by Harvey's *De Generatione Animalium* (1650). Harvey selected the chicken as an example of oviparous generation and deer as an example of viviparous generation. Each of these was "an exemplar or representative of all the rest, which, as being most known to us, will give light to the rest, and become a platform to which all the other[s]

9. "The Discovery of a Perfect Plant in Semine," p. 451. He erred in describing an undescended mammalian ovum as fertilized.

10. G. R. Potter gives 1734 as the date for the poem in "Henry Baker, F.R.S. (1698–1774)" (1932), pp. 301–03.

11. Grew had not known about plant sexuality when he wrote *The Anatomy of Vegetables Begun* (p. 147). He later said the idea occurred to him and Sir Thomas Millington at the same time in 1676: *Anatomy of Plants*, p. 171.

12. Ibid., p. 172. He believed that the receptacle was the female organ.

may be reduced by way of analogy." [13] Harvey's comments on the validity of analogies in nature gave clear sanction, if any was needed, to analogies with plants:

> For nature being divine and perfect, is always consonant to herself in the same things. And as her works do either agree or differ (namely in kind, species, or some analogy) so her operation . . . is the same or different in them.[14]

In 1667 Nicholas Stensen suspected that there might be a mammalian ovum; Swammerdam and deGraaf (1641–73) confidently wrote about it in 1672.[15] Enthusiasm at the apparent discovery led Malpighi, Swammerdam, and Malebranche (1638–1715) to conclude that all the mysteries of generation had been cleared. Their ambition for total explanation was satisfied by an "ovist" hypothesis which held that the mammalism ovum and the eggs of birds, before they had been fertilized, contained all the parts of the future organism in compact form. The male fluids merely hastened the growth of a preformed embryo and did not have to penetrate the ovary with a material contribution.

One of the most striking examples of the influence of the idea of botanical analogy was the manner in which Nehemiah Grew tailored his notion of plant generation to fit the ovist hypothesis. He sought to maintain that the sperm-like particles of pollen from the "apices" (anthers) performed their function merely "by falling on the uterus," and did not have to touch the ovules. He drew an analogy with birds, where there was supposed to be "no intromission but only an adosculation of parts." [16] N. Dedu of Montpellier described the transfer of beliefs:

> Après que dans ce dernier temps quelques célèbres anatomistes eurent avancé que les testicules des femmes n'étaient proprement que des ovaires, que chacune des petites boules ou vésicules qui les composent étaient des oeufs, qu'au moyen de ces oeufs, les femmes comme les poules fournissaient toute la matière nécessaire pour la génération, et que les hommes comme les coqs, ne fournis-

13. *Anatomical Exercitations Concerning the Generation of Living Creatures* (1653), p. 390–91.

14. Ibid., sig. A7^{v}–A8. Cf. Newton's phrase in *Opticks*, Qu. 31 (1717), p. 376: "Nature is very consonant and conformable to her self."

15. Needham, *A History of Embryology* (2d ed. 1959), pp. 162–63. The mammalian ovum was not actually seen until 1827.

16. *Anatomy of Plants*, p. 173.

saient que certains esprits naturellement destinés à rendre ces oeufs prolifiques; quelques auteurs modernes ayant aussi découvert dans la plante des petites boules ou vésicules, qui ne sont apparamment que l'insertion des fibres, ont voulu que toutes choses tirassent leur origine des oeufs. Ils ont soûmis les plantes à cette loi, et ont prétendu que leurs vésicules fussent des ovaires, que les semences fussent des oeufs, qui, contenant en miniature toutes les parties de la plante, n'eussent besoin pour éclore que d'être fomentés par la chaleur du soleil et arrosés par le suc de la terre.[17]

In *Historia Plantarum* (1686) John Ray showed great interest in Grew's theory, although he was not willing to deny the male all influence on the offspring. Between the stigma and the ovule lay the solid body of the pistil; the early embryologists had to solve the problem of how the male influence was conveyed through its substance. Grew and Ray, unable to solve this difficulty, assumed that the male influence was immaterial:

> It does not argue against [the sexuality of plants] that these particles . . . do not penetrate into the uterus or seed; for they do not do so in fish, whose eggs are fertilized from a considerable height. . . . [The sperm's] vapor and subtle effluvia alone are sufficient to fertilize the egg and to vivify the embryon inside.[18]

In 1691 Ray published *The Wisdom of God Manifested in the Works of the Creation,* containing new observations on plant generation. The pollen must exert some influence on the development of the ovule, even if an immaterial one, because in some animal hybrids the male had "a great, if not the greatest, stroke in generation." [19] Ray named the immaterial influence "plastic nature." In the second edition of 1692 he contrived a syllogism to prove his point. The male influence affected the ovule. The pistil could not be penetrated by a material substance. Therefore the male influence was immaterial. He abandoned the anatomy of plant generation "to the more sagacious philosophers to inquire." [20] We may gain from Ray's content-

17. *De l'âme des plantes* (1685), pp. 262–63. This "strict analogy" was remarked by George Adams, *Micrographia Illustrata* (1746), p. 218. Cf. Bradley, "The Generation of Plants" (1724), pp. 9–10.

18. *1,* 17.

19. P. 219. Note that this argument presupposes that plants are analogous to animals.

20. Ibid., (2d ed. 1692), part 1, p. 97.

ment with this solution a foretaste of later beliefs about subtle fertilizing fluids and the complacency toward anatomical observations which was to characterize those who held the beliefs. In 1694 Ray wrote, "the apices . . . are the principal part of the flower, and it is our opinion that the pollen they contain is directly analogous to the seminal animalcules of animals, endowed with prolific virtue and serving to fertilize the female." [21]

Sebastian Vaillant (1669–1722) took a similar position in 1717. "Seulement la vapeur, ou l'esprit volatile qui se dégageant des grains de poussière, va féconder les oeufs." [22] He argued that the bright purple pollen of some poppies left no traces of its color in the ovules which it had fertilized. He should not have expected this to happen. The pollen of the spermatophyte plants is not a simple fertilizing particle which finds its way into the ovule but an asexual generation of the plant rather similar to the sporophores of lower plants. It may lie dormant for a time until placed on a stigma moist with the sugar solution secreted by mature female flower parts, whereupon it sends forth a tube which grows easily in the tissue of the style and carries gametes to the ovule, which is fertilized by them.

Opposed to the ovists among theorists of animal generation there arose a group, usually called the "animalculists," who believed that the embryo was preformed within the seminal animalcule. We have seen how Leeuwenhoek described the embryo plants in their seeds within the ovary. In 1703 Samuel Morland supposed that they had pre-existed in the pollen. The penetration of the pistil presented no difficulties to Morland, who unblushingly assumed that the style was hollow to permit the pollen grains to pass through to the ovules. This was a characteristic mechanist interpretation because it countenanced gross fertilizing corpuscles. Morland recurred to Malpighi's analogy between the styles of plants and Fallopian tubes. While conceding that the plant tubes must be very narrow, he was nevertheless certain that nature's lavish provision of pollen would insure the passage of some grains "through so narrow a conveyance." Morland was highly critical of Grew's "spirituous emanations or energetical impress." [23] He added that wind would shake or rain wash the pollen down the style, and supplied a plate showing a hole through which he supposed the pollen grains to enter the seed. He was well pleased to "observe the analogy between animal and vegetable generation as

21. "Praefatio," *Stirpium Europearum* (1694), sig. B4–B4ᵛ.
22. *Discours sur la structure des fleurs,* p. 16.
23. Morland, "The Parts and Use of the Flower" (1703), p. 1475.

far as [it] was necessary there should be an agreement between them." We may style Morland's interpretation the "pollenist" hypothesis and that of Grew, Ray, and Vaillant the "ovulist" hypothesis, to emphasize the parallel with animalculism and ovism as explanations of generation in animals. Étienne François Geoffroy (1672–1731) observed in 1711 that the embryo did not appear in maize grains until the pollen had dehisced. He sucked water through a lily pistil, citing its hollowness as a proof for his assertion that tubes in the style permitted the passage of whole pollen grains.

> If one cuts the pistil transversely in the narrowest part he will find as many canals as there are divisions of the stigma. These canals go along to reach each cellule which encloses two ranks of seeds ranged in a spongy placenta.[24]

Patrick Blair maintained the ovulist position in 1720. He had taken the side of the mechanists in the dispute with Bradley over the nature of circulating fluids; in plant generation he argued for an immaterial influence. If this looks inconsistent it is only because Blair took positions "to make good the analogy." [25]

> As the work of generation in animals does not proceed from their animal or sensitive but from their vegetative life, which being the same as in plants, that operations must be performed after the same manner in both. Therefore as there is a necessity of two different sexes in animals, it must be so in plants too.[26]

He argued against the pollenists "that the farina in substantia cannot enter the vasculum seminale, or if it do, that there is no direct passage for it to enter each particular seed . . . then I hope both their queries, suppositions, and assertions must fall." [27] Philip Miller's hybrid cabbages in the Chelsea Physick Garden demonstrated that embryos were not preformed but created by the union of two influences. Blair supposed that this was an argument against the pollenists (it applied equally well to ovulists). "Did each grain of this farina

24. "Sur la structure des parties des fleurs," p. 220. See his summary of the ovulist-pollenist positions, pp. 228–29. He ingeniously cited one of Giovanni Pontano's Eridanus poems [1481] describing a female date palm at Otranto which bore no fruit until it could "see" a male in Brindisi, in support of his belief that windblown pollen might be carried great distances: Pontano (1426–1503), *Carmina ecloghe—elegie—liriche,* ed. J. Oeschger (Bari: G. Laterza and Sons, 1948), p. 408. Bradley published a translation of ten lines in *A Philosophical Account* (1721), p. 103.

25. *Botanick Essays,* p. 302.

26. Ibid., pp. 231–32.

27. Ibid., p. 279.

enter the pistil to its proper uterus this mongrel kind would never be produced."[28] Penetration into the ovary by pollen grains "is no more probable than that a Musket ball can pass through a thick Rampart wall."[29] Blair's preface of 1724 was an exceptionally abusive attack upon Richard Bradley. John Martyn (1699–1768) found "such marks of *delirium,* that I persuaded Mr. Strahan not to publish them by any means."[30]

The ovulist–pollenist controversy did not have to become a futile wrangle from fixed positions. Continued investigation of the subject could have disclosed the true anatomy of plant reproduction. The quarrel had gone on for years when Richard Bradley turned to the subject in 1721. He tried to avoid dogmatic argument and offered his own solution of the penetration difficulty "only as an hypothesis."[31] His beliefs about plant generation led toward the development of a theory based on subtle fluids. While a refinement in the texture of explanations constituted a gain for the possibility of true explanation by doing away with references to penetrating pollen grains and immaterial influences, it diverted attention from the fruitful problem of the penetration difficulty and gave rise to unfounded speculations. The existence of hybrids would receive a more creditable explanation, and the analogy with animal reproduction would be saved, but at the price of ambiguity in descriptions and the abandonment of close anatomical investigation.

Bradley began by describing the fertilization of animals, whereby little worms in the semen entered the womb to undergo metamorphosis into embryos. Should two vermicules be admitted to the ovum, "We shall find two foetus under the same covering, or else a

28. "Observations upon the Generation of Plants" (1721), p. 218. The earliest known reference to a plant hybrid occurs in a letter from Cotton Mather (1663–1728) in December, 1716 to James Petiver describing a friend whose yellow maize planted to the leeward side of red and blue maize had "ye same colour communicated unto them." The same man attempted to deter thefts of his squashes by planting gourds among them, only to discover that the squashes became "so infected and embittered by the gourds, that there was no eating of them" (BM Sloane MS 4,065, f. 155). Cf. Zirkle, "Some Forgotten Records of Hybridization" (1932). Miller's description of hybrids was dated 19 Oct. 1721. The presumptive explantation of hybrids offered by Leeuwenhoek would have accorded with the pollenist thesis, but it was overlooked.

29. "The Preface" (1724), p. [93].

30. Letter of 16 June 1754 to Bishop Richard Rawlinson, inside the front cover of the *Rawlinson MS.* Martyn objected to Blair's shrill slander that "the herbwomen in Covent Garden taught him [Bradley] how to make the monthly directions for the Kitchin": Letter of 23 June 1724 to Patrick Blair from John Martyn.

31. *A Philosophical Account,* p. 114.

monstrous double foetus joined together . . ." [32] This conjecture indicated a rare insight into questions of generation and a promise which Bradley fulfilled by the virtuosity of his speculations on plant generation. He sought to "examine if the generation of plants does not carry along with it some analogy to that of animals," hoping "to produce more solid arguments for the generation of animals than the ovarists [ovulists] have done." [33] In 1717 he had taken the extreme pollenist position, asserting that there was "a pipe to the uterus" which he devised an illustration to show.[34] In 1721 he was more doubtful:

> I agree that it is not sufficient to prove only that the prolific dust of the apices may fall upon the pistils of the flowers; we must conduct it even into the very cells of the seeds and I own that it is very difficult to comprehend how this dust can get there, but because we find a difficulty in anything are we therefore to conclude it is impossible? . . . A few observations, which time may produce, will set this matter in a clearer light.[35]

We observe Bradley in the process of abandoning the mechanist position of the penetration of gross particles of pollen, just as he had forsaken the belief in gross circulating fluids. By 1724 Bradley had abandoned hope of finding tubes to the ovary. He tried to overcome the penetration difficulty by a detailed investigation of "the analogy between plants and animals." No one had yet shown how the cock fertilized the egg, but eggs undoubtedly showed "the cock's tread" after copulation. Perhaps there were passages open only during the heat of conjugal passion. At other times the parts would be "fixed and contracted." [36] It seemed reasonable to suppose that "In coitu the parts I speak of are more relaxed . . . [and there is] passage sufficient to admit the male seed into the uterus, or even into the ovaries." [37] No doubt flowers were analogous to birds and their styles

32. Ibid., p. 106. He dismissed notions of preformation as "bare supposition." For experiments on hybrids see *New Improvements* (1717), part 1, p. 22; also *Ten Practical Discourses* (1727), pp. 87–90. Also Paul Dudley, "Observations on Plants in New England" (1724), pp. 198–99.

33. *A Philosophical Account,* p. 101; also 103.

34. *New Improvements* (1718), part 3, Pl. 3, Fig. 2, A (opp. p. 287): the drawing shows a tulip style with a fissure which he called the uterus, although it did not touch the receptacles; also (1717), part 1, p. 15.

35. *A Philosophical Account,* pp. 112–13.

36. *New Experiments* (1724), p. 17.

37. Ibid., p. 18.

were more relaxed "under the influence of the sun." While they were thus "dilated" the pollen found easy passage.

The suggestion which pointed most clearly to subsequent speculation about subtle fluids was made in 1717, when Bradley wrote that pollen might be assumed to possess "a magnetic virtue" because beeswax attracted light bodies when rubbed.[38] Another suggestion was that pollen grains burst in water to reveal "a multitude of grains and that the passage into the seat of the egg-nest [ovary] is capable of receiving many of them at one time." [39] Bradley's idea that pollen grains contained fine particles which might act by magnetic virtue was an adumbration of the later theory of subtle fertilizing fluids contained in vesicular pollen grains. Before continuing with this narrative we must pause to take note of the consequences of plant sexuality for the scale of function.

Aristotle's assertion that plants did not have separate sexes was contradicted by the discovery that such species as hemp and French mercury were dioecious, which is to say that male flowers occur on one plant and females on another. Rudolph Jacob Camerarius of Tübingen (1665–1721) described segregation experiments whereby he isolated plants bearing female flowers from those bearing male flowers and found the females sterile.[40] Jacob Bobart (1599–1680) is said to have found in 1682 that an isolated female lynchis (*Melandrium*) would be sterile.[41] Camerarius contradicted his knowledge of these plants by asserting that plants were by nature hermaphrodites and fertilized themselves. Perhaps he regarded dioecious plants as exceptions, or even as single individuals. He cited Swammerdam's recent discovery of hermaphroditism in snails and observed that form of sexuality to be the exception among animals but the rule among plants. He took this example from Grew and Ray, who both cited the analogy between self-fertilizing plants and hermaphroditic animals. Most of the writers on plant generation supposed that plants must fertilize themselves. Samuel Morland drew a flower with stamens reaching far above the pistil so that self-fertilization or "autogamy" would be possible. Geoffroy maintained that the stamens "are always disposed so that the extremity of the pistil necessarily receives the powders which they pour out." [42] Bradley believed "the pistil is always so placed that the apices which surround it are either equal

38. *New Improvements,* part 1, p. 14.
39. *New Experiments,* pp. 14–15.
40. *De Sexu Plantarum* (1694), pp. 19–21.
41. Blair, *Botanick Essays,* p. 293.
42. "Sur la structure des parties des fleurs" (1711), p. 221.

in height with it or about it, so that their dust falls naturally upon it."[43] Blair, who thought that the pollen fertilized by immaterial emanations, contrived an argument to show that it was physically impossible for pollen to reach the top of the pistil in upright flowers with short stamens, or in pendant flowers with very long stamens which overreach the pistil. This struck him as excellent proof, not that flowers cannot fertilize themselves, but that they must do so by immaterial effluvia![44]

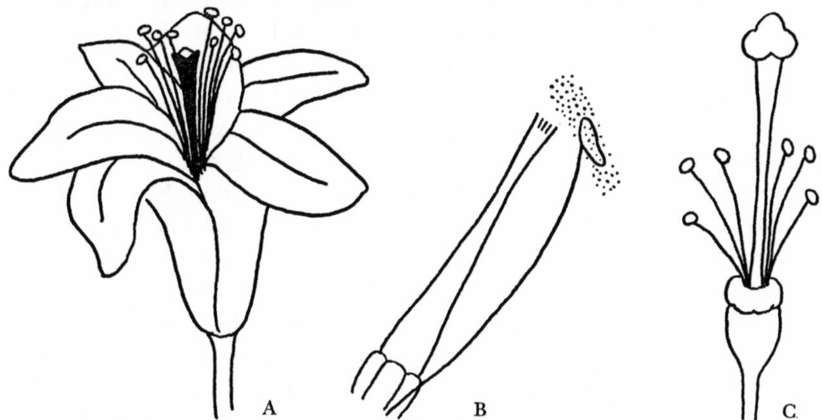

FIG. 1. Self-fertilization in the flower, 1703–1720. A. Pollen automatically enters the pistil.* B. Pollen automatically enters the pistil.† C. Fertilization must be by immaterial influence.‡

* Morland, "Parts of the Flower," Fig. 23 of plate opp. p. 1449.
† Bradley, New Improvements, part 1, Fig. 1 opp. p. 24.
‡ Blair, Botanick Essays, Fig. 3 of Pl. I opp. p. 284 [drawing by Pat Tidwell].

John Hill wrote in the *Monthly Review,*

> Nature has provided for the entrance of this fine matter into the pistil or uterus of the plant by making the bodies which support its capsules longer than the pistil in such flowers as stand erect, and shorter in such as hang downward; so that in both cases, when the capsules burst, this farina falls on the pistil, and, making its way down to the embryo seeds, impregnates them.[45]

43. *New Improvements,* part 1, p. 15.

44. Blair retained his belief in necessary autogamy even when Philip Miller showed that bees transported pollen from flower to flower: Blair, "Observations upon the Generation of Plants" (1721) pp. 216–18.

45. [Hill], Review of the *Philosophical Transactions, Monthly Review, 4* (Nov. 1750), 54–56.

Necessary autogamy was a corollary of the orthodoxy of graded function. There had to be some way of defining plant reproduction that would ascribe to plants functions less elaborate than those of animals. It was argued that plants fertilized themselves while animals fertilized each other, except for a few lower kinds that were hermaphrodites.

Richard Bradley was influenced in yet another way by the notion of a scale of beings. He supposed that the worm observed in the semen of animals entered the uterus, ascended the scale of beings until it reached the level of the intended species, and was born. "We may regard the form of the worm or animalcule in the generative liquor of animals as an instance of the certainty of a future metamorphosis."[46] In this passage Bradley hinted at a notion of embryo development very similar to the recapitulation theory which was to receive so much attention in the nineteenth century.

Speculation on subtle fertilizing fluids was strikingly exemplified in Louis Bourget's *Lettres philosophiques* (1729); he offered a theory to reconcile Newtonian attraction, the "conspiring movements" of Leibniz, and the pressure of ether described by Malebranche.[47] It was necessary to consider life forms as arranged in a series from the simplest through plants and zoophytes to the most complex animals. That explained why the hair and teeth of higher animals showed a kind of vegetation.[48] Reproduction was explained as the result of a "liqueur fort spiritueuse" in the pollen, or "parties plus subtiles de la liqueur."[49]

> La mécanisme organique n'est autre chose que la combinaison du mouvement d'une infinité des molécules éthériennes, aériennes, aqueuses, oléagineuses, salines, terrestres etc.[50]

Stephen Hales asked the readers of his *Vegetable Staticks* (1727) "to indulge conjecture" on the subtle matter in the pollen, which surrounded the plant "with an atmosphere of sublimed sulphureous pounce" serving "to attract and unite with itself elastic or other refined active particles."[51]

> And if to these united sulphureous and aerial particles we suppose some particles of light to be joined, for Sir Isaac Newton

46. Bradley, *A Philosophical Account* (1721), p. 105; also 111–12.
47. [1723], p. 51.
48. Ibid., p. 58.
49. Ibid., p. 149.
50. Ibid., p. 164.
51. Pp. 356–57.

has found that sulphur attracts light strongly, then the result of these three by far the most active principles in nature will be a punctum saliens to invigorate the seminal plant; and thus we are conducted by the regular analysis of vegetable nature to the first enlivening principle of their minutest origin.[52]

Hermann Boerhaave (1668–1738) was not sure how the penetration difficulty could be overcome. He hinted at subtle fluids:

Being admitted into the orifice of the pistil, it is either conveyed thence into the utricle [ovary], to fecundify the female ova; or it is lodged in the pistil, and by some magnetic power draws the nourishment from other parts of the plant into the embryos of the fruit.[53]

During his stay in Holland Linnaeus published the *Fundamenta Botanica* (1735), embodying the principle features of his system of botany.

Plants arise through the presence of pollen upon the naked stigma, where the grains are burst and the seminal aura flows out to be absorbed by the humors of the stigma.[54]

At a meeting of a philosophical club in Leyden in 1737 he was invited to view the seminal animalcules. He would not admit that the animalcules were worms or "corpora organisata" of any kind.[55] It is at least possible that Linnaeus refused to acknowledge the presence of moving bodies in semen because he could think of nothing analogous in plants. In his influential dissertation "Sponsalia Plantarum," published in 1749, Linnaeus gave a lengthy gloss on the aphorisms of the *Fundamenta Botanica* dealing with generation.[56] "The microscopes of Lieberkühn showed to us quite clearly" that the supposed animalcules were mere "dull corpuscles." Most of the embryo, ac-

52. Ibid., p. 357. Gesner, "De Fructificatione" (1743), Thesis IX, traces the development of subtle fluid theories from the "volatile spirit" of Vaillant and the "sulphureous attracting power" of Hales.

53. *A New Method of Chemistry, 1* (2d ed. 1741), p. 141 n.

54. [1735], aph. 145.

55. *A Dissertation on the Sexes of Plants* [1760], trans. Smith (1786), p. 9; also see [Linnaeus], "Generatio Ambigena," *Amoen. Acad., 6* (1764), 4–5. Also Pulteney, *A General View of the Writings of Linnaeus* (2d ed. 1805), pp. 49–50.

56. Linnaeus claimed the dissertation as his own in a letter of 23 Aug. 1746 to Haller: Smith, ed., *Correspondence of Linnaeus, 2* (1821), 390. See W. T. Stearn, "The *Amoenitates Academicae* and the Authorship of Linnaean Dissertations," in Carl Linnaeus, *Species Plantarum;* A *facsimile of the first edition 1753, 1* (London: Ray Society, 1957), 51–64. Also Pulteney, n. 55 above, p. 335.

cording to Linnaeus, was present in the egg before fertilization and came to resemble the female parent; the superficial external features and habits of the offspring were impressed upon the embryo by a subtle fluid contributed by the male parent, which the offspring came to resemble in those respects. He supposed that this notion explained the characteristics of hybrids.[57] Linnaeus recounted Bernard de Jussieu's observations on a grain of maple pollen placed in water:

> The moment some liquid touches a particle of pollen there is a discharge in the shape of a cross from four valves. These observations afford an opportunity for the following conclusions, namely that the pollen grains are hollow within, containing something peculiar to themselves, which at the first touch of liquid is discharged from the globules, which burst asunder and emit these very subtle contents. This observation adds not a little light to the generation of animals by analogy with the seminal vermicules.[58]

We recall Linnaeus's belief that the spermatic fluid contained inert fertilizing globules like pollen grains. In *Philosophia Botanica* (1751) Linnaeus defined pollen as "a vegetable dust which breaks open when moistened by the appropriate liquor and emits an elastic substance invisible to the naked eye." [59] "All pollen is vesicular and contains impalpable matter, which it explodes." [60] Linnaeus witnessed the formation of pollen tubes in the style of a lily after he had placed pollen on the stigma. He thought the tubes resulted from the passage of subtle matter and was content to observe merely that the pollenists had been wrong:

> We perceive little rivulets, or opaque streaks, running from the stigma towards the rudiments of the seed. Some time afterwards, when the drop [of liquid] has totally disappeared [from the stigma], the pollen may be observed adhering to the stigma, but of an irregular figure, having lost its original form. No one therefore, can assent to what Morland and others have asserted,

57. [Linnaeus], "Sponsalia Plantarum" [1746], p. 80; also [Linnaeus], "Fundamentum Fructificationis" [1762], *Amoen. Acad. 6* (1764), 279–304. Also [Linnaeus], "Generatio Ambigena" [1759], ibid., pp. 1–16. Also Pulteney, p. 553.

58. "Sponsalia Plantarum," p. 87. Jussieu does not seem to have published this observation. Duhamel (1700–81), who was present at the time, described it in *La physique des arbres* (1758), part 1, p. 223.

59. Par. 88.

60. Ibid., par. 143.

> that the pollen passes into the stigma, pervades the style, and enters the tender rudiments of the seed, as Leeuwenhoek supposed his worms to enter the ova.[61]

Such an observation might well have led to observations of the growth of pollen tubes in the style had the "streaks" not been attributed to subtle matter.

Linnaeus had drawn upon the observations of John Turbervill Needham (1713–81), the English Catholic priest in Paris, who viewed an "infusion" of lily pollen in water in 1743. "I plainly perceived a rope of exceeding small globules to be ejaculated with some force from within." [62] He observed another bursting pollen grain "shed a long train of globules adhering to each other, and enveloped in a filmy substance." In 1745 he published a small volume of very original microscopic observations. Upon examining the pistil he found "rows of [stigmatic] papillae, each with an aperture proportioned to the size of the globules of farina; its canals, etc. appropriated in the exactest and nicest manner for conveying the impregnating substance of the farina to the uterus or ovary." [63] He thought the pollen grain descended into the pockets on the stigma until it could go no farther, whereupon "it injects the impregnating substance with which it is replete into the tubes that lead to the uterus." [64] He refused to join Morland, Geoffroy, and Bradley in believing that the grain itself traveled to the ovules, because many flowers had solid pistils. "The subtlest of its parts only penetrates into the tubes." [65] Needham saw pollen tubes which had grown in the style and described them as much finer than the stigmatic irregularities. He did not make the crucial observation which would have shown the tubes growing in the style. He did see the gametes emerge from a pollen grain placed in water. He concluded only that the fertilizing matter was "inconceivably fine, subtle, and penetrating." [66]

> I thought I observed some alteration in these minute bodies, as if the shell or case had emitted through a small aperture and shed a long train of minute globules, which appeared but as

61. *Dissertation on Sexes of Plants* [1760], pp. 28–29.
62. Needham, "Microscopical Observations on the Farina of the Red Lily" (1743), p. 639.
63. *An Account of Some New Microscopical Discoveries,* pp. 64–65.
64. Ibid., p. 68.
65. Ibid., p. 72.
66. Ibid., p. 76 n.

> points in the microscope, involved in a filmy substance, as the eggs of some aquatic insects are.[67]

The bursting grains in water resembled nothing so much as "an Æolipyle violently heated."

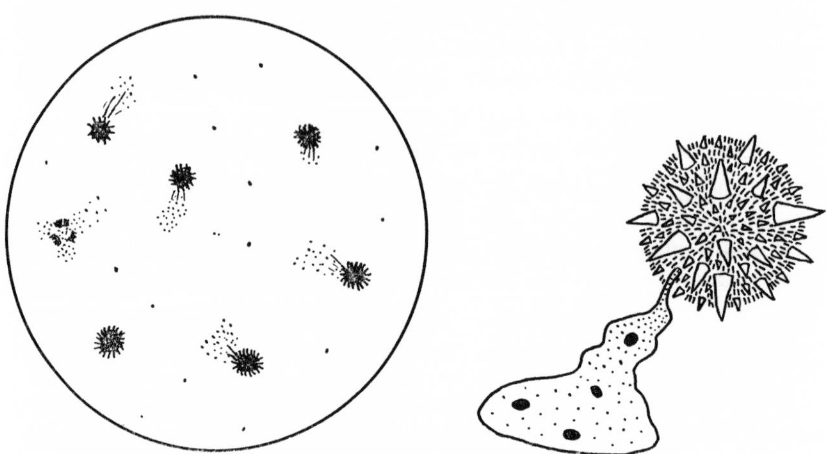

FIG. 2. The subtle contents of vesicular pollen.*

* Needham, *Microscopical Discoveries,* Fig. 4 and 5 of Pl. IV. Linnaeus reproduced the illustration of the discharging pollen grain in *Philosophia Botanica,* Fig. 151 of Pl. VIII opp. p. 302 [drawing by Pat Tidwell].

The interpretation of microscopical observations almost always depends upon prevailing opinions about life and matter. Needham was led astray by the idea of immanence. We must remind ourselves that, whatever its defects, the subtle fluid physiology was an improvement over corpuscular mechanism so far as the texture to be attributed to organisms was concerned. It is interesting to speculate on what a mechanistic physiologist might have made of the pollen tubes; perhaps he would have suspected that they had grown in the pistil. We have no way of knowing.

Needham's concept of "exuberating ductile matter actuated with a vegetative force" permitted anologies with prevailing beliefs about

67. Ibid., p. 73. Cf. C. D. Darlington, "The Place of Botany in the Life of a University" (Oxford: Clarendon Press, 1954), pp. 9–10, for an estimate of the way primitive microscopes used before the discovery of the achromatic doublet made it difficult to study physiology. Another harmful effect of the low resolving power of eighteenth-century microscopes was the scope they permitted for speculation. It was not that nothing at all could be seen, but that speculators were able to imagine they had seen whatever they liked.

subtle fluids in animal generation.[68] One of the most remarkable examples of analogy in the history of embryology was Needham's comparison of a pollen grain to the spermatophore of cephalopods, a device which ejects the sperm of squid and cuttlefish in a number of small discharges. It had been seen by Swammerdam, who knew its function, but Needham gave "the first detailed account" and it is occasionally called Needham's organ.[69] From his own account of pollen discharging its contents in 1743, Needham was led almost inevitably to a unique analogy between pollen grains and these "milt-vessels":

> The analogy between the vegetable and animal world in this particular [generation] will appear to be still greater than has been hitherto imagined, as the nature of the farina fecundans and its action upon the application of water, not unlike that of the milt-vessels mentioned above, imply something of a similar mechanism within the globules contrived for the same purpose.[70]

In 1765 there was yet another microscopic examination of the pollen tubes, under a supposed magnification of 859 diameters, with the tiny single lenses dropped from molten glass by Father Giovanni Maria della Torre of Naples. With such a microscope the "impregnating corpuscles" might be studied to advantage in delicate plants "where the style is slender and transparent [so] they may be distinguished in their passage." [71] The *Philosophical Transactions* carried an illustration of a style with many tubes in 1765 but they were not traced to the agency of the pollen.

68. "A Summary of Some Late Observations" (1748), p. [620].

69. David H. Tomsett, "Sepia," *L.M.B.C. Memoirs on Typical British Marine Plants and Animals* (Liverpool Univ. Press, 1939), no. 32, pp. 136–41 and fig. 77–78.

70. *Some New Microscopical Discoveries,* p. 62. Needham showed Buffon's influence in his belief in universally diffused living corpuscles. He was led astray in the most frightful way when he observed that gravy, no matter how tightly sealed in sterilized flasks, soon swarmed with life. See Paul Hazard's lively account of these "marvellous results" in *European Thought in the Eighteenth Century from Montesquieu to Lessing,* trans. J. Lewis May (Yale Univ. Press, 1954), pp. 136–37. John Hill charged Needham with materialistic tendencies: *Monthly Review, 4* (Nov. 1750), 58. Hill's *Lucina Sine Concubitu* (1750) was a satire of this and similar beliefs. Hill's own system of generation was based on the absurd idea that the "vascular substance" of the stem grows up through the stamen and is planted as a fragment of living plant in the ovary: *Outlines of a System of Vegetable Generation* (1758), pp. 37–46. See his criticisms of analogy, p. 4.

71. Stiles, "Concerning Some New Microscopes" (1765), p. 261 and Pl. 8, Fig. 19. On the Torre microscope see *Priestley, The History and Present State of Discoveries Relating to Vision, Light, and Colours* (London: J. Johnson, 1772), p. 745. Also George Adams, *Essays on the Microscope* (1787), pp. 10–11.

Most naturalists were content with the notion of subtle fertilizing fluids, and their attention shifted away from questions of minute sexual anatomy. James Parsons wrote of an "exalted fluid" which constituted the "impregnating effluvium" in 1752.[72] Joseph Gottlieb Koelreuter (1733–1806) published an important work on plant generation in 1761 which established the importance of insects in transmitting pollen and reported several valuable hybridization experiments. He believed that male and female fluids mixed on the stigma and exerted an immaterial influence on the ovary. He was correct in calling the bursting pollen observed by Jussieu, Duhamel, and Needham an unnatural effect, but did not realize they had skirted a fundamental discovery. "The organized [körnichte] material of the pollen, which Needham took for a collection of germs, is nothing other than the substance of the human semen in a raw, unripe form." [73] Michel Adanson wrote in 1763 that fertilization was not effected "by the intromission of the powder of the stamens" but by a subtle vapor "just as tenuous, as animated, and as active as that which envelops electrified bodies; it insinuates itself into the tracheae of the style and passes from their termination on the stigma to the placenta." [74] Marmaduke Berdoe assumed that generation was accomplished by "the most active sparks of the electric fluid." [75] Lazzaro Spallanzani wrote that fertilization was effected by the "spermatic vapor" of the pollen and not by the "gross sensible part." [76] Christian Konrad Sprengel's (1750–1816) famous book on plant generation in 1793 was published after years of painstaking field observation and microscopy. He described many modifications of flower parts for achieving pollination but explained the penetration of the pollen's influence in the same way. He was much taken with the "Ähnlichkeit der Befruchtungsart" between plants and animals:

72. *Philosophical Observations on the Analogy between the Propagation of Animals and That of Vegetables,* p. 81.

73. Koelreuter, *Vorläufige Nachricht von einigen das Geschlecht der Pflanzen betreffenden Versuchen und Beobachtungen* (1761), p. 7. Von Sachs, *History of Botany* [1875], pp. 411–12, asserts that hybrids could not be explained before Koelreuter's idea. But Leeuwenhoek offered a presumptive explanation in 1693, and Linnaeus wrote a great deal on the subject.

74. Adanson, *Familles des plantes, 1* (Paris: Vincent, 1763), 121.

75. *An Enquiry into the Influence of the Electric Fluid* (1771), p. 99; also 100–05.

76. "A Dissertation Concerning the Generation of Certain Plants" (1784), pp. 322–23. Réaumur wrote in *Art de faire eclorre et d'élever en toute saison des oiseaux domestiques . . . , 2* (Paris: Imprimerie Royale, 1749), 329–30, that Newtonian attraction was being used to solve all the mysteries of generation. Also Charles Bonnet, "Idées sur la fécondation des plantes" (1774), p. 265. He wrote that Newton and Hales had disclosed the subtlety and activity of pollen and its affinity for light.

Once it is on the stigma the pollen grain penetrates the style, not with its own body which is many times too large, but with the fertilizing essence which it contains, through the pistil and into the ovary, and influences the germ just as the male sperm does the female ovary in the animal world.[77]

In an influential handbook on botany published in 1819 Kurt Sprengel (1766–1833) attacked the mechanistic "pollenist" hypothesis advanced by "the natural historians of the early part of the eighteenth century, that there is a direct passage of the pollen into the ovary."

We must allow its privilege to analogy, which informs us, that in the lower animals, particularly in the molluscs, impregnation is accomplished without the passage of any material substance from the impregnating organ into the receptacle of the seed. In this case it is purely a galvanic process, in which, by means of the chain of different organs lying together, the vital activity is unfolded to the degree necessary for the production of new individuals. A process exactly similar takes place in the vegetable kingdom. The pollen, brought into contact with the stigma awakens in it, as well as in the germen [ovule], a new life.[78]

The pollen tube was not satisfactorily observed until 1830 when Giovanni Battista Amici (1786–1863) turned his improved microscope to a freshly fertilized section from the stigma of a yucca plant: "C'est le boyau lui-même qui peu à peu s'allonge, descend par le style, et va se mettre en contact avec l'amande." [79]

This discovery pretty well disposed of galvanic fertilization and subtle fluids. It upset the analogy between plant and animal generation, curiously enough, because the spermatozoa were still considered a species of worm.[80] Gottfried Reinhold Treviranus (1776–1837) sought to correct this notion in 1835 by asserting that spermatozoa bore a better analogy to pollen than to worms. He thought "the term

77. *Das entdeckte Geheimniss der Natur im Bau und in der Befruchtung der Blumen* (1793), p.)(2. Also Brisseau-Mirbel, *Traité d'anatomie et de physiologie végétales,* 2 (1801–02), 52.

78. Sprengel and deCandolle, *Elements of the Philosophy of Plants* [1819], p. 253; also 254.

79. "Note sur le mode d'action du pollen sur le stigmate" (1830), p. 331. For this discovery see Wodehouse, *Pollen Grains* (1935), pp. 15–105.

80. For examples of confusion on this matter see F. J. Cole, *Early Theories of Sexual Generation* (1930), pp. 16–36. Also J. F. Blumenbach, *A Manual of the Elements of Natural History,* trans. R. T. Gore [from 10th ed.] (London: W. Simpkin and R. Marshall, 1825), p. 277. John Hill classified spermatozoa as worms: *An History of Animals* (1752), pp. 8–9 and Pl. 1.

'animal pollen' would be a more appropriate name for the organized parts of animal semen than the appellation seminal animalcule."[81]

> The reader will not fail to recognize a strong analogy between the organized parts of animal semen and the pollen of plants. The latter, just like the former, is composed of an aggregate of vesicles surrounded by a common integument, and containing the proper fructifying matter; and which, when moistened by the fluid that exudes from the stigma and nectaries at the time of their maturity, quit their investment.[82]

While spermatozoa lack the encasing microspore of pollen grains, this false analogy may have helped to overthrow the belief that worms, rather than human cells, were the fertilizing agents in semen. The understanding of the pollen tube, like almost every other development in our history of theories of plant generation, was deeply influenced by the idea of botanical analogy.

81. "On the Organized Bodies Found in the Seminal Fluid of Animals, and Their Analogy to the Pollen of Plants," p. 343.
82. Ibid., p. 340.

4

The Triumph of Botanical Analogy

i. Linnaeus, Analogy, and the Scale of Beings

Carl Linnaeus (1707–78) retained throughout his life a child-like sense of identification with the world of nature, except the reptiles, to which he reacted with unscientific abhorrence. His sensitive character was particularly susceptible to the appeal of general ideas. He wished his life to be "hallowed" or metaphysically sanctioned by the discovery of what he imagined to have been the divine plan for the creation.[1] He was given Vaillant's essay on plant sexuality in 1726 by Dr. Rothman at Växjö and his enthusiasm for the discovery colored much of his subsequent work.

> The organs of generation, which in the animal kingdom are by nature generally removed from sight, in the vegetable kingdom are exposed to the eyes of all, and that when their nuptials are celebrated, it is wonderful what delight they afford to the spectator by their most beautiful colors and delicious odors.[2]

1. A. J. Boerman, "Carolus Linnaeus, a Psychological Study" (1953), p. 153. One receives a similar impression from many of Linnaeus's writings. See Knut Hagberg, *Carl Linnaeus* (1952) on the MS *Nemesis Divina,* a book of dark sayings and anecdotes to show the active influence of evil. Also Pulteney, *Writings of Linnaeus,* (2d ed. 1805). Note the introduction to *Critica Botanica* [1737], trans. Sir Arthur Hort (1938), pp. xxi–xxvi, or the addresses to Jehovah in various editions of the *Systema Naturae.* Also "Oeconomia Naturae" [1749] or *Reflections on the Study of Nature,* trans. J. E. Smith (London: George Nicol, 1785). Also *Lachesis Lapponica . . . ,* trans. Smith (London: White and Cochrane, 1811).

2. [Linnaeus], "Oeconomia Naturae" [1749], p. 16. At the age of 22 (1729) he

When Linnaeus set out to establish as an axiom of botany the existence of sexes in plants he argued from their analogy with animals. "To illustrate the generation of plants, we must take our first lights from the animal kingdom and pursue the chain of nature till it leads us to vegetables." [3] In the *Fundamenta Botanica* (1735) he stated that plants, while they lacked sensation, were "equal with animals" in the possession of life, as was proved by similarities in origin, nutrition, aging, disease, death, movement, internal propulsion of fluids, and general anatomy.[4] All that lives proceeds from eggs. The seed is the egg of plants. Therefore, as "it is contrary to all experience for eggs to hatch without having been fertilized, so it is with plants." [5]

> Therefore the calyx is the bedchamber, the corolla the curtains, the filaments the spermatic vessels, the anthers the testes, the pollen the sperm, the stigma the vulva, the style the vagina, the germen the ovary, the pericarp the fecundating ovary, and the seed the ovum.[6]

This anthropomorphic description of generation was followed by a general statement of botanical analogy:

> The belly of plants is the ground; the chyliferous vessels, the root; the bones, the trunk; the lungs, the leaves; the heart, the heat [of plant tissues]; hence the ancients described a plant as an inverted animal.[7]

Harvey was named as the authority for the phrase "Omne vivum ex ovo" which began aphorism 134.[8]

As for the cryptogams, whose life cycle was not then understood, he wrote that Linnaeus, Micheli (1679–1737), Vallisner (1661–1730), Jus-

---

wrote a small MS tract entitled "Praeludia Sponsaliarum Plantarum in quibus physiologia earum explicatur, sexus demonstratur, modus generationis detegitur, nec son summa plantarum cum animalibus analogia concluditur." Uggla, *Linnaeus* (1957), Plate 4a, reproduces the title page. Cf. Rousseau's "ecstasy" and "rapture" at the "thousand little acts of fructification I observed": *Rêveries du promeneur solitaire* [1782]; *Confessions . . . ,* 2 (London: J. Bew, 1783), 215–16. Also his letter of 21 Sept. 1771 to Linnaeus, in Smith, ed., *Correspondence of Linnaeus,* 2 (1821), 553.

3. Linnaeus, *Sexes of Plants* [1760], p. 15.
4. Aphorism 133.
5. Ibid., aphorism 138.
6. Ibid., aphorism 146.
7. Ibid., aphorism 147.
8. "Sponsalia Plantarum," p. 73.

sieu, Réaumur, Bobart, and Tournefort (1656–1708) had seen their seeds or "eggs."[9] In "Sponsalia Plantarum" [1746] he mentioned segregation experiments in which female plants isolated from males bore no fertile seeds, but devoted more space to elaborating his argument from analogy. We might fairly say that the idea of botanical analogy was the central concept of Linnaean botany (Plate 3).

Linnaeus made the sexual anatomy of plants the basis for his celebrated artificial system of plant classification, which divided all species into twenty-four classes. The classes were keyed to the number or relation of the stamens, except the last class: "clandestine marriage" or cryptogams. The number of stamens is not an adequate index of relationships of affinity and descent among plants. The popularity of the Linnaean system among amateurs who were for the first time able to refer a flower to a systematic catalogue should not obscure the fact that very few botanists thought it arranged plants according to their true affinities. Linnaeus listed exceptions to the categories in his more comprehensive taxonomic manuals and stated clearly what some amateur botanists were distressed to discover, that the sexual system was artificial, a useful organizing device perhaps, but not an attempt to express true relationships.

In the *Classes Plantarum* (1738) Linnaeus listed sixty-four natural orders of plants (and one of corals) as an adumbration of a natural system. "The method which preserves more natural orders is said to be more natural and vice versa."[10] Systematic relationships are manifested by specimens arranged in groups (the natural orders of which Linnaeus spoke), to which the system (the method, in Linnaeus's words) gives clue by the use of selected characteristics. A natural system would provide adequate characters for groups of plants which had been arranged according to their true affinities. One of Linnaeus's most arresting beliefs was that only one representative of each natural order need have existed at the Creation. This comment is the first suggestion of the phylogenetic basis of modern systematics.[11] Throughout his life Linnaeus believed that the characters for any system of plants should be drawn from the fructification: number, disposition, and relation of flower parts and sections through the ovary. But the

9. Typical of the mistaken ideas about cryptogams in the eighteenth century was the description by Noël Antoine Pluche (1688–1761), *Spectacle de la nature, 1* (Paris: la Veuve Estienne, and Jean Desaint, 1732), 407–11. Cf. Gesner, "De Fructificatione" (1743), pp. 88–89.

10. Col. 484.

11. Linnaeus, "Fundamentum Fructificationis" [1762], *Amoen. Acad., 6* (1764), 19 ff. Also *Genera Plantarum* (6th ed. 1764), III–IV.

"sexual system" or artificial method, based on the stamens alone, linked species with dissimilar flowers and separated others with flowers similar in almost all respects but the number of stamens.[12] We may note a further difference between an artificial system and a natural one. An artificial system derives its appeal from the simplicity of its characters and depends upon an a priori assessment of characters rather than their adequacy to predict relationships of true affinity. The characters of a natural system, on the other hand, are obtained by induction from arranged specimens. We shall offer a conjecture about the latent processes of Linnaeus's reasoning about the manner in which the specimens for a natural system were to be arranged.

Linnaeus wrote, "I myself have worked for a long time to devise a natural system, and while I was able to add some things to it I was unable to perfect it; and I shall continue as long as I live."[13] He was fully aware that natural orders preserving overall floral affinity would not follow merely from the number and relation of stamens; he wrote to Haller in 1737:

> I am ready to agree with you that the stamens and pistils lead to no natural system; having adopted a method founded thereon as a substitute, to excite curious observers to examine these parts of the fructification, hitherto reckoned so trifling and unimportant; for an alphabetical arrangement was always intolerable to me. Besides, an attention to the organs in question may have its use, though not altogether for the purpose of natural classes.[14]

He wrote to Haller a few months later, "Far be it from me ever to uphold artificial arrangements . . . I wish we knew more about natural classes."[15] Had Linnaeus been an empiricist, he would have presented successive editions of the *Genera Plantarum* and *Systema Naturae* with plants listed according to the natural orders he recognized in the "Fragmenta Methodi Naturalis" in 1738. Other botanists might then have revised his system as more subtle relationships of

12. L. C. Miall listed the following violations of true affinity by the classes of the artificial system: *Zea, Holcus,* and *Anthoxanthum* were separated from the grasses; *Veronica* from the Schrophularaceae; *Salvia* and *Lycopus* from the *Labiatae; Sanguisorba, Poterium,* and *Alchemilla* from the Rosaceae. The system associated *Mercurialis* (Euphorbiaceae) with *Hydrocharis* (Hydrocharitaceae); *Valerian* (Valerianaceae) with the Iridaceae; *Potamogeton* (Potamogetonaceae) with holly (Aquifolaceae); and arrowhead (Alismataceae) with oak and beech (Fagaceae). *The Early Naturalists* (1912), p. 326.

13. *Classes Plantarum* (1738), col. 484.

14. Letter of 3 April, in Smith, ed., *Correspondence of Linnaeus,* 2 (1821), 229.

15. Ibid., p. 311. Letter of 3 Jan. 1738 N.S.

affinity were discovered and new plants found. Such an enterprise would have been consistent with the regulative values of accuracy and conformity to nature involved in the concept of limited explanation. It seems likely that what Linnaeus hoped to discover was a sequence of groups that might be presented as a linear series or scale of natural orders. Only by 1750 or 1751 did he come to realize that this could not be done. The fragment of a natural method in the *Classes Plantarum* arranged plants in a numerical sequence of orders, listing genera in single linear columns. The series seems to represent decreasing elaborateness of flowers, with the cryptogams and corals (still regarded as plants) at the end. Was not Linnaeus trying to pattern his natural system after the scale of beings?

> There is, as it were, a certain chain of created beings, according to which they seem all to have been formed, and one thing differs so little from some other, that if we hit upon the right method we shall scarcely find any limits between them. This no one can so well observe as he who is acquainted with the greatest number of species [i.e. Linnaeus himself]. Does not everyone perceive that there is a vast difference between a stone and a monkey? But if all the intermediate beings were set to view in order, it would be difficult to find the limits between them. The polypus [hydra] and the sea-moss join the vegetable and the animal kingdom together, for the plants called Confervae [algae] and the animals called Sertularia [marine polyzoa and hydroids] are not easy to distinguish. The corals connect the animal, vegetable, and fossil world.
>
> Hence the botanists of this age have been busy seeking out natural classes, which is surely a matter of great moment and an extensive investigation.[16]

He mentioned an instance wherein he had transferred a genus from one natural order to another. It would never have occurred to a botanist to place genus *Turnera* among the columniferous plants (and in 1738 he did not do so) were it not for the characteristics of one of the columniferous plants, the musk-mallow (*Malva*). "*Malva,* as soon

16. [Linnaeus], "Quaestio Historico Naturalis, Cui Bono?" [1752], pp. 248–49. For other references to the scale of beings see the "Imperium Naturale" in the *Systema Naturae* or aphorism 3 of the *Fundamenta Botanica*. Cadwallader Colden criticized the artificial system and argued strongly for a natural system based upon the scale of beings in a letter to J. F. Gronovius in December of 1744. *Colden Papers, 3* (1920), 89–92.

as it was examined, connected the *Turnera* with the columniferous plants." [17] In 1751 he placed *Turnera* in order 34, "Columnifera," in the "Fragmenta quo ego proposui," published as part of the *Philosophia Botanica*.[18] It may have been by the discovery of such links that Linnaeus hoped to arrange the entire plant kingdom in a linear series reaching from plants with no flowers to those with the most complicated ones.

There can be no question of the importance Linnaeus attached to the idea of a scale of beings. He wrote in 1760, with reference to the sex of plants:

> We must pursue the great chain of nature till we arrive at its origin; we should begin to contemplate her operations in the human frame and from thence continue our researches through the various tribes of quadrupeds, birds, reptiles, fishes, insects, and worms, till we arrive at the vegetable creation.[19]

The idea of botanical analogy, which Linnaeus used in arguing for the existence of sexes in plants, was itself a corollary of the scale of beings. In 1738 he had tried to arrange plants in linear series. His shift of Turnera shows that he tried to perfect the scheme between 1738 and 1751. Why did he not continue with this effort? The answer, simply stated, is that it could not be done. If we have presented Linnaeus's ideas correctly, a phrase in a letter written in 1750 to Johann Gesner of Zurich (1709–90) becomes very significant. He seems to state that he could not arrange plants in a single linear scale in which each group was joined both to the group above and the one below:

> The plants themselves have been disposed by the great Creator according to their affinities, in such a manner as if they had been written on a chart or geographical map in which the boundaries between closely adjacent regions are very difficult to distinguish.

17. Ibid., p. 249. Also *Classes Plantarum,* cols. 502, 505.

18. P. 31. Between 1738 and 1751 Linnaeus made extensive revisions in the order of the genera in orders VI, XXIX, XXX, XXXIII, XXXVI, and XLIII. Within the orders three sets of three genera were rearranged and eight pairs of genera reversed in sequence. The genera added to the orders between 1738 and 1751 were placed sometimes in the middle of a sequence, sometimes at the beginning, and sometimes at the end. Linnaeus would not have made such changes if he did not mean the serial order of the genera to be significant.

19. *Sexes of Plants,* pp. 8–9. Contrast this movement from the complex to the simple with Hooke's more mechanistic progression from the simple to the complex.

> They acknowledge a dual affinity which no mortal could easily overthrow.[20]

In the *Philosophia Botanica* (1751) he wrote, "Plantae omnes utrinque affinitatem monstrant, uti territorium in mappa geographica." [21] August Thienemann interpreted this comment as a criticism of the idea of a scale of beings:

> For Linnaeus a class or genus represented a country on a political map, surrounded by a ring of other countries. The borders between any two can be long or short, according to their similarity.[22]

Nils von Hofsten writes that Linnaeus's idea of nature was "a single-lined chain of links." [23] Arthur Cain's acute analysis of the logic underlying Linnaeus's concept of genus and species disclosed a conformity to Aristotelian modes of reasoning.[24] Each of these conclusions illuminates a small area of our conjecture, which we state as follows. From 1738 or earlier until 1750 and 1751 Linnaeus hoped to found a natural system of plant taxonomy on a linear series of plant groups. He despaired of this arrangement after 1751 because he had found the groups of plants interlocked with each other like pieces of a Chinese puzzle.

After 1751 Linnaeus became more interested in morphological notions that flowers were the essential parts of plants, as though to compensate himself for the failure of the linear series and provide some sort of metaphysical sanction for the artificial system. In an autobiographical sketch he wrote:

> The sexes of plants, which have sometimes been maintained and sometimes opposed and denied, he proved in so clear a manner that all his adversaries were silenced; and who could do it better than Linné? For he had examined all known plants—an undertaking that required a man's whole time. Nay, he went so far as to found on this most essential part of vegetables the whole of his Methodus Plantarum or Systema Sexuale.[25]

20. Letter of 13 Feb. [Sir] Gavin deBeer, "The Correspondence between Linnaeus and Johann Gesner" (1949), p. 235.

21. P. 27.

22. "Die Stufenfolge der Dinge" (1910), p. 250.

23. "Linnaeus's Conception of Nature" (1957), p. 88. He thought that by dual affinity Linnaeus meant the scale of functions which von Hofsten calls "different degrees of complication."

24. "Logic and Memory in Linnaeus's System of Taxonomy" (1958).

25. Pulteney, *Writings of Linnaeus* (2d ed. 1805), p. 556.

Linnaeus sought proof that flowers were essential parts of plants in Cesalpino's notion of prolepsis (anticipation), which made it appear that all the plant's tissues unfolded one by one to reveal the flower. Linnaeus sponsored a number of dissertations on this subject between 1755 and 1764. The cortex was supposed to develop into the perianth, the "liber" into the corolla, the "lignum" into the stamens, and the medulla into the pistil.[26] The cortical substance of plants was supposed to perform nutrition and the medulla to constitute the sexual essence. The same was held to be true of animals, in whose generation the female contributed the essence and the male, the external parts.[27] The buds of flowers were held to be analogous to the pupal stages of insects; the expanding flower, to the emerging winged forms. Swammerdam had developed an analogy of this kind. In 1755 Linnaeus styled the process "the metamorphosis of plants"; "Swammerdam et Needham hanc, inter insecta et vegetabilia analogiam manifeste deprehenderunt." [28] In a valuable study of Goethe's not altogether dissimilar idea of plant metamorphosis Adolph Hansen investigated Linnaeus's notions of metamorphosis and concluded that they were "scholastische Nonsens." [29] The morphological doctrine of prolepsis and the analogy of metamorphosis were elaborate instances of special pleading. It all went to prove that the stamens on which he based his artificial system were the essential parts of plants. Linnaeus had found

26. "Metamorphosis Plantarum" (1755). Also "Prolepsis Plantarum" [1763]. Also *Systema Naturae . . . ,* 2 [*3*] (12th ed. Stockholm: Lars Salvius, 1767), 8–9.

27. "Theses Medicae," prop. J. C. D. Schreber, *Amoen. Acad.,* 6 (1764), 40–43; also 324–41, 365–83. Also Pulteney, *Writings of Linnaeus,* p. 446.

28. "Metamorphosis Plantarum" p. 370. Cf. Swammerdam, "A general analogy, or comparison of the mutations and accretions as to parts and limbs, as well as in eggs, worms, and nymphs, as in insects among themselves: also in their mutations, and accretions which we observe in an animal of the red-blood species and a vegetable clearly exhibited at one view" [1685], in *The Book of Nature . . . ,* trans. Thomas Flloyd, revised by John Hill (London: C. G. Seyffert, 1758), p. 138. Also John Beale, "Correspondence of Pith with Seeds" (1669).

29. *Goethes Metamorphose der Pflanzen: Geschichte einer botanischen Hypothese* (1907), n. 1, pp. 184–85. Metamorphosis was for Linnaeus "der gewünschte Übergang zu seiner Theorie" of taxonomy (p. 196). Goethe himself called the notion "eine oberflächliche Bemerkung, welche näher betrachtet sich nirgend bestätiget." *Versuch über die Metamorphose der Pflanzen* (2d ed. Stuttgart: Gotta'schen Buchhandlung, 1831), p. xvii. Hansen ignores the historical continuity of speculation on metamorphosis when he argues that Goethe's speculations (which have found defenders) had nothing at all to do with those of Linnaeus (p. 198). Too much of a distinction can be made out between Linnaeus as a student of dead plants and Goethe, of living ones. E.g. James Boyd, *Notes to Goethe's Poems,* 2 (Oxford: Basil Blackwell, 1958), 115. Also Gillispie, *The Edge of Objectivity* (1960), pp. 192–93. Linnaeus was a rhapsodist of nature and quite an enthusiast himself.

a metaphysical warrant at last, but it was not so satisfying as a natural system based upon the scale of beings.

We have observed the manner in which Grew, Ray, Camerarius, Bradley, Blair, and others escaped the consequences of plant sexuality for the scale of functions by ascribing hermaphroditic generation to plants, which they shared only with the lower animals. In "Sponsalia Plantarum" [1746] Linnaeus wrote that snails and earthworms were hermaphrodites, worker bees sexless, and the hydra altogether asexual. The idea that plants shared only the lowest category of sexual generation with animals should have begun to wear a bit thin. If dioecious plants were not proof enough that plants reproduced monosexually, Linnaeus had better evidence still. He was the discoverer of dichogamy, or differential maturing of male and female flower parts, which he observed in the plantain tree (*Musa paradisiaca*) and the prickly cassava (*Jatropha urens*). "I clearly observed that no seeds would ever be produced in this species [*Musa*], unless several plants placed together were to flower nearly at the same time." [30] So far as I have been able to discover, Linnaeus's remarks on this subject were confined to several sentences in "Sponsalia Plantarum." His failure to make this observation more general probably lay with the orthodoxy of graded function. Dichogamy was again observed by Christian Konrad Sprengel in the summer of 1789 when he noticed protandry (stamens mature before the pistil) in willow-herb (*Epilobium*) and love-in-the-mist (*Nigella*). In 1791 he observed proterogyny (pistil matures before the stamens) in spurge (*Euphorbia*). "The contrivances of many hermaphrodite flowers, which I was first to discover, secure that no individual may be fertilized by its own pollen." [31] T. A. Knight wrote that "nature intended that a sexual intercourse should take place between neighboring plants of the same species." [32]

Linnaeus had observed proterogyny before 1746 but was not alert to its implications. In *Kalmia* the stamens spring out to scatter the pollen, often across neighboring flowers. Linnaeus noticed this and assumed it was a device to insure autogamy. He wrote that *Zea mays*

30. "Sponsalia Plantarum," pp. 102–03. Cf. Gesner, "De Fructificatione" (1743), p. 85.

31. Sprengel, *Das entdeckte Geheimniss der Natur* (1793), col. 17. "So scheint die Natur es nicht haben zu wollen, dass irgend eine Blume durch ihrer eigenen Staub befruchtet werden solle" (col. 43).

32. "An Account of Some Experiments on the Fecundation of Vegetables . . . ," *Phil. Trans., 89* (1799), 202. But see Smith, *Introduction to Botany* (1807), pp. 318–339, for a later example of the influence of the orthodox Linnaean position.

was always autogamous, even though it is often protandrous.[33] He surmised that the pollen of *Iris* was pushed up to the stigma along channels in the petals by gentle breezes. This assumption was outrageous because autogamy is a virtual impossibility in *Iris*. Even fertilizing insects must leave pollen from another flower on the stigma before making their way down to the anthers. In *Campanula* autogamy is made unlikely by marked protandry. Linnaeus wrote that the pollen rose to the stigma in "certain canals," an impossibility even if the stigma was found to be mature before the pollen was all gone. He described the emergence of the pistils in protandrous composites, but this struck him as a form of self-pollination. In many such flowers the pollen has disappeared before the style splits to reveal the stigmatic papillae. Linnaeus's claim about canals in *Campanula* and rising pollen in *Iris* bears some analogy to the epicycles of Ptolemaic cosmology. The appearance Linnaeus was out to save was the notion that plants generally fertilized themselves and did not transgress upon the more elaborate reproductive processes of the higher animals.

Linnaeus relied upon the idea of botanical analogy as his main proof for plant sexuality. For the sake of analogies between plants and animals he had denied the existence of spermatozoa (believing instead that the sperm contained inert fertilizing corpuscles). When he observed pollen tubes he thought he had seen evidence of subtle fertilizing fluids. He devoted his energies to a taxonomic system which he knew to be artificial because he could not base a natural method on the scale of beings. He observed proterogyny in two species of plants but, under the influence of the orthodoxy of graded function, he failed to make the discovery sufficiently general and advanced false accounts of autogamy in *Campanula* and *Iris*. We shall shortly find that he gravely misinterpreted the nature of certain marine animals so he could assign them to a middle position on the scale of beings between plants and animals.

The orthodoxy of graded function was interpreted by some writers as meaning that plants could not be sexually differentiated at all. In 1754 Charles Alston (1683–1760), the superintendent of the botanic garden and lecturer in botany at the University of Edinburgh, attacked every one of the proofs for aphorism 145 of the *Fundamenta Botanica*, as stated in "Sponsalia Plantarum." One of his points may be stated as follows. What has been alleged of the sexes of plants depends upon their fertilizing themselves; but some plants, particu-

33. He accepted this statement uncritically from Logan, "Impregnation of the Seeds of Plants" (1736).

larly those observed by Linnaeus, cannot fertilize themselves; therefore, what has been advanced concerning their sexual generation is untrue. The pistils of composites often rose high above the male florets before giving the appearance of maturity. The pistil in *Campanula* far outreached the stamens.[34] The stamens of *Iris* were hidden below the segments of the stigma, making autogamy impossible. As for the canals for wind-blown pollen, "What eye ever saw these canals or rimae with the pollen rising in them?" [35] The castor-oil plant (*Ricinus communis*) had all its female florets above the males; automatic self-fertilization was impossible.[36] Alston also attacked Linnaeus's use of analogies to prove points where "general induction" was required. These were genuine weaknesses in the argument as Linnaeus had advanced it.

Alston's attempt at refutation was motivated by outraged propriety. He refused to quote Linnaeus's description of the pansy (*Viola tricolor*) in "Sponsalia Plantarum," finding it "too smutty for British ears." [37] The female parts had been described as white and elegantly handsome, gaping wantonly before the stamens. It was one of Linnaeus's most poetic passages. "No imagined analogy between plants and animals can warrant or excuse the fulsome and obscene names imposed by sexualists on the different parts of the fructification of vegetables." [38] Plants were lower than animals and more inert; that settled the matter.

In 1762 William Smellie (1740–95), who later translated Buffon and superintended the first edition of the *Encyclopedia Britannica* (1773), read an attack on the concept of plant sexuality to his "Newtonian Society" in Edinburgh.[39] The lecture was published in 1790 as part of his *Philosophy of Natural History*. Smellie denied sex to plants simply because it seemed to contradict the orthodoxy of graded function. He did not appreciate Linnaeus's intricate proposition that plants, aphids, coelenterates, and snails constituted a category of self-

34. Alston, "The Sexes of Plants," pp. 264–65.
35. Ibid., p. 265.
36. Ibid., p. 270.
37. Ibid., p. 266. See "Sponsalia Plantarum," p. 90.
38. Alston, *The Sexes of Plants*, pp. 308–09. Siegesbeck had also accused Linnaeus of indecency. As late as 1849 William Darlington (1782–1863) omitted explicit references to the sex organs of plants from an edition of the botanical correspondence of John Bartram: Zirkle, "Some Forgotten Records" (1932), pp. 444–45.
39. Kerr, *Memoirs of William Smellie*, 2 (1811), 102. Lord Kames suggested to Smellie that he prepare lectures "not on natural history as a science, but on the philosophy and general economy of nature." These were published as *The Philosophy of Natural History* in 1790 and 1799.

fertilizing hermaphrodites inferior to the more advanced animals which reproduced monosexually. Smellie mentioned the hermaphroditism of the vinefretter (aphid), millipede, hydra, and infusoria. As these animals were "destitute of all the endearments of love, what should induce us to fancy, that the oak or the mushroom enjoy these distinguished privileges?" [40]

Smellie performed a segregation experiment upon a female "Lychnis dioica" (*Melandrium rubrum*), which he found to bear seeds after a summer in a vacant lot in Edinburgh, "surrounded with houses of five and six stories high and distant from any male lychnis about an English mile." [41] The plant is entomophilous and must have been fertilized by an insect. Smellie was not concerned with the investigation of pollination and argued that the fertility of a plant alleged to be female proved that the so-called males were not necessary. "This beautiful theory [of sexuality], derived from a mistaken analogy, has no foundation in nature." [42] Smellie was far happier with the notion of a scale of beings attended by corresponding grades of functional complexity.

John Rotheram of Newcastle (1750?–1804), who had been a pupil of Linnaeus, answered Smellie with a pamphlet in 1790. He held that analogy was merely "a collateral argument," not the only proof of plant sexuality. He made short work of Smellie's lychnis: "You do not assure your readers that the female lychnis was free from insects during its florescence, and it is a plant well known to be inhabited by numerous insects." [43] Rotheram did, however, recur to Linnaeus's idea that the mode of generation in plants was shared only with the lowest animals: "Of all other individuals in the animal kingdom [snails, worms, etc.] approach nearest to the nature of a vegetable." [44] Smellie had argued that reproduction could not be ascribed to plants without challenging the functional superiority of those animals which were asexual or hermaphrodite. Rotheram replied that plants enjoyed only the lowest form of sexuality and need not be said to transgress upon animals. The debate was an astonishing exercise because Linnaeus and Rotheram knew of dioecious plants, just as Camerarius, Blair,

40. Smellie, ibid., *1*, (1790), 246.

41. Ibid., p. 258.

42. Ibid., p. 263; also 245–46.

43. *The Sexes of Plants Vindicated*, p. 27.

44. Ibid., p. 4. Readers of the Linnaeus-Ellis correspondence discover that Linnaeus shared a quaint view, widespread at the time, about the annual disappearance of swallows: that they wintered in the mud of estuaries. Rotheram showed himself an orthodox Linnaean by arguing for this view (pp. 36–42), against Smellie's contention that they migrated.

Gesner, and Bradley did. The existence of monosexual plants, not to mention Linnaeus's observation of dichogamy, defeated the whole argument.

Not all opposition to the sexes of plants was based on blind adherence to the orthodoxy of graded function. There was an objective difficulty noticed by several experimenters. Camerarius had found in the 1690s that segregation experiments did not always succeed when performed on hemp, French mercury, and Turkish maize.[45] These plants bear anemophilous flowers not fertilized by insects, so their fertility is not so easily explained as that of Smellie's lychnis. Mercury, hemp, and maize may on occasion bear a male flower on a female plant; Camerarius did not realize this. Alston cited the occasional appearance of viable seeds after such experiments as proof that seed-bearing plants could be fertilized without any need for so-called males.[46] In 1760 Linnaeus performed "a beautiful and truly admirable" segregation experiment on hemp. Undisturbed plants bore seed; those from which the male florets had been removed were completely barren.[47] For the moment the question seemed settled. But in 1779 and 1780 Spallanzani managed to produce fertile seeds from a citron pumpkin after enclosing the female flower in an airtight bottle. He removed any male florets from female hemp plants, isolated the plants in a closed space, and planted the seeds after they appeared. Fifty-three out of fifty-eight germinated. "The perfect fructification of hemp is entirely independent of the action of the fecundating dust." [48] Perhaps plants had pre-existing embryos like those Haller thought he found in chickens.

> We have a new and striking point of analogy between plants and animals to be added to the many others long known; and hence

45. *De Sexu Plantarum* (1694), pp. 76–78.

46. Koelreuter attacked Alston for misplaced emphasis in interpreting Camerarius' failures: "Historie der Versuche, welche vom Jahre 1691 an, bis auf das Jahr 1752 über das Geschlecht der Pflanzen angestellt worden sind . . . ," in J. C. Mikan, ed., *Opuscula Botanici Argumenti* (1797), pp. 181–83. Also Blair, *Botanick Essays* (1720), p. 241. The mercury was the worst choice possible for a segregation experiment because it seems to be, in a sense, parthenogenetic. *M. annua* occasionally forms seeds without fertilization. A. Kerner von Marilaun (1831–98) performed segregation experiments in the central Tirol where nothing could have fertilized his *annua,* but they formed fertile seeds. So far as I know, nothing similar has been alleged of spinach or maize. For a discussion of this interesting matter and further citation, see Paul Knuth, *Handbook of Flower Pollination, 1* (1906), 60–62 and *3* (1909), 370.

47. Linnaeus, *Sexes of Plants,* pp. 33–34. In "Sponsalia Plantarum" he traced Camerarius' failures with hemp to the fact that hemp may be dioecious.

48. Spallanzani, "Concerning the Generation of Certain Plants" (1784), p. 296.

> the suspicion that these two tribes of organized beings compose, perhaps, only one immense family, receives strong confirmation.[49]

There is no evidence to suggest that Spallanzani deliberately misinterpreted his results through a desire to prove the analogy he remarked. There can be no doubt, however, that for investigators of plant life the idea of botanical analogy was coming to constitute a regulative orthodoxy.

ii. Problematical Organisms

A series of discoveries about coelenterates and polyzoa published between 1741 and 1760 seemed to establish the existence of zoophytes—forms intermediate between plants and animals. There was a reciprocal relationship between these discoveries and the idea of botanical analogy. The existence of zoophytes vitiated most of the simple characters that might be relied upon to distinguish plants from animals, thus encouraging a belief in the idea of botanical analogy which, in turn, influenced the manner in which the discoveries were interpreted. The organisms were judged to rank between plants and animals, not because of their simplicity of structure, but because their functional capacity was ambiguous. Today the simplest forms of life are judged to hold something like a middle place, not above the highest plants in a linear series, but as representatives of the primitive life forms from which plants and animals evolved along divergent paths. In the eighteenth century an organism was judged to rank below the simplest animals, near the highest of the plants if it showed asexual budding or grew in colonies fixed to the ground.

An apparent confirmation of ideas about a low category of reproduction and the existence of a scale of beings was provided by Abraham Trembley (1710–84), who observed a strange plant-animal in ornamental ditches at Sorgvliet, an estate near The Hague where he was employed as a tutor. In January of 1741 he wrote to Charles Bonnet,

> I have studied it ever since June last, and have found in it striking characteristics of both plant and animal. It is a little aquatic

49. Ibid., p. 315. Fougeroux de Bondaroy (1732–89), Duhamel's son-in-law, thought he, too, had discovered evidence of pre-existing plant embryos: "On court moins de risque, je l'avoue, d'étudier l'histoire naturelle en suivant une route tracée par l'analogie." "Mémoire sur la fécondation des plantes," [Rozier's] *Observations sur la physique, 5,* (1775), 27.

> being. At first sight everyone imagines it to be a plant; but if it be a plant, it is sensitive and ambulent; if it be an animal, it may be propagated by slips or cuttings, like many plants.[1]

The animal he described was the fresh-water hydra, a coelenterate familiar to amateur miscroscopists. Leeuwenhoek, who described it in 1703, had called it an animalcule. He observed the body extend itself or become shorter, and watched as a bud "forsook its mother's belly." [2] Soon afterward another article was sent by an anonymous author who, expressing chagrin that Leeuwenhoek had published first, claimed to have observed the creatures several months before him. The writer made better drawings of them, also including one with buds.[3] Neither had any trouble whatever in deciding that the hydra was an animal. After Trembley started investigating the creatures in the summer of 1740 he was so aware of analogies with both plants and animals that it took him until March of the following year to decide which it was.

The animal observed by Trembley was the small (quarter inch) *Chlorohydra viridissima,* which resembled a plant in its brilliant green color. He isolated specimens to see if they would reproduce, which they did, but he never saw any copulation "entre eux d'analogue à ce qui sert à féconder la plupart des animaux." [4] He devised an emasculation experiment of the sort frequently performed by botanists who removed the stamens of flowers. He removed the tentacles from eight polyps to see if they "had the same use as those of the flowers of plants." He placed them in isolated tanks where they continued to bear young by asexual budding, which could not have happened if the tentacles were analogous to flower parts.[5] Although the polyp contracted when disturbed and displayed other motions, Trembley thought for a time that it might be an especially sensitive plant. The budding process did not offer a conclusive analogy with that of plants because the buds seemed able to separate themselves from the main stalk.

On November 25, 1740, he performed an experiment which Réau-

1. Quoted by George Adams the younger, in *Essays on the Microscope* (1787), p. 395.
2. "Green Weeds and Animalculae," p. 1307 and Fig. 9.
3. Anon., "Two Letters" (1703), Figs. 1 and 2.
4. *Mémoires, pour servir à l'histoire d'un genre de polypes d'eau douce* (1744), p. 188.
5. Ibid., pp. 191–94. "Nous n'avons rien découvert dans ces animaux qui fût analogue aux fleurs de plantes, et à la graine qu'elles produisent" (p. 206).

mur was to repeat again and again, each time with astonishment. Trembley cut a polyp in two, supposing that no animal could survive such a test and that its death would prove it indeed an animal. "I judged that if two parts of the same polyp lived after being separated and each developed into a perfect polyp it would be evident that these organized bodies were plants." [6] To his astonishment the creatures survived. Each half put forth the missing parts after ten days had passed, in contradiction to all accepted views on the indivisibility of the vital principle in animals. "Following the intention with which I performed the experiment, I had to conclude positively that the polyps were plants, of the sort which come from slips." [7] The functional capacity of the creature was certainly ambiguous. "Je fus donc alors réduit à aller encore plus en tâtonnant, que je ne l'avois fait jusques-là." [8] As Trembley observed the polyps feeding upon pond life, migrating about their glass to follow sunlight, and progressing rather like geometrid caterpillars by a series of stylized but apparently spontaneous motions, he came to the conclusion that they were indeed animals. He puzzled for a time over Boerhaave's distinction between the external roots of plants and the internal roots (mesenteric lacteals) of animals, but this criterion did not seem to apply to the polyp.

Trembley's careful experiments are a measure of the difficulties faced by a sound experimentalist owing to contemporary confusion about the difference between plants and animals. He was indifferent to the idea of botanical analogy and sought clear proof that the polyp was either plant or animal in nature, unlike later speculators who tried to make it out to be a little of each. The "generally received rules" were criticized because they provided no criteria where a simple animal was concerned: [9]

> Il est trop dangereux, en fait d'histoire naturelle, d'abandonner l'expérience, pour se laisser conduire à l'imagination. On risque de n'arriver, en suivant cette route, qu'à des hypothèses peu sûres, et qui peuvent devenir nuisibles aux progrès de cette science, si on a le malheur de se prévenir pour elles.[10]

6. Ibid., p. 13.
7. Ibid., p. 16.
8. Ibid., p. 190.
9. Ibid., p. 302. In his first letter to Réaumur (15 Dec. 1740) he described the polyp as an animal: *Trembley Correspondence* (1943), p. 11. He was doubtful on 16 Feb. 1741 (p. 23) and certain of its animal nature by 25 March 1741 (p. 63).
10. Ibid., p. 308.

John Baker's close analysis of Trembley's experiments and observations establishes his importance in the history of experimental biology.[11] But despite the cautious tone of Trembley's work, the polyp he discovered lent encouragement to subsequent speculations in natural history.

The first word to reach England about the polyp was contained in a letter from Buffon to Martin Folkes (1690–1754) written in 1741. The discovery clearly showed that "nature proceeds by nuances and that all that can exist does." [12] J. F. Gronovius (1690–1760) wrote that the polyp was an imperfect animal, rather like a zoophyte or fungus.[13] In 1743, before Trembley had published, Henry Baker's *Attempt towards a Natural History of the Polype* described the experiments and some specimens sent to Martin Folkes. As news of the discovery spread the animals were observed by many naturalists, including Martin Folkes, Henry Miles, John Ellicott, (1706?–72), James Parsons, and several anonymous correspondents. It seems to have been expected that naturalists would keep a tank of water with polyps, feed them worms or small water insects, change their water with solicitude, and tenderly keep them free from "vexatious vermin" with a hair-pencil.[14] Baker concluded that the polyp was an animal. Its regenerative powers led him to remark, "We can scarce hesitate to look upon it as a real fresh-water starfish." [15] In 1742 an anonymous letter to the Royal Society from Cambridge was prompted by "what has lately been reported concerning the insect."

> The best philosophers have long observed very strong analogies between the two classes of beings, and the moderns, as they have penetrated further into nature, have every day found reason to extend that analogy; some have even with great probability talked of a scale of nature, in which she, by an insensible transition, passed from the most perfect of animals not only to the most imperfect and thence to the most imperfect of vegetables, but even through coralline bodies and minerals to the very earths and stones, which seem the most inanimate parts of our globe.
>
> Now in such a scale, who is the man that will be bold to say, just here animal life entirely ends and here vegetable life be-

11. *Abraham Trembley of Geneva* (1952).
12. Harcourt Brown, "Buffon and the Royal Society of London" [1944], p. 159.
13. "Concerning a Water Insect . . ." (1742), p. 220.
14. Cf. Baker, *Natural History of the Polype* (1743), p. 8.
15. Ibid., p. 45. Réaumur pointed out the analogy between regeneration in the polyp and in starfish: "Préface" (1742), p. lii.

> gins? . . . And might a man not even be excused if he should modestly doubt whether plants and vegetables may not themselves be considered as a very low and imperfect tribe of animals; as animals might, in like manner, be considered as a more perfect and exalted kind of vegetables? [16]

Cadwallader Colden called the polyp "a notable instance of the chain between vegetables and animals and which probably extends through the whole creation from the lowest degree of vegetation in minerals to the most perfect animal." [17] In 1743 Henry Fielding (1707–54) published an anonymous satirical pamphlet set up to resemble an article in the *Philosophical Transactions,* supposing that gold coins might also multiply by being cut in half. The correspondent professed himself unable to decide "whether this be really an animal or a vegetable, or whether it be not strictly neither, or rather both."

> What hath principally dissuaded me from an opinion of its being an animal is, that I could never observe any symptoms of voluntary motion, but indeed the same may be said of an oyster, which I think is not yet settled by the learned to be *absolutely* a vegetable.[18]

Despite this satire, the *Philosophical Transactions* published in 1744 an article by John Bartram (1699–1771) claiming that the "fibrous roots" of some mussels indicated a vegetable nature. Did not oysters grow rather like figs, in clusters, and were not all shellfish "somewhat analogous to plants"? [19] Lamettrie (1709–51) wrote in "L'Homme-machine" (1748) that the uniformity of nature and the analogies between the plant and animal kingdoms made it easier to believe in an "imperceptibly graduated chain" of beings.[20] Buffon wrote:

> We see that there is no absolute and essential difference between animals and vegetables, but that nature descends by subtle gradations from what we deem the most perfect animal to one which

16. "Part of a Letter," pp. 228–29.

17. Letter of Dec. 1743 to Peter Collinson: *Colden Papers, 3* (1920), 45. See the praise for Trembley's discovery in Jacques Delille's poem, *Les trois règnes de la nature, 2* (1808), VI. *Gentleman's Mag., 15* (1745), 197, wrote: "What astonishing discoveries have been made within the last four years! The polypus on one hand, as incredible as a prodigy, and the electric fire on the other, as surprising as a miracle!"

18. *Some Papers,* p. 10, 11.

19. *Phil. Trans.,* no. 474 (1744), 157–58.

20. *Œuvres, 2,* (1764), 101. "L'Homme-plante" ibid., 14–15, 26–27.

is less so, and again from this to the vegetables. The fresh-water polyp may perhaps be considered as the lowest animal, and at the same time as the highest plant.[21]

Aram Vartamian has argued that regeneration encouraged materialistic theories of physiology.[22] The polyp converted no Englishmen to materialism. It was too easy to believe that regeneration was a vegetable property shared only with plants and not characteristic of higher animals.[23] James Parsons (1705–70) assumed that polyps and willow trees possessed a "secondary organization" subsidiary to the primary soul. Whenever a polyp was cut in pieces or a shoot removed from a tree, the secondary powers of inner tissues would cause a new part to grow. "Why should that analogy and uniformity cease here which are everywhere else so manifestly carried on in the animal and vegetable creation?" [24] (Plate 4). Many naturalists investigated regeneration. Charles Bonnet estimated that three million worms might arise from one if it were cut into eight pieces and redivided every year for six years.[25] Such discoveries, although they disclosed problems that could only be solved after the development of a cell theory many years later, obscured the distinction between the animal and plant kingdoms. The polyp seemed to be a perfect example of a zoophyte, a creature in a middle state between plants and animals.

Coral polyps also became objects of speculation. In 1599 Ferrante Imperato (1550–1625) had compared tubular corals to beehives and ascribed other coral formations to animal concretion. He did not, however, see the polyps.[26] John Ray classified the stony corals as plants. In 1705 Leeuwenhoek wrote of roots at the nidus of coral

21. *Histoire naturelle* . . . , *2* (Paris: Imprimerie Royale, 1749), 9.

22. "Trembley's Polyp, La Mettrie, and Eighteenth-Century French Materialism" (1950), pp. 259–86.

23. Vartamian contends that because the polyp was called a plant by Leeuwenhoek and discovered to be an animal by Trembley, animal vitality came to be viewed as less complex. But Leeuwenhoek thought the polyp was an animal, Trembley hesitated to call it one, and many speculators described it as an intermediate form.

24. *Philosophical Observations on the Analogy between the Propagation of Animals and That of Vegetables,* p. 200. Cf. Erasmus Darwin, *Phytologia* (1800), pp. 97–103. For the polyp and the scale of beings, also see Bonnet, *Contemplation de la nature* (1764), *1*, 203–46 and *2*, 75–76. Abbé François Para du Phanjas thought the divisibility of the polyp meant that it must be a plant, albeit a very sensitive one: *Théorie des êtres sensibles:* . . . , *1* (Paris: Barrois & Cellot, 1788), 224–26 [1772].

25. Traité d'insectologie: . . . *2* (Paris: Durand, 1745), 29. Also Baker, *Abraham Trembley* (1952), pp. 155–58. Vorontsova and Liosner, *Asexual Propagation and Regeneration* (1960), pp. 111–17.

26. *Dell'historia naturale* . . . (Naples: Constantino Vitale, 1599), pp. 713–24.

formations: "We allow that substance to receive its nourishment and increase after the same manner as other plants."[27] In 1708 Geoffroy found the coral to be "a true plant approaching the nature of stone."[28] Luigi Marsigli (1658–1730) illustrated "fiori bianchi" which he had seen to protrude from the coral's branches; when he removed the coral from the water the flowers disappeared.[29] Marsigli's observation was welcomed as a pleasing confirmation of the vegetable nature of corals. Boerhaave wrote, "Coral has been suspected by the naturalists of all ages for a sea plant, but the moderns have demonstrated it such."[30]

Richard Bradley thought to elevate corals and sponges by assigning them to an intermediate rank between minerals and plants. "It has some analogy to plants [and] . . . I cannot see any reason why we may not place coral amongst the submarine plants."[31] In 1730 Samuel Dale (1659?–1739), a physician and antiquary of Braintree, Essex, published a natural history catalogue which detailed numbers of corals and sponges. He thought they were plants, although akin to the zoophytes or "plant animals as some term them."[32] Thomas Shaw (1694–1751) described "little roots" which contracted when the coral structure was removed from water. He thought the little roots compensated the plant for the absence of a single large one.[33] In 1740 Linnaeus listed the following among "Zoophyta": Sepia (cuttlefish), Tethys (nudibranch?), Limax (slug), Asterias (starfish), and Medusa (jellyfish). We find the following among the cryptogamic plants: Spongia, Isis (*Corallium*), Lithoxylum (*Gorgonia*), Millepora, Tubipora, Madrepora, Cellepora, and Sertularia (polyzoa, colonial hydroids, and some seaweeds).[34]

Jean André Peyssonel (1694–1759) began his observations of coral

27. "Microscopical Observations on Red Coral," p. 128.

28. "Observations sur les analyses du corail," p. 104.

29. *Brieve ristretto del saggio fisico intorno alla storia del mare* (1711), p. 13; see Pl. 2, Fig. 2. He first described this appearance in a letter to the Abbé Bignon dated 18 Dec. 1706: "Coral has been suspected by the naturalists of all ages for a sea plant, but the moderns have demonstrated it such."

30. *A New Method of Chemistry* [1727], *1*, 135. He cited Marsigli.

31. *A Philosophical Account* (1721), p. 15; also 13–14. Also Antoine de Jussieu (1748–1836), "The Analogy between Plants and Animals, Drawn from the Difference of Their Sexes" [1719], p. 29. Also Noël Antoine Pluche, *Spectacle de la nature, 1* (1732), fourteenth day.

32. *The History and Antiquities of Harwich* . . . (London: C. Davis and T. Green, 1730), pp. 337–40. He reserved the name "Zoophytae" to jellyfish.

33. *Travels or Observations Relating to Several Parts of Barbary and the Levant* (Oxford: at the Theatre, 1738), pp. 385–86.

34. *Systema Naturae* . . . (2d ed. Stockholm: 1740), p. 63.

at Marseilles in 1719. In 1721 he saw the "flowers" observed by Marsigli but did not examine them closely. On April 28, 1723, he discovered that the flowers were in reality little animals. "Ce que nous prenions pour fleurs etoient des Veritables Insectes, . . ." [35] In February of 1725 he put fragments of living coral into a vase of sea water: "and I observed that what we believed to be the flower of this pretended plant cannot be anything but an insect like a little sea-anemone [ortie] or polyp." [36]

> Repeating my observations on the other branches I saw clearly that the little holes one sees in the rind of the coral are the tunnels that these orties come out of—these holes correspond to the little cavities or cellules in the rind, whose traces may be seen in the substance of the coral itself, these cavities are the niches or habitations of the coralline orties.[37]

In a paper submitted to the Académie des Sciences in 1727 he argued that the interior core of the branching structures displayed no analogies with plant stems. Réaumur took it upon himself to condense the paper and publish it anonymously to save Peyssonel from ridicule.

The discovery of the animal nature of corals should be considered the disclosure of something objectively true rather than a corollary of the idea of botanical analogy, even though it conformed to the general tendency to view all plants in terms of animals. The opposition provoked by the discovery may sometimes be considered as an expression of the orthodoxy of graded function, which resisted the attribution of an animal nature to corals rather as the same concept had led to denials of plant sexuality. Réaumur wrote that more elaborate analogies with plants could save the conventional opinion:

> Mais n'avons-nous pas les fleurs qui s'épanouissent le jour et qui se ferment la nuit: d'autres qui s'ouvrent le soir, et se ferment le matin? L'épanouissement et le ressèrrement des pétales du corail est plus subit que celui des fleurs dont nous parlons. Mais est-il plus que ne le sont les mouvements de la sensitive [plant]? [38]

In 1741, after Trembley's observations of the polyp, Réaumur drew the obvious inference that coral flowers might be animals. At his urging Bernard de Jussieu (1699–1777) went to the coast of Normandy

35. MS, *Traité du Corail* [1751], p. 39 [f. 20].
36. Ibid., p. 70 [f. 35].
37. Ibid., p. 71 [f. 36].
38. "Observations sur la formation du corail," p. 278.

in September of that year to investigate "avec la loupe et le microscope." Jussieu saw the polyps of *Alcyonaria* and the polypides in polyzoa. In 1742 Jussieu went to Dieppe, where he observed a madrepore with "polypes," a tubularian, an alcyonarian, a *Flustra,* and a cellepore. All were indisputably animals.[39] Réaumur wrote to Trembley, "We have now to surmise that the flowers of coral discovered by Count Marsigli can only be polyps." [40] In the preface to the sixth volume of his *Mémoires pour servir a l'histoire des insectes* (1742) Réaumur professed agreement with Jussieu's findings and named Peyssonel as the author of the article written in 1727. In 1748 Trembley was in England and pointed out coral polyps to the Duke of Sussex and William Watson.[41] In May of 1751 Peyssonel, then Royal Physician in Guadeloupe, sent a manuscript of four hundred pages to the Royal Society identifying the soft spots at the tips of tubularian corals as the "gîte des orties ou insects coralines." [42] He maintained that all corals and many other marine productions were the work of minute marine animals.

The belief that corals were animal in nature encountered vigorous opposition from defenders of graded function, who were unwilling to elevate a plant to so high a status. Stukeley, Parsons, and Hill denied that it was an animal. Vitaliano Donati sought to make corals conform to an abstract compromise between plants and animals.

William Stukeley argued that, while corals did not have true roots to draw sustenance from the floor of the sea, they might be considered analogous to air plants. One would be very "diffident of his eyesight, if he does not, without the least hesitation, think em to be real plants." [43] Stukeley drew comfort from the observation that coral formations bore no analogy to spider webs or honeycombs. The "true & precise" analogy would be found with little animalcules which inhabited, but did not create, the algae of ponds and ditches.[44]

> I have never been at the bottom of the ocean, have not had an opportunity of making researches into this particular branch of natural history. Nor is there any need of it, to obtain satisfac-

39. "De quelques productions marines" (1742).
40. *Trembley Correspondence* (1943), pp. 116–17. Letter of 3 Dec. 1741.
41. Peyssonel (Watson), "An Account of a Manuscript" (1752), p. 462.
42. Peyssonel (Flourens), "Analyse d'un ouvrage" (1838), p. 341.
43. MS, "On corals & corallines" 13 May 1752, p. 2.
44. Ibid., p. 9.

tion in this matter. I must needs speak, what reason loudly dictates.[45]

Watson replied on May 28, 1752, that Peyssonel had not maintained that all sea plants were animal productions, but that corals, sponges, lithophytes, and numbers of polyzoa unquestionably were.[46] Stukeley produced a piece of red coral which had been found in the Riber Ribble in Lancashire which he imagined to date back to the "Noachian deluge." [47] The doctrine of "polypus's" was "fully as absurd, as equivocal [spontaneous] generation." [48] In June Stukeley argued that all the animals found in corals were alike, a single species of adventitious inhabitant in the different species of sea plants. If the lime of corals bore no analogy to the chemistry of land plants it was because corals were sea plants impregnated with marine salts. Their texture struck him as very analogous to the "channel work, or medullary pipes" of plants.[49]

James Parsons, author of the ingenious analogy between regeneration in polyps and willow trees, was indignant at suggestions that corals were animals and, in reply, rang all the changes on the idea of nature. Because of the empirical difficulties of observing an animal living in the depths of the sea one had to overcome the limitations of sense by analogy, "by comparing them to something else as near to them as may be," in order "to range them in the rank which they were designed to hold by divine providence." [50] He tried to refute analogies with lime-secreting molluscs and Trembley's polyp. Peyssonel's claim that coral polyps built reefs as bees constructed combs was said to neglect the absence of any hollow cavities such as those in beehives.[51] He turned instead to analogies with plants, such as fixed roots and branched growth. Water, which deposited hard growths in tea kettles, must also deposit the stony substance of corals in its circulation through their stems, with whose cross sections

45. Ibid., p. 8.
46. Watson MS, Letter of 28 May 1752, p. 1. *The Journal Book of the Royal Society* [copy], *21* (1751–54), 141–46, contains an account of the debate at this meeting.
47. MS, "On Corals, Corallines &c." 28 May 1752, p. 1.
48. Ibid., p. 3.
49. MS, "On Corals &c." 11 June 1752, p. 9; also p. 14.
50. "The Formation of Corals" (1752), p. 507.
51. The polyps of madreporan corals secrete layers of lime in rosettes conforming to the base of their central cavity. Tubular corals close their tubes behind them. Peyssonel did not claim that cavities were left in corals when the animals were removed.

Parsons claimed to find analogies in Grew's illustrations of plant stems. "Poor helpless jelly-like animals" could not erect reefs or other formations, which had "the appearance and characteristic marks of vegetables." [52]

In 1745 Linnaeus wrote a dissertation on corals, presenting in succession the familiar arguments that they were mineral formations, plant growths, and the work of animals. He avowed that each argument seemed conclusive. Further information was necessary before the nature of corals could be decided.[53] He included corals neither in the *Flora Svecica* in 1745 nor the *Fauna Svecica* in 1746. In 1748, on the authority of Jussieu, he moved "lithophytes" or stony corals into the fourth order of *Vermes* which included tubipores, madrepores, millepores, and Sertularia (colonial hydroids, polyzoa, and some seaweeds).[54]

Vitaliano Donati (1717–63), professor of botany at Turin, described marine animals in a very interesting way in his natural history of the Adriatic Sea in 1750. Any system of taxonomy should follow the scale of beings. "Should we gain an exact understanding of mosses and fungi, we should probably complete the link between terrestrial plants and insects." [55] Donati argued that the scale of beings was not limited to terrestrial forms, but that another scale might be found in the sea. "Nell'osservare li prodotti della natura, non ritrovo une sola e semplice progressione, o catena di cose, ma ne ritrovo moltissime uniformi, perpetue, constanti" [56] "In each of these orders or classes nature forms her series and has her insensible passages from link to link along her chain." Regeneration in the polyp and in Bonnet's worms showed that the same functional capacity might be possessed by both marine and terrestrial forms. "Ma chi sà che la natura prolunghi la serie delle plante e degli animali, stessi sino nel regno

52. Parsons, "Formation of Corals," pp. 511–13.

53. "Dissertatio de Coralliis Balticis," pp. 186–87.

54. *Systema Naturae* . . . (6th ed. Stockholm: Godfrey Kiesewetter, 1748), pp. 8–9, 76. Note that this shift did not depend upon John Ellis's writings about the "Sertularia." Also see aphorism 76 of *Philosophia Botanica* in which Linnaeus acknowledged that Peyssonel "restored them to their right place, to which they certainly belong, the animal kingdom."

55. *Della storia naturale marina dell'Adriatico,* p. xxi. Excerpts from the work were published in *Phil. Trans.* in 1751.

56. Ibid., p. xx. Thienemann points out that this passage was in effect a criticism of the notion of a linear series. This was not, however, Donati's motive. He sought to include marine organisms in the scale of beings. The division into chapters in the French translation of 1759, which Thienemann cites, was different from that in the first edition. This distorted the argument somewhat.

dell'acque?" [57] Donati tried to prove his assertions about a marine scale of beings by describing three classes of intermediate beings: polyparies, plant-animals, and animal-plants. Along the scale, with "regular and almost insensible progressions, nature passes from production to production." [58] The first step in the ascent from plants to animals included corals, which were plants in the overall aspect although their reproductive organs were the polyps or little animals:

> Voi qui vedete vegetazione di planta, e propagazione d'animale. Ora giudicate, se il corallo all'uno piuttosto che all'altro regno debba appartenere, o si più ragionevolmente un luogo medio se gli convenga.[59]

The "piante-animali" constituted the second step. These were more fleshy than corals and included sponges. He gave an excellent microscopic illustration of sponge tissue and assumed that an eight-inch marine worm he found in one was the polyp which created it. As a representative of the higher "animali-piante" he mentioned a "Thethys spherique," a round sponge of Lamarck's genus Tethya (probably *Tuberella tethyoides,* Keller).[60] Unlike most sponges, it seemed able to move about or at least to drift from place to place. The series seemed to confirm "the order to which nature holds, not only in her passage from genus to genus, but even from class to class." [61] In 1755 he wrote to Vallisner describing a new kind of sea growth in which a "true plant" and a "true animal" composed the same organism:

> The plant vegetates all by itself, without receiving nutriment from the animal, and the animal without receiving anything from the plant; but if one dies the other perishes, and both arise from the same germ.[62]

57. Ibid., p. xxi.
58. Ibid., pp. xxvi–xxvii.
59. Ibid., p. lii. Cf. Donati, "New Discoveries" (1751), p. 104. Also Griffith Hughes, ". . . Concerning a Zoophyton, Somewhat Resembling the Flower of the Marigold," *Phil. Trans.,* no. 471 (1743), 590–13 and Pl. 3, Fig. 1. Hughes called a sea anemone successively a flower, a sensitive flower, and an animal.
60. Donati's illustration may be compared with Yves Delage and Edgard Hérouard, *Traité de zoologie concrète,* 2 (Paris: C. Reinwald, 1899), part 1, 168–69 and Pl. 13.
61. Donati, *Storia naturale* (1750), pp. lxii–lxiii.
62. Letter of 14 Nov. 1755, in Roncetti, ed., *Lettere inedite scientifico-letterarie* (1845), p. 129. For a bibliography of Donati see V. A., *Lettere inedite del Dottore Vitaliano Donati* (Ancona: A. G. Morelli, 1883), pp. 11–17.

He probably observed a colonial hydroid or a colony of protozoa, "un anello nuovo in natura, e che connette mirabilmente l'animale col vegetale." [63]

John Hill's *General Natural History* (1751) classified the corals, sponges, and allies as plants.[64] In *Essays on Natural History* (1752), Hill poured scorn on naturalists who had confused mineral growths and plants, or considered the cochineal insect or the kermes (the pregnant female of *Coccus ilicus,* once gathered for dye manufacture) as excrescences of plants: "Still later than all this, the polyp, even while it moved, and felt, and ate before us, was by many declared a vegetable." [65] Then Hill proceeded to fall into the same error of which he accused the others. He accused Réaumur and Jussieu of "an error of the first magnitude in natural philosophy" for having asserted that corals were animal structures, simply "from their finding animals lodged in several parts of them." [66] One might find larvae in trees and leaf-mining insects in plants without calling trees the products of larvae or leaves the product of leaf-miners. Hill observed the marine animals and, indeed, found "insects" in them. He thought they were accidental to the growth, which was to be considered a plant. He observed the life cycle of *Alcyonium* but identified the polyps he saw bud and float away from the "parent vegetable" as bursting pollen. It struck him as unprecedented and marvelous that they grew (although without taking root) where they fell and did not have to fertilize female flowers at all.[67] Perhaps this observation helped to confirm Hill's opinion that pollen was a particle of living tissue from the medulla of plants.

After some doubt, the hydra was admitted to be an animal. The stony corals were then advanced into the lower ranks of the animal kingdom, although in somewhat equivocal terms. We must take note of a controversy which developed over the "Sertularia" which Linnaeus had listed as animals in 1748. These were the "corallines" described as animals by Peyssonel in the lost half of his 1751 manuscript. Some had been observed by Jussieu in 1741 and 1742; he, too, had called them animals. It only remained for their anatomy to be investigated, whereupon their relationship to the other marine animals

63. Ibid., p. 130.

64. 2, 6–24.

65. pp. 4–5.

66. Ibid., p. 27. This would have been a fair criticism if applied to Donati's observation of worms in sponges.

67. Ibid., pp. 171–75. See his section "Zoophytes," in *A Review of the Works of the Royal Society* (1751), pp. 79–91, in which he attacked John Bartram, Griffith Hughes, and Henry Baker.

might be made plain. John Ellis (1710–76), a London merchant who used his position as King's Agent for the Province of West Florida (1764) and Agent for the Island of Dominica (1770) to cultivate the natural history of those places, turned his attention to some of these neglected animals, which he called "corallines." Most of them resemble the corals in their mode of life, although their colonies are flexible because the animals do not secrete such large amounts of lime. Some were marine polyzoa or "sea-mosses"—colonial, sessile animals which display extraordinary polymorphism. One type of animal is a living enclosure (the zooecium), sometimes with a small appendage (the avicularium), which closely resembles the head of a bird of prey, complete to the detail of a snapping beak. The other form is the "polypide," which in a sense inhabits the zooecium, possessing a digestive tract and differentiated muscular tissue, not found in coelenterates. From time to time the polypide collapses into a "brown body" which the zooecium ejects and replaces. These animals are now assigned to phylum Polyzoa and ranked near the arthropods, well removed from phylum Coelenterata (the hydroids, jellyfish, corals, alcyonarians, sea anemones, and allies, as well as Trembley's polyp). Some of the more delicate polyzoa and colonial hydroids bear a startling resemblance to sea plants, and few who saw them in a tidal pool would suspect otherwise (Plate 5).

In his reply to Stukeley on May 28, 1752, William Watson observed that "some species of coralline" had been described as animals by Peyssonel,

> But other species of coralline, so denominated by botanists, & are truly plants do not come under his consideration; neither does any of the large family of Fucus.[68]

John Ellis was fond of making montages representing underwater scenes out of his collection of corallines from Anglesey and Dublin. He was probably led to suspect they were animals by the debate between Parsons and Stukeley. On June 18, 1752, four of his montages were exhibited to the Royal Society. On the same day he wrote to Philip Webb (1700–70) that his collection was to be classified on a principle different from that of Ray, Tournefort, Morison (1620–83), and Dillenius (1687–1747). He had recognized that his "tubular coralline" was the work of animals because it did not have a vegetable

68. Watson MS, Letter of 28 May 1752, p. 1. Cf. Peyssonel (Watson), "An Account of a Manuscript" (1752), p. 464.

cortex and had "dead animals on its Tops." [69] He referred to an "Eschara" (*Bugula*) which seemed "to be the aggregate nests of Insects in the manner of the bees honeycomb." [70] In 1753 he wrote that corallines, "hitherto claimed by the botanists," were analogous to coral and therefore animals.[71] Both of the corallines he described in his letter to Webb in June of 1752 had been described by Jussieu in 1742. Ellis erred in assuming that all the corallines described by Ray and Tournefort must be animals, even though Peyssonel and Watson had warned that some were seaweeds. His error was due in part to inexperience and in part to his insistence upon a single criterion for distinguishing plants from animals. He asserted that only animals secreted lime, whereas there are in fact numerous varieties of calcareous algae.[72] Ellis included polychaete worms in his essay and failed to distinguish coelenterates from polyzoa. He wrote to Dr. David Skene of Aberdeen that he was not interested in systematics: "I am neither equal to the task nor have I time to enter on a regular system." [73] Ellis's amateurism involved the study of corallines in great confusion. Some of the attacks upon his writings came from observers who found that Ellis had not distinguished calcareous algae from colonial hydroids and polyzoa. For this reason it is difficult to be sure that his attackers were motivated by the orthodoxy of graded function.[74]

The tendency toward equivocation in Linnaeus's dissertation on corals in 1745 reappeared as exuberant speculation on the subject of corals and corallines, which he believed, as had Donati, to be plants with animated flowers. In 1758 he defined them as "Animalia composita, efflorescentia, stirps vegetans." [75] In his 1760 essay on plant sexuality he wrote that zoophytes were plants with marked affinities to animals: "Their flowers are sensible and vibrate spontaneously." [76] This was

69. Ellis MS, Letter of 18 June 1752. Cf. *Essay on Corallines* (1755), p. 31 and Pl. 16, Fig. c. Also *The Journal Book of the Royal Society* [copy], *21* (1751–54), 175.

70. Ibid. Also *Essay on Corallines* (1755), pp. 70–71.

71. Ellis, "Observations on a Remarkable Coralline" (1753), p. 117.

72. Sir Sidney Harmer remarked the "curious irony of fate" whereby one of the papers for which Ellis was awarded the Copley Medal in 1768 had maintained the animal nature of calcareous algae: "Presidential address" (1929), p. 90.

73. *Calendar of the Ellis Manuscripts,* ed. S. Savage (1948), p. 71.

74. Job Baster, "Observationes de Corallinis" (1757) alleged that Ellis was altogether wrong because some of his corallines were seaweed. Pallas, in *Elenchus Zoophytorum* (1766), noted that the "jamaican" (p. 53), "anglica" (pp. 48–49), "alba" (pp. 50–51), "dichtoma" (p. 51), and "ramulis" (p. 50) corallines were in fact plants; pp. 418–19 (page numbers in parentheses refer to Ellis, *Essay on Corallines*).

75. *Systema Naturae . . . 1* (10th ed. Stockholm) 789–821

76. *Sexes of Plants,* p. 12. Also [Linnaeus], "Animalia Composita" [1759]. Also Pulteney, *Writings of Linnaeus,* 2d ed., pp. 560–61.

"scholastische Nonsens" and Ellis criticized him for it. Linnaeus undertook to defend this notion in a fatuous letter which indicates very well the extent to which he was dominated by general ideas about nature:

> Zoophyta are constructed very differently, living by a mere vegetative life, and are increased every year under their bark like trees, as appears from the annual rings in a section of the trunk of a Gorgonia [sea fan]. They are therefore vegetables, with flowers like small animals, which you have most beautifully delineated. All submarine plants are nourished by pores, not by roots, as we learn from Fuci [seaweeds]. As zoophytes are, many of them, covered with a strong coat, the Creator has been pleased that they should receive nourishment by their naked flowers. He has therefore furnished each with a pore, which we call a mouth. All living beings enjoy some motion. The zoophytes mostly live in the perfectly undisturbed abyss of the ocean. They cannot therefore partake of that motion which trees and herbs receive from the agitation of the air. Hence the Creator has granted them a nervous system that they may spontaneously move at pleasure. Their lower part becomes burdened and dies, like the solid wood of a tree. The surface, under the bark, is every year furnished with a new living layer, as in the vegetable kingdom. Thus they grow and increase; and may even be truly called vegetables, as having flowers, producing capsules, etc. Yet as they are endowed with sensation and voluntary motion, they must be called, as they are, animals; for animals differ from plants merely in having a sentient nervous system, with voluntary motion; nor are there any other limits between the two.[77]

Job Baster (1711–75) upheld the Linnaean notion in 1761. He thought the mixed nature of zoophytes a decisive proof for the existence of parallel scales of functions and beings. The Leibnizian principle of continuity was held to have anticipated, even to have predicted, the discovery of such organisms. Whatever was advanced to distinguish plants from animals, "these definitions nevertheless come together in zoophytes." [78] As late as 1775 Ellis found it necessary to attack the notion of plant-animals. "To conjecture [such] a monstrous metamorphosis [is] repugnant to the general analogy of nature." [79]

77. Letter of 16 Sept. 1761, *Correspondence of Linnaeus, I,* 151–52.

78. "Dissertationem hanc de Zoophytis," p. 110. On Leibniz and the chain of being see Lovejoy, *The Great Chain of Being* (1936), pp. 144–81, 223–25, 233.

79. "On the Nature of the Gorgonia; That it is a Real Marine Animal, and

Sponges, it might be added, were not well understood during this period. They are at present classified as phylum Porifera and are considered simpler animals than the coelenterates. Sponges have specialized collar cells to maintain a circulation of water through their pores but no polyps. Peyssonel found extraneous organisms in sponges and concluded in an article on "the worms that form sponges" that they had built the sponge as a refuge and "walk indifferently into the tubular labyrinth." [80] The manuscript of Peyssonel's article reveals that he was led into error by assigning too great a value to analogies. The existence of corallines and lithophytes, he wrote, "m'avoint fait conjecture, qu'il en etoit de meme pour les Eponges." [81]

> Il semble qu'il en est de meme de la Phisique comme de la geometrie, une proposition expliquée, un problême résolu, une vérité démontrée, donne une infinité d'autres connoissances aussi certaines que les premieres connües, quel advantages ne tire-t-on par de la quarante-septième du premiere livre d'Euclide dans la Phisique egalamt.[82]

Other naturalists recognized that sponges were simple animals without polyps. Pallas (1741–1811) called the sponge an "animal ambiguum" in 1766.[83]

There can have been few sequences of discovery so subject to the influence of general ideas as that leading from Trembley's observations on the polyp to Linnaeus's interpretation of corals. Each new discovery was subject to greater distortion as a result. The catalogue of errors about problematical organisms leads away from the narrative of discovery with the notion that algae constituted a polypary or refuge constructed by water animals and the discovery of a vegetating fly.

A report about a strange plant-animal found in the Lesser Antilles was published by the Royal Society in 1763:

Not of a Mixed Nature, between Animal and Vegetable" [1775], p. 7. In the *Systema Naturae* . . . 12th ed., Tom. 1 [2] (Stockholm: Lars Salvius, 1767), 1304, Linnaeus accepted Ellis's opinion that all lime-secreting forms were animals, even though this meant the inclusion of calcareous algae. Also *Correspondence of Linnaeus, 1*, 220–21, 260–61. On later taxonomy of the hydroids and polyzoa see Thompson, *A History of British Zoophytes* (1838), pp. 52–77.

80. "Of the Worms That Form Sponges" (1758), p. 593.

81. Peyssonel MS, "Dissertation sur les Eponges . . . " [1757?], p. 13 [f. 120].

82. Ibid., p. 1 [f. 114].

83. *Elenchus Zoophytorum* (1766), p. 375. Also Ellis and Solander, *Zoophytes* (1786), p. 183. Cf. Hooke, *Micrographia* (1665), pp. 135–40. On the later taxonomy of sponges see Daudin, *Cuvier et Lamarck, 1* (1926), 440–44.

> In the month of May [this fly] buries itself in the earth and begins to vegetate. By the latter part of July the tree is arrived at its full growth and resembles a coral branch, and is about three inches high and bears several little pods, which dropping off become worms and from thence flies, like the English caterpillar.[84]

Here was a prodigy almost as great as sea plants with animal flowers! Linnaeus wrote to George Edwards (1752–1823) in 1764:

> My thoughts are so taken up with these productions, that I cannot sleep without dreaming of them. I conjure you, by the Author of Nature, to write to me the first day you can spare to explain this phenomenon.[85]

William Watson wrote to John Hill about the report, which would have been a welcome addition to the scale of beings. Hill's reply was crushing; he named the object a saprophytic clavaria which often grew from decaying cicadas that had died in the pupal stage. We may imagine the relish with which he wrote to the Royal Society: "So wild are the imaginations of man; so chaste and uniform is nature." [86] In an essay "Sur l'analogie, & le passage du végétal au vital" (1769), Turbervill Needham cited the vegetating fly as a creature intermediate between plants and animals.[87] One is reminded of the famous tree of Pius II, thought to grow on the coast of Scotland, which dropped barnacles into the water, where they grew into geese.

In 1767 speculation was aroused by Rudolph Eric Raspé's claim that mushroom spores, if placed in water, turned into animals. John Ellis examined spores and found that the motion Raspé (1737–94) had attributed to them was imparted by "very minute animalcules." [88]

84. Letter from an army officer in Dominica. Watson, "Vegetable Fly" (1763), pp. 271–72.

85. *Correspondence of Linnaeus, 2,* 504. See Edwards, *Gleanings of Natural History . . . , 3* (London: for the author 1764), 263–64 and Pl. 335.

86. Watson, "Vegetable Fly," p. 273. See Pl. XXIII, p. 448. Also Andreas Elias Büchner, "Falso Credita Metamorphosis Summe Miraculosa Insecti Cuiusdam Americani," *Nova Acta Physico-Medica Academae Caesareae Leopoldino-Carolinae, 3* (1767), 437–42 and Pl. 7, Figs. 12–13, opp. p. 592.

87. Spallanzani, *Nouvelles recherches sur les découvertes microscopiques . . .* (Paris: Lacombe, 1769), part 1, pp. 239–61 and Pl. 6, Figs. 2, 3. This assertion was attacked by Fougeroux de Bondaroy in *Mém. Acad. Roy. des Sci.* (for 1769), 467–76 incl. 2 plates. Cf. Berdoe, *An Enquiry into the Influence of the Electric Fluid* (1771), for analogies among flowers, chick embryos, and a root which produced an "animal substance" (pp. 111–41, 170–71).

88. Ellis, letters to *St. James's Chronicle,* 1767.

Word of the discovery had reached Linnaeus, who created a new realm of nature, "Chaos," to contain the animals which grew from mushroom spores.[89] In a dissertation on the "Mundus Invisibilis" Linnaeus argued that as the kermes insect became immobile in its mature stages when fixed to the bark, the spores of mushrooms might really be little animals which also grew into plants:

> Verbo: uti Zoophyta e vegetabili efflorescunt in Animalcula, ita contraria naturae lege Fungi ex Animalculis adolescere in Vegetabilia, si confirmetur haec Fungorum genesis.[90]

John Woodward had supposed in 1699 that green films on flasks containing plants were vegetating matter and not plants at all. In 1779 Joseph Priestley wrote that coatings of algae which grew on the side of water-filled vessels could "neither be of an animal or vegetable nature, but a thing sui generis."[91] Jan Ingenhousz (1730–99) supposed that water might be "changed into this vegetation," which released part of the water as oxygen.[92] Priestley replied in 1781 that he supposed the green matter was a primitive plant arising from spores in the water.[93] The matter did not rest there. In 1787 Sir Benjamin Thompson (1753–1814) announced that the green coatings were "evidently of an animal nature."[94] Ingenhousz wrote in 1789 that he had been at "une peine infinie pendant plus de trois ans consécutifs, pour tâcher de déterminer la nature de cette substance."[95] He believed algae to be composed of little insects, faintly green when viewed separately, but bright green in masses.[96] Sometimes one had to break a green crust before the animals could be seen. Minute green points of the substance probably grew into the animals which might later be seen to inhabit it.[97] Felix Fontana is said to have believed

89. *Systema Naturae* . . . , 12th ed., 1 [2] (1767), p. 1326. Also Ellis, 'Observations on a Particular Manner of Increase in the Animalcula of Vegetable Infusions," *Phil. Trans.*, *59* (1769), 138–52 and Pl. 6.

90. "Mundus Invisibilis" [1767], p. 404.

91. *Experiments and Observations Relating to Various Branches of Natural Philosophy* . . . , *1* (London: J. Johnson, 1779), 342.

92. *Experiments upon Vegetables* (1779), p. 90.

93. Priestley, *Experiments and Observations* . . . , *2* (Birmingham: Pearson and Rollason for J. Johnson of London, 1781), 32–63.

94. "Experiments on the Production of Dephlogisticated Air," p. 124.

95. "Sur l'origine et la nature de la matière verte de M. Priestley . . . ," *Nouvelles expériences*, *2*, 8. Cf. Pl. 1, opp. p. 574.

96. Ibid., pp. 24–25.

97. Ibid., p. 33.

that algae were formations analogous to coral structures, built by the animalcules found in pond water.[98]

In 1802 Justin Girod-Chantrans (1750–1841) published a monograph in which he asserted that many kinds of algae were polyparies built as refuges by pond animals:

> The time is not far off when these marine productions, which have been placed among plants of the lowest order, will climb the scale of beings to take their place at the head of the vegetables, immediately below the marine and freshwater polyps.[99]

He had glimpses of their structure through a microscope and concluded that they bore a striking analogy to corals. The question was settled decisively by Jean Senebier (1742–1809) and others shortly afterward, and the algae were put very firmly back into the vegetable kingdom.

One after another plants had been made out to be animals. One wonders that any plants were left in the vegetable kingdom at all. Speculations on plant-animals and vegetating flies were a direct consequence of the discovery of apparently intermediate functional capacities in lower animals, always with reference to a scale of beings wherein the difference between plants and animals was contingent upon functional capacity. We may now more easily understand efforts to extend the analogies between plants and animals to cover all possible points of comparison. It is to this development, supported by several observations about "The Super-Life of Plants," that we now turn.

iii. The Super-Life of Plants

Seventeenth-century mechanists held that plants which furled their leaves and appeared to sleep (tamarind and clover were often mentioned) did so as a mechanical reaction to the agency of heat. Jacques Philippe Cornut (1606–51) is said to have observed that sleeping flowers

98. Alexander Tilloch, Comments on "the green matter which vegetates in water" [Tilloch's] *Philosophical Mag., 6* (1800), 312–14.

99. *Recherches chimiques et microscopiques sur les conferves, bisses, tremelles, etc.,* pp. 7–8. Much of his confusion arose from observations of swarm-spores, which he compared (p. 22) to ants attending aphids. Cf. Franz Ungar (1800–70), *Die Pflanze im Momente der Thierwerdung* (Vienna: 1842 or 1843), which he cites in "Einiges zur Lebensgeschichte der *Achyla prolifera," Linnaea, 17* (1843), 129–152 and Pl. 4.

of anemone would reopen inside a closed, dark box if their stems were placed in warm water. At Oxford, Robert Sharrock (1630–84) found that seedlings would direct their growth toward the open part of a window in pursuit of "the freshness and freeness of the air that the plant enjoys." [1] Richard Bradley thought that climbing plants were attracted to their supports "as a lodestone attracts iron to it." [2] Stephen Hales supposed that heliotropic plants followed the sun because the more rapid evaporation of water from the sunlit side of the stem caused a loss of turgidity.

The idea of botanical analogy was to divert naturalists from mechanical explanation and experimental investigation. Observe Linnaeus's reaction to Hales's discovery of respiration by the leaves:

> Leaves moving and breathing correspond in this way to the lungs of animals, but we cannot allow that they are [placed in motion by the plant itself] like the tails affixed to animals; we must deny voluntary motion to them in this.[3]

Linnaeus honored the orthodoxy of graded function by asserting that the leaves of plants were moved by the wind rather than by the plant itself. On the subject of sleep in plants he was not so cautious. *Draba* (grass) threw itself down at night as though to protect its pollen from the night air. *Trifolia* (clover) and *Oxalis* (sorrel) folded up their leaves before storms. The flowers of *Tragapogon,* called John-go-to-bed-at-noon in England, opened at dawn and closed at noon. *Parkinsonia, Tamarindus, Aeschynomene,* and other plants expanded their leaves in the daytime and collapsed at night. Many other plants enclosed their flowers in leaves at night, as though to protect them. Linnaeus compared sickly hothouse plants to courtiers who failed to take sufficient exercise and seems to have been influenced by the analogy, because he stated that motions must be useful to plants.[4] In the *Philosophia Botanica* (1751) he mentioned plants which predicted storms by closing their flowers, flagged, turned about, opened and closed their flowers, and furled their leaves like sails. He listed

1. *Propagation and Improvement of Vegetables* (1660), p. 41. Sharrock placed seedlings in a window "where there was a quarry out" (i.e. a pane of glass). For earlier writers on the sleep of plants see P. R. Bell, "The Movement of Plants in Response to Light" (1959), pp. 2–7. Also Pfeffer, *Die periodische Bewegungen der Blattorgane* (1875), pp. 163–70.
2. *A Philosophical Account* (1721), p. 34.
3. *Philosophia Botanica,* aphorism 147.
4. "Sponsalia Plantarum," pp. 68–69.

forty-six "vigilant flowers" which opened and closed at set times.[5] In 1755 he published an essay entitled "Somnus Plantarum" which received wide attention. He was at pains to justify his use of the word sleep:

> How plants can lack nerves and sensations and yet perform the motions of sleep and vigilance it is impossible to say, but surely there is nothing wrong [with supposing] that the Creator gave most if not all plants something analogous to sleep, because no creature can last for long without periods of rest, which in this place it may be possible to all of the sleeping plants; I dare to name it [sleep] what it has from the first been seen to be to avoid coining a new word which would be obscure for a time and might fail to be accepted.[6]

He devised a teleological criterion to distinguish the sleep of flowers from the sleep of leaves. Petals closed in order to protect the pollen, whereas leaves furled because they benefited from their rest. Linnaeus was confused by a tamarind that closed its leaves even in a heated greenhouse where there was no need to protect the fruit.

Speculation on the cause of sleep in plants was arrested for a time by John Hill, who performed a series of mechanical experiments on the subject. Hill's adoption of an experimental approach may have been related to the fact that he was one of the few British naturalists who rejected theories of subtle matter. He had once attacked speculative Newtonian monism as atheistic.[7] Hill found certain fibers whenever he dissected moving plants and assumed that a physical agency must act upon them. Only heat, air, moisture, or light could be considered as physical causes. Linnaeus's observation of the tamarind had eliminated heat. It seemed doubtful that air could be the physical cause of sleep motions. He soaked some plants and kept others dry; motions continued in both groups, eliminating moisture from consideration as a cause. When Hill tried cutting off the light from an *Abrus* (Leguminosae) he found that sleep movements invariably followed. He rushed into print in 1757 with a pamphlet entitled *The Sleep of Plants, and Cause of Motion in the Sensitive Plant Explain'd,* which he dedicated to the King and addressed to Linnaeus.

5. Pp. 273–74. Daniel Solander wrote to John Hunter, probably in 1776, that out of 13,000 known species of plants, 448 showed sleep motions, 195 had moving stems, 107 moved their leaves to follow the sun, 6 were affected by touch, and 1 moved its leaves constantly: Hunter, *Essays, 1* (1861), 355–56.

6. P. 336.

7. *Thoughts Concerning God and Nature* (1755), 395.

> It is in our power therefore to bring on this state of repose at pleasure, and by the admission or exclusion of light, to make the plant at our own time put on all its changes.[8]

Hill did not speak of light as a kind of ether which might be converted into solid bodies, but as an active mechanical impulse which was the material cause of the motions of plants by means of "a motion occasioned by its rays among their fibers." [9] He was as eager as any seventeenth-century mechanist to construct a mechanical explanation. William Kenrick (1725?–79) ridiculed the notion of plant volition, perhaps with Hill's correction of Linnaeus in mind:

> Say, "The broad oak, when thunders roar,
> "Fears till the thunder-storm be o'er;
> "Conscious of doubt and dread by turns,
> "Stands trembling as the forest burns;
> "Alive, awake, to nature's laws,
> "From nature's scenes experience draws;
> "Throbbing its trunk with hopes and fears,
> "Grown old in wisdom as in years." [10]

Another category of plant motions are those of irritability, conspicuously manifested by the sensitive plant, *Mimosa pudica*. The pinnulae of this plant collapse pair by pair down each subpetiole when touched. The movement is effected by reversible changes in the turgescence of special structures, the pulvini, at the base of each pinnule, subpetiole, and leaf (Plate 6). Stimuli are transmitted by the circulation of hormones, probably aided by the agency of tiny electric currents, along specialized fibers which run through each leaflet to the petioles and down the main rib of each compound leaf. The mysterious motions of the plant were regarded as unimpeachable evidence for the idea of botanical analogy.

8. P. 30.

9. Ibid., p. 18. Hill performed similar dissections on *Mimosa pudica* and observed fibers running from receptor to effector tissues. He did not remark turgescence changes in the pulvini. The sensitive plant also closed its leaves when removed to a dark place, which he explained by the removal of light pressure from the leaves. Such a cause might appear to account for sleep but could not explain the plant's reaction to the application of pressure by physical blows. Von Sachs, in *History of Botany* [1875], p. 550, credits Dutrochet with the first useful discoveries on the sensitive plant. Bell, in "The Movement of Plants in Response to Light" (1959) refers principally to tropic movements and does not mention Hill. Pulteney, in "The Sleep of Plants," (1758) does Hill more justice (p. 314).

10. *Epistles Philosophical and Moral* (London: T. Wilcox, 1759), Epistle 8, lines 37–44 (p. 306).

Tommaso Campanella (1568–1639) wrote that "No one should doubt the senses of plants—they are born, nourished, grow, produce seeds and young even as animals do." [11] He did not know about the sensitive plant, mentioning the heliotrope and the *Nymphaea lotus* of the Euphrates, which rose from the water to salute the sun each day. Martin Lister, ever alert for analogies, supposed that the "sudden shrinking of some plants, [and] the frequent closing and opening of flowers" in others, were "manifest acts of sense." [12] Caspar Bose wrote in 1728 that the movements of plants in following the sun or closing their leaves when touched, and the existence of zoophytes (sea anemones, not corals), indicated that plants enjoyed sensation. He argued against the mechanistic physiology of Grew, Dedu, and Mariotte and cited the fabulous Tartarian lamb as a plant which enjoyed sensation all over its body.[13]

Robert Hooke experimented on living specimens of *Mimosa* in 1661. A blow, an incision in a pinnule, or a drop of nitric acid was observed to cause all the pinnulae above the affected spot to close and those below to collapse pair by pair down the subpetiole. He supposed that a blow pressed liquors out of the subpetioles and down the rib of the leaf, causing the pinnulae to come together. He did not

11. *De Sensu Rerum et Magia . . .* (Frankfurt: Egenolphum Emmelium, 1620), Bk. 3, chap. 14 (p. 251). Cf. Linnaeus, *Sexes of Plants,* pp. 47–48 for the Euphrates lily. Campanella sought to maintain correspondences between earthly and celestial things and did not investigate causes. Pliny did not believe Apollodorus's account of the sensitive plant: *Historia Naturalis* xxiv. 17.

12. "Acts in Plants Resembling Those of Sense" (1673), p. 5137.

13. *Dissertatio Botanico-Philosophica de Motu Plantarum Sensus Aemulo.* Another writer who apparently believed in the Scythian lamb was Demetrius de Lacroix, who included a woodcut of the creature in his poem *Connubia Florum* (1728), also p. 15. Also Erasmus Darwin, "The Loves of the Plants" (1789), Canto I, and in later editions a plate copied from John Evelyn, *Terra . . . ,* ed. A. Hunter (York: A. Ward for J. Dodsley, 1786), p. 48. Darwin did not make a point of denying its existence. John Ray had done so in 1686. Sir Hans Sloane, Johann Philipp Breyn (1690–1764), and Denis Diderot (1712–84) thought the mythical creature was a curio manufactured from fern roots by wily Chinese merchants: *Phil. Trans.,* no. 247 (1698), 461–62 and Fig. 5 opp. title page; no. 390 (1725), 353–60 and plate opp. title page; [Diderot], "Agnus Scythicus," in *Encyclopédie, 1* (1751), 179–80. Erasmus Darwin's brother, Robert Waring Darwin (1766–1848), agreed in *Principia Botanica* (3d ed. 1810), p. 171. Cf. Bacon, *Sylva Sylvarum* (1626), Cent. VII, par. 609 (p. 155). Henry Lee explained that the legend arose from naive descriptions of the cotton plant: *The Vegetable Lamb of Tartary* (1887), pp. 31–60. Also A. W. Exell, "Barometz: the Vegetable Lamb of Scythia," *Nat. Hist. Mag., 3* (1931–32), 194–200. With the exception of Darwin's poem, and he was critical enough to include it only as a poetic fable, I have found no writer later than Bose who believed in the *Agnus scythicus* on grounds of analogy. The specimens of Sloane and Breyn had been too conclusively shown false.

observe the liquors but had no doubt that the motions could be explained on mechanical principles:

> He that had the ability and leisure to give you an exact anatomy of this pretty plant, to show you its fibers and visible canals, through which this fine liquor circulateth or is moved, and had the faculty of better and more copiously expressing his observations and conceptions—such a one would easily from the motion of this liquor solve all the phenomena and not fear to affirm that it is no obscure sensation this plant hath.[14]

Hooke failed to disclose the "constituting contrivance." He imagined that the "humble or sensible plant," once explained, would cast a good deal of light on animals, the next step upward in "nature's transition from one degree to another" along the scale of functions.[15] The course of explanation was to proceed in a manner opposite to that which Hooke suggested. Any light cast upon the subject for the next one hundred and twenty years was to be reflected from the animal kingdom, through the medium of the idea of botanical analogy.

John Ray found the reactions of the sensitive plant very difficult to explain and conceded that the plant seemed to "display this quality [of sense] in no obscure fashion."[16] He could not discover a mechanical cause for the motions and offered as a hypothesis an analogy with the lungs of animals. He thought both leaves and lungs were turgid and expanded when filled with fluids, and were flaccid and collapsed when the fluids were evacuated. Ray denied that the plant controlled the movement of the fluids by valves which could be opened and shut at will.[17] Richard Bradley, who also favored mechanical explanations, offered no hypothesis as to the cause of the motions. Linnaeus noted similar movements in Mimosa and Oxalis (*Biophytum sensitivum*) but would not ascribe them to a voluntary power or true sensation.[18]

Albrecht von Haller distinguished between the contractibility which some tissues displayed and the power of communicating pain or sensation possessed by others. These were the celebrated categories of irritability and sensibility. He maintained that the irritability of animal fibers "distinguished them from vegetables."[19] His denial of irri-

14. Hooke, *Micrographia* (1665), p. 120. Also Pl. 11, Fig. 2.
15. Ibid., p. 124.
16. *Historia Plantarum, 1* (1686), 2.
17. Ibid., p. 978.
18. "Somnus Plantarum," pp. 335–36.
19. *A Dissertation on the Sensible and Irritable Parts of Animals* (1936), p. 44.

tability to plants was soon challenged by naturalists who believed that the property might reside in the sensitive plant. Bonnet supposed that irritability, residing in the gelatinous tissues of plants, was the cause of their motions.[20] In actual fact this was to say nothing whatever about the cause, because the term irritability described motions which might be excited in muscular tissue independent of hypothetical physical agencies. To those who used it, the term was satisfying only because it suggested analogies with animals. In 1767 Benjamin Stillingfleet translated Giambattista dal Covolo's essay on the irritability of flowers. This work described the mechanism whereby the pistil of a single thistle floret was forced out of its protective sheath. Bent strands of tissue were observed to straighten and advance the pistil. The filaments moved if touched, just as irritable muscles did in animals. Microscopic examination revealed no apparent causes.

> What is there now remaining for a naturalist? What but a modest silence? As I can go no farther in search of causes I must content myself with finding out names and not lose this opportunity, perhaps not less curious than any other whatever . . . Let me then call this contracting power the irritability of flowers, a quality perhaps never so fully shown as here, unless in relation to the fibres of the muscles. . . . And lastly, may it not be said, that the filaments of [these] flowers are not muscles? [sic] [21]

In a dissertation on the irritability of plants Johann Friedrich Gmelin (1748–1804) described motions of irritability in roots, trunks, petioles, peduncles, buds, spines, stipules and bracts, leaves, receptacles, calices, petals, nectaries, the anthers and filaments of stamens, the germens, styles, and stigmata of pistils, pericarps, and seeds. He listed 600 plants with irritable anthers and some 40 plants with irritable leaves. He denied that the motions arose from sensibility, idiosyncrasies and antipathies, nervous spirits, the spiritus mundi, humectation, motion of humors, suppressed perspiration, or electric matter.[22] The motions were to be regarded as true irritability. The plants displayed irritability in moist tissues as a result of excitations in fibers,

20. *Contemplation de la nature,* 2 (1764), 60–66. Also Peter Camper, (1722–89), *Oratio de Analogie inter Animalis et Stirpes* (1764), for enthusiastically stated analogies of nutrition, sexuality, perspiration, respiration, circulation, parental affection, and sensation.

21. Dal Covolo, *Concerning the Irritability of Some Flowers* [1764], pp. 40–41; "Filaments" refers to the strands of tissue.

22. *Irritabilitatem Vegetabilivm* (1768), pp. 5–6.

which could be produced by a variety of physical stimuli.[23] Gmelin was not concerned with the close experimental analysis of the motions of any one plant, but the discovery of apparent irritability in as many parts of as many different kinds of plants as possible. Not until the experimental researches of John Hunter, John Lindsay, and Thomas Knight would it become possible to refer to any protracted observations on isolated phenomena of irritability or tropisms in plants. Their investigations will be discussed as part of a revival of experiment in natural history, coincident with the development of the science of biology. We may observe, however, that the researches of the first two were not published in their own lifetimes. Between 1770 and 1815 the subject of plant irritability was in the hands of speculative essayists who gave the idea of botanical analogy its most complete expression.

Alexander Hunter (1729–1809) wrote in his essay "On Vegetation and the Analogy between Plants and Animals" that geotropism in the radicles of seedlings seemed "to carry with it some appearance of instinct." [24] Some time around 1770 Richard Watson (1737–1816), professor of chemistry at Cambridge and later bishop of Llandaff, wrote his essay "On the Subjects of Chemistry and Their General Division." He was unable to discover a chemical criterion distinguishing plants from animals. As animals were "wholly nourished from vegetables, it might be expected a priori that the products obtainable by a chemical analysis from the two kingdoms should be different rather in quantity than quality, and that we should not from thence discover any criteria by which they might be distinguished from one another." [25] In fact, he was utterly unable to distinguish plants from animals. Plant motions were just as "definite and distinguishable" as those of corals, sponges, and molluscs.

> Now to refer the muscular motions of shellfish and zoophytes to an internal principle of volition, to make them indicative of the perceptivity of the being, and to attribute the more notable ones of vegetables to certain mechanical dilatations and contractions of parts occasioned by external impulse, is to err against that rule of philosophising which assigns the same causes for effects of the same kind. The motions are . . . equally distinct and uniform

23. Ibid., p. 29.
24. *Georgical Essays, 1* (1770), 89.
25. [First printed, although not published, in 1771.] p. 158.

> and should be equally derived from mechanism or equally admitted as criterions [sic] of perception.[26]

Not generation, nutrition, organization, life, health, sickness, or death was a criterion adequate to distinguish animals from plants. "Both are subject to be frost-bitten and to consequent mortifications, both languish in excessive heats, both experience extravasations of juices from repletion and pinings from inanition."[27] Watson found that lead and tin burned like rotten wood and that zinc burned like charcoal. "Why should the phlogiston of metals be thought of a nature wholly different from the [organic] oil?"[28] Perhaps all the strata of the earth's crust were of organic origin and "all matter is, or hath been organized, enlivened, animated." He wrote of "an uninterrupted concatenation" in the works of God, whereby all species, genera, and kingdoms were "mingled together" or distinguished in the mind of the Creator by divinely perceived "lines of division too minute for our observation."[29]

These sentiments were influenced by a complacent theological argument that God's infinite goodness "seems to delight in the conferring of existence upon every degree of perceptive being."[30] From this assumption it followed that God strove for the widest possible distribution of perception in organisms. Some remarks on plant sensation to be found in eighteenth-century essays were inspired as much by this "pleasure principle" as by apprehensions about plant life.

Soame Jenyns (1704–87) wrote in his essay "On the Chain of Universal Being" (1782) that the sensitive plant and lower animals seemed to share equally in the capacity for reaction to stimulus:

> Solidity, extension, and gravity, the qualities of mere matter, being united with the lowest degree of vegetation, compose a stone; whence this vegetative power ascending through an infinite variety of herbs, flowers, plants, and trees to its greatest perfection in the sensitive plant, joins there the lowest degree of animal life in the shellfish, which adheres to the rock; and it is

26. Ibid., pp. 142–43.
27. Ibid., p. 149.
28. Ibid., p. 162.
29. Ibid., pp. 169–71.
30. Cf. [Joseph Addison], *Spectator*, no. 519 (25 Oct. 1712). Also Willey, *The Eighteenth Century Background* (1940), chap. 3, "Cosmic Toryism." Also Baker, *Abraham Trembley* (1952), p. 230. Cf. Aristotle, *Historia Animalium* viii. 1. Also Priestley, *History of Elictricity* (1767), p. xx.

difficult to distinguish which possesses the greatest share [of sensitivity], as the one shows it only by shrinking from the finger, and the other by opening to receive the water which surrounds it.[31]

In 1768 living specimens of a remarkable new sensitive plant were sent to John Ellis by William Young of Philadelphia. It was the *Dionaea muscipula,* or Venus' fly trap, an insectivorous plant of the Atlantic pine barrens. Ellis wrote in October of that year, "I have never met with so wonderful a phenomenon." [32]

'Tis a new sensitive plant and formed in such an extraordinary manner as if the great author of nature intended it to receive some nourishment from the animals it seizes. For in the internal part of the two lobes of each leaf are three erect little spines [the trigger hairs] among the little red [digestive] glands marked with dots in the print. These glands seem to be the irritable part. As soon as a fly or other insect touches these, when the leaves are young and vigorous, the lobes immediately close upon it and the spines either stick into it or serve to prevent its escape, where it remains till it dies. . . . This is an entirely new genus. I have sent its characters to Linnaeus, our father in botany, which I suppose he will adopt.[33]

Linnaeus adopted the name suggested by Ellis in his description. "The sensibility and figure of the leaves of the Dionaea has put my old friend Linnaeus into raptures." [34]

Another remarkable plant was *Desmodium gyrans,* the telegraph plant. The plant slept at night but in the daytime, above a temperature of 72°, the small lateral leaflets moved steadily around in elliptical orbits.[35] In 1778 Charles Linnaeus the younger intruded a description of the plant upon a letter he was writing to a Spanish botanist to announce the death of his father. The wonderful thing about the movements of the Hedysarum, as it was then called, was their spontaneity. The leaflets moved "not all at once nor all in the same direc-

31. P. 8.
32. *Correspondence of Linnaeus, 1,* 235.
33. Letter of 11 Oct. 1768 to Mary, Duchess of Norfolk. Ibid., *2,* 72–73.
34. Savage, ed., *Calendar of the Ellis Manuscripts* (1948), p. 71. Letter of Nov. 1768 to Dr. David Skene of Aberdeen. For his first letter to Linnaeus describing the plant: "In this you will have a feast," see p. 37.
35. Cf. Charles Darwin, *The Power of Movement in Plants* (1880), pp. 361–65. Also [Jackson], *Sketches of the Physiology of Vegetable Life* (1811), pp. 34–36, for a rather emotional description.

tion."[36] The writer who described the plant in the second edition of the *Encyclopedia Britannica* expressed wonder that its lateral leaflets were "in constant motion without any external impulse," and observed that the motions might be observed "for the space of 24 hours in the leaves of a branch which is lopped off from the shrub if it is kept in water."[37] In 1785 Robert Bruce described yet another sensitive plant, an *Averrhoa* whose "leaves, on being touched, move very perceptibly." Rays from a burning glass or an electric shock also caused the motions.[38]

Joseph Priestley wrote that his materialistic theory of psychology was "rather favorable to the notion of such organical systems as plants having some degree of sensation."[39] George Bell (1755–85) declared in 1777, "Such is the analogy between vegetables and animals, that the knowledge of the nature of the one illustrates that of the other."[40] Bell cited the "wonderful activity" of the Mimosa, Hedysarum, and Dionaea.

> That these plants *live,* will be granted; but I suspect that they likewise *feel.* I doubt whether we are right in confining the capacity of pleasure and pain to the animal kingdom.

"This view of the life of vegetables raises botany to the rank of philosophy. It adds fresh beauty to the parterre, and gives new dignity to the forest."[41]

In 1785 Thomas Percival of Manchester (1740–1804) advanced his "Speculations on the Perceptive Power of Vegetables." He inferred from the analogies between plants and animals that they possessed a common living principle which "naturally implies" sensitivity. Sensitivity in turn implied the "capacity for enjoyment." Even if that capacity were very small among vegetables, the aggregate of happiness in the vegetable kingdom would "be found to exceed our most en-

36. *Correspondence of Linnaeus, 2,* 537.

37. *Encyclopaedia Britannica, 5* (2d ed. Edinburgh: J. Balfour, 1780), 3566. Also Broussonet (1761–1807), "Mouvements des animaux et ceux des plantes" (1784).

38. "The Sensitive Property of the Tree *Averrhoa carambola,*" p. 356.

39. "A General View of the Doctrine of Vibrations," in *Hartley's Theory . . .* (London: J. Johnson, 1775), p. xx.

40. "De Physiologia Plantarum," p. 419. Also Lord Kames, "Plants and Animals Compared," *The Gentleman Farmer* (1776), pp. 385–98.

41. Ibid., pp. 418–19. B. Sprague Allen, *Tides in English Taste 1619–1800: a Background for the Study of Literature* (Harvard Univ. Press, 1937) describes the rising popularity of natural landscape gardens during the eighteenth century. It is not altogether impossible that notions about the sexuality and sensibility of plants encouraged the new taste and seemed to require a new setting for plants.

larged conceptions." Corals and allies had been acknowledged as animals. Perhaps all plants might now be recognized as sensitive beings. Considerations of teleology led him to attribute animal instincts to plants. The radicle would pursue the soil suited to it even if the seedling was inverted. The motions of the Dionaea served to supply the plant with food. The notion of plant sensation was consonant "to those higher analogies of nature which lead us to conclude that the greatest possible sum of happiness exists in the universe." [42]

Sir James Edward Smith (1759–1828) observed that the stamens of barberry sprung up "with considerable force" if a stimulus was applied to the inside surface of the filament. He mentioned similar contrivances in *Opuntia tuna* (Cactaceae) and the Dionaea and Mimosa. "All these movements are, I think, certainly to be attributed to irritability." [43] Bonnet had once urged upon Smith the notion that the entire plant showed irritability, but Smith argued that this was true only of certain specialized parts. He considered the motions inexplicable because he could not discover "anything particular in the structure" of the effectors. He sought to restrain speculation on the subject and urged detailed investigations of the structures that effected the motions. He pointed out that irritability and sensibility were sometimes combined in the same part in the animal kingdom. He doubted that this happened in plants. The distinction he wished to draw was not clear but his tone was restrained and his hypotheses specific. Few essayists displayed such restraint, and no real progress was made in questions of plant motion until naturalists set aside thoughts of analogy with animals.

William Smellie wrote that plants were "not only conscious of their existence but enjoy degrees of happiness proportioned to their natures and the purposes they are destined to answer in the general scale of animation." [44] The philosophical naturalist would not contemplate organisms "individually, but by their rank and the relations they have to the constituent parts of the general system of nature." [45] The many analogies between plants and animals and the extreme difficulty of

42. P. 126.

43. "The Irritability of Vegetables" (1788), p. 162. Also his *Introduction to Physiological and Systematical Botany* (1807), pp. 3–4. Also von Humboldt, *Florae Fribergensis* (1793), pp. 148–52.

44. *The Philosophy of Natural History, 1* (1790), 77.

45. Ibid., p. 525. Unlike the "cosmic Tories" who assumed that this system tends to man's highest happiness, Smellie held that man's perceptions were so acute as to involve him in pain and despair. With greater sensibility "no man could bear to live" (p. 526).

distinguishing them seemed to imply "that both these kingdoms constitute the same order of beings and that nature, in the formation of them, has operated upon one great and common model." [46] As the hairs, nails, beaks, and horns of animals showed something like vegetation in their mode of growth, growth and nutrition in the two kingdoms must depend upon similar mechanisms. The processes of growth evaded microscopical elucidation or mechanical explanation: "I shall confine myself at present to such remarks as are purely analogical." [47]

Smellie adhered strictly to the orthodoxy of graded function, and admitted the validity of analogies only if they were drawn along very small segments of the scale of beings. He refused to ascribe organization to minerals in the same sense the word had when applied to plant tissues. The use of fibrous asbestos to link plants and animals depended upon "one of those strained analogies which are too often employed by theoretical writers." [48] The orthodoxy of graded function, which had led him to deny sexuality to plants, also implied that plants lacked sensation, although he allowed them a measure of irritability.[49]

One of the most elaborate statements of the idea of botanical analogy was Robert Hooper's *Observations on the Structure and Economy of Plants; to Which Is Added the Analogy between the Animal and Vegetable Kingdom* (1797). Hooper (1773–1835) listed page after page of analogies based upon nutrition, sexuality, respiration, growth, birth, and death. He, too, denied sensation to plants. With Smith, Smellie, and Hooper it is possible to discern the beginning of the ebb of the tide of speculation about analogies from the high-water mark reached with Bell and Percival. Of later writers on this subject none was able to produce new evidence that plants enjoyed sensation, or any ingenious new attributes of analogy.

Charles White (1728–1813), a surgeon in Manchester, published *An Account of the Regular Gradation in Man, and in Different Animals and Vegetables; and from the Former to the Latter* in 1799. He claimed to have received the idea for his book from a graded series of skulls displayed in Manchester by his friend John Hunter.[50] Hunter

46. Ibid., p. 43. See the letter of 10 April 1800 from Sir Joseph Banks to T. A. Knight on the "one uniform plan" followed by nature: Knight, *Papers* (1841), p. 29.

47. Ibid., p. 25. As circulatory vessels eluded sight, they had to be inferred by analogy; pp. 21–22, also 520–26.

48. Ibid., p. 12.

49. Ibid., pp. 11–12.

50. P. 41.

had said at the time that plants and animals comprise different kingdoms because plants lacked stomachs. White succeeded in blurring that distinction by citing writers who denied that the central cavity of coelenterates was a true stomach. He discussed analogies in circulation, moulting, generation, and sleep and included a table patterned after the "certainly ingenious" scale of Bonnet. White was interested primarily in the higher forms on the scale of beings and sought to construct a series from man down through the apes to birds, based on speculations by Lavater (1741–1801) and Camper about the relationship between receding brows and intelligence. A corollary of White's argument was the inferiority of Negroes, whom he supposed to occupy the level between brutes and men [51] (Plate 7).

In 1811 Maria Elizabeth Jackson published *Sketches of the Physiology of Vegetable Life,* an attempt to make the study of plant physiology fashionable by relating plant functions to those of animals. Were "vegetables . . . possessed of faculties which may entitle them to a place amongst the animal orders of the creation?" [52] For the answer "facts and analogy must combine their evidence." Most anatomical differences between plants and animals were vitiated by the existence of zoophytes without brains, nerves, or differentiated muscular tissue. In this argument as in those of Smellie and Charles White we may observe the effect of problematical organisms on the distinctions between plants and animals. Mechanical causes for growth, tropisms, and the manner in which the tendrils of climbing plants located support had not been found.

51. Ibid., pp. 41–85. Cf. the "curious morsel," 6. The eighteenth-century passion for completeness sought beliefs about racial inferiority in order to fill an empty spot on the scale of beings. White's essay and other writings provided a theoretical justification for many of the "defensive beliefs" involved in modern race prejudice relating to the intelligence and morality, cleanliness, fleetness of foot, sexuality and endurance of Negroes. The role played in modern prejudice by such beliefs is discussed by John Dollard, *Caste and Class in a Southern Town* (3d ed. New York: Doubleday Anchor Books, 1957), 369 ff. It was asserted in rebuttal that Negroes were dark merely because they had lived in the tropics. Cf. James Maclurg, *Experiments upon the Human Bile* (1772), pp. 210–13. [Henry Home, Lord Kames], *Sketches of the History of Man* (Edinburgh: W. Creech, 1774). Benito Jerónimo Feijoo y Montenegro (1675–1764), "A Display of the Intellectual Faculties of the Various People, with Remarks on the Talents of the Different Ones," *Essays . . . , 4* (London: for J. Brett, 1780), 329–62. Samuel Stanhope Smith (1750–1819), *An Essay on the Causes of Complexion and Figure in the Human Species . . .* (Edinburgh: C. Elliott, 1788). Gode-von Aesch, "Physiognomics," *Natural Science in German Romanticism* (1941), pp. 217–39. Also Lovejoy, *The Great Chain of Being* (1936), pp. 233–36. Prejudice does not depend upon defensive beliefs, but the beliefs themselves seem to have depended in part upon the chain of being.

52. P. 6.

> Will it be too daring to predict that the variety of wonderful phenomena, which hourly present themselves to our view in the study of vegetable economy, will in a short time universally be ascribed to the same power of volition we unhesitatingly grant to animals of the most inert nature? [53]

She doubted "whether a marked distinction will ever be discovered between these two great orders of nature." [54]

Also in 1811, James Perchard Tupper, a former student of James Edward Smith, published *An Essay on the Probability of Sensation in Vegetables,* which gathered together all the speculations of the preceding century to prove that plants enjoyed all the powers of animal life but volition. He believed they had sensation and also instinct, by which he meant contrivances for self-preservation.[55] Tupper cited phototrophic movements, motions of tendrils in climbing plants, geotropism in roots, plants which closed their leaves before storms, contrivances for fertilization, and sleep in plants. These seemed to be instinctive in that they could be used by the organism only for the purposes intended by the Creator. Tupper thought that birds built nests and spiders spun webs after the same manner. His cardinal principle was "not to ascribe similar effects to different causes." [56] The tapeworm did not have nerves but was capable of reacting to stimuli; perhaps plants functioned in the same way.

> Hence it is evident that organs different from the general character of nerves can, and do, perform their functions in some animals; consequently, it can be no very extravagant conjecture to entertain, that this analogy extends to vegetables, which, in so many other respects bear so near a similitude to animals in their physiology.[57]

53. Ibid., p. 29.
54. Ibid., p. 100.
55. This assertion had been denied explicitly by Oliver Goldsmith, *An History of the Earth, and Animated Nature* (London: J. Nourse, 1774), *2,* 1–14; *8,* 161–69. Tupper, *Sensation in Vegetables* (1811), p. 16, does not mention Goldsmith but patterned his argument as though to answer him.
56. P. 48.
57. Ibid., p. 56. Tupper had in mind an article by Sir Anthony Carlisle (1768–1840) "Observations upon the Structure and Oeconomy of those [intestinal] Worms called Taeniae," *Trans. Linn. Soc., 2* (1797), 253–54. Carlisle thought tapeworms might have a portion of "nervous matter" diffused through their bodies. Thomas Cooper (1759–1839), the materialist and radical who accompanied Priestley to America in 1794, held similar beliefs about analogy: "On Vegetable Life" (1814). One "J. R. W." criticized Cooper, whereupon he replied with a spirited essay, depicting a courtroom in which testimony was elicited from Linnaeus, Buffon, and

Tupper subscribed to the theological argument that sensation must have been conferred upon plants for the sake of universal happiness.[58] He was so firmly convinced of the validity of the scale of beings that he averred no single link could be lost, because that would constitute defiance of God's injunction to increase and multiply.[59]

Eighteenth-century naturalists denied or overlooked every distinction between plants and animals that they might have been expected to consider. Despite the extravagances of speculation encouraged by the idea of botanical analogy, particularly Linnaeus's interpretation of zoophytes and the notion that plants enjoyed sensation, it would not be correct to conclude that its consequences for the eventual development of true knowledge in biology were altogether harmful. Largely through its appeal to speculators, the idea had effected a change in the usual opinion of plant life. The analogies with minerals advanced by seventeenth-century mechanists were rejected in favor of analogies with animals, which represented progress toward a more accurate assessment of the complexity of plant life. The pursuit of analogies helped to ease the abandonment of the desire for total explanation. Botanical analogy could be used to discourse of many functions in plants, and this comprehensiveness tended to satisfy, but even the speculators who sought its sanction realized that it left causes unexplained. The next step, taken by very many early nineteenth-century biologists, was to seek to become independent of such inherited ambitions. Botanical analogy and the ether were half measures in this development that were discarded when the scientific community agreed upon the need to enforce the principle of limited explanation. The revolution in technique had been foretold by the empiricism of Haller and Newton, but for those who would not accept such discipline all at once, ideas of suble fluids and analogy had permitted some of the satisfactions of total explanation. Below the surface of apparent continuity a fundamental change of opinion about scientific

---

Sir Humphry Davy in support of the idea of analogy: "Of Vegetable Life" (1815). Also see his note in J. Priestley, fils, *Memoirs of Dr. Priestley . . .* (London: J. Johnson, 1807), pp. 315–16. Also Cooper, *Tracts Ethical, Theological and Political* (Warrington: by W. Eyres for J. Johnson of London, 1789), p. 241. Among later writers who tried to sustain the idea of botanical analogy (with no new arguments) were Renn Hampden (1793–1898), *Philosophical Evidence of Christianity* (1829); J. S. Duncan (1769–1844), *Analogies of Organized Beings* (1831); Edwin Lees (1800–87), *The Affinities of Plants with Men and Animals* [1833]; and George Field (1777?–1854), *Outlines of Analogical Philosophy* (1839).

58. *Sensation in Vegetables,* pp. 79–81.

59. Ibid. (2d ed. 1817), pp. 127–43, "On the Perpetuity of Every Species of Living Beings [sic] Originally Created."

method was slowly effected. After the turn of the century it becomes possible, in many different courses of investigation, to characterize biology as a positivistic science employing experiment and more modest programs of observation according to the principle of limited explanation.

5

From the Idea of Nature to the Science of Biology

The turn of the century was a time of rapid change in the study of natural history. Articles published in scientific journals became increasingly specialized between 1790 and 1810. The progress of permanently significant biological discoveries was hastened. Instances of cross-citation and translation became more common in the archival literature, showing a more rapid communication of discoveries and increasing interdependence of effort. For present purposes it seems best to analyze in terms of ideas the writings of four men who presided over the change, with particular attention to the ideas of immanence and botanical analogy.

We shall characterize the change as the development of a science of life which came to replace the ideas of the naturalists as the leading concern of serious investigators of organic nature. Through the subtle institutional and intellectual processes so well described by Thomas Kuhn in his recent study of scientific revolutions, a new age of discovery and experimental work was begun.[1] To call the new generation biologists rather than naturalists is not to deny that the quickening development of the life sciences depended almost entirely upon established precepts of scientific method and familiar practices of observation. The process whereby whole constellations of concepts and acceptable simplifications re-form and succeed one another along courses dictated by fashion, experience, and increasing sophistication need

1. Kuhn, *The Structure of Scientific Revolutions* (1962).

not always be radical and revolutionary. But our evidence will show that many scientific writers of the time thought of themselves as new men, using their inheritance of values and concepts to serve more truly scientific concerns.

The biologists, not so prone to speculative excess, rejected the ideas upon which so much eighteenth-century writing had been based. Empiricism and rigorous modes of interpreting experimental results brought a positivistic tone to biological science. The harmony once believed to exist between life and the energies of matter was disrupted. Organic bodies had come to seem very remote from any abstractions that might be drawn from physics or chemistry to describe them.

Eighteenth-century naturalists had described life as the aggregate of externally collected energies or the sum of the attractive and repulsive powers of individual particles within an organism. The biologists were to conceive of life as dependent upon internal metabolic processes and exchanges of energy. This conception had to be honored by the adoption of more rigorous methods of investigating organic phenomena. The notions of life adopted by nineteenth-century biologists were to foster among them more severe experimental techniques, suited to the investigation of processes vaguely defined and virtually unexplained. The result was quite naturally a more cautious manner of applying analogies and an attitude of empiricism.

Erasmus Darwin has been praised as an exponent of modern beliefs about life. We must investigate his writings to see if such an attitude may indeed be discovered. An examination of the works of Lamarck, Sir Humphry Davy, and John Hunter will set the difference between the naturalists and the biologists in a clearer light and help us to understand how it came about.

i. Erasmus Darwin

Erasmus Darwin (1731–1802) followed typical eighteenth-century habits of mind, notwithstanding his recognition of evolution as the principal process of organic development. An analysis of his meaning will contradict any attempt to ascribe a new "biological" sensibility to him.[1]

The fact that Darwin wrote three long poems about nature does not of itself indicate that he had new opinions about the poetic value

1. Cf. Desmond King-Hele, *Erasmus Darwin 1731–1802* (London: Macmillan, 1963) for a more generous estimate of his originality and interests.

of scientific knowledge or that some change in the content of his beliefs about nature had made them more amenable to poetic expression. This can be demonstrated by a brief survey of other eighteenth-century scientific poems.

Camerarius' experimental proof of plant sexuality had been hailed by one of his contemporaries in these lines:

> There the farina we may see,
> Down from th'aspiring summits flow,
> The greatest part of flow'rs we know
> Hermaphrodites to be. . . .
> As the shell-fish in the briny main,
> At the same time from one part give,
> What with the other they receive,
> Both sexes they [plants] contain.[2]

Demetrius deLacroix's *Connubia Florum* (1728) and Adrien van Royen's *De Amoribus et Connubiis Plantarum* (1732) were also inspired by the discovery of plant sexuality. In deLacroix's poem a character visits a palace of flora where he is introduced to Sebastian Vaillant and permitted to view the wonders of plants with the "piercing eyes of Ray and Malpighi." At the command of Cupid, "L'esprit séminal s'exhale, frappe la voute qui le réflechit, pour passer avec plus d'impétuosité dans les canaux imperceptibles de la trompe, jusques dans la substance intérieure du placenta." [3] The poet professed a lifelong interest in the nature of the soul, the structure of the universe, and the fundamental causes of all things.[4]

In his *Spring* (1728), James Thomson (1700–48) described an "attractive Plant" imbibing "the live Æther." [5] Thomas Pennant called Thomson "the naturalist's poet," and Thomas Percival praised him for having wandered in "sequestered walks" where he had acquired "by the most minute attention, a knowledge of all the mysteries of nature." [6] Gilbert White (1720–93) wrote poetic descriptions of wildlife:

2. Camerarius, *De Sexu Plantarum* (1694), pp. 80–84, trans. John Martyn and published in Blair, *Botanick Essays* (1720), pp. 326–30.

3. deLacroix, *Connubia Florum*, p. 7.

4. Ibid., p. 3. For the sensitive plant, see pp. 17, 21.

5. Lines 511, 517. See also McKillop, *The Background of Thomson's Seasons* (1942), p. 60, on the nitro-aerial salt. Also Nicolson, *Newton Demands the Muse* pp. 55–73 on poetic descriptions of Newton's ether.

6. *Natural History and Poetry* (1789), p. 252. Also Pennant, *British Zoology . . .*, *I* (London: Benjamin White, 1768), viii. Also Aikin, *Natural History and Poetry* (1777).

What time the may-fly haunts the pool or stream,
When the still owl skims round the grassy mead,
What time the timorous hare limps forth to feed;
That be the time to steal adown the vale,
And listen to the vagrant cuckoo's tale; [7]

In *The Minstrel* (1779) James Beattie (1735–1803) described a youth aspiring "through number, time, and space" to scientific knowledge. Fancy "no more / Wantons on fickle pinion", "But, fix'd in aim, and conscious of her power, / Sublime from cause to cause exults to rise".[8] Percival argued that natural philosophy was a fitting source for poetic materials because it "infinitely exceeds in extent, elevation, and grandeur that of the ancients." [9]

In a study of natural science and German romanticism Alexander Gode-von Aesch cites a number of poets who sought to write Lucretian epics of science reflecting the synthesis of interrelated forces. André Chénier (1762–94) describes the origin and progress of physical nature and society in "Hermes" [1792]:

Souvent mon vol, armé des ailes de Buffon,
Franchit avec Lucrèce, au flambeau de Newton,
La ceinture d'azure, sur le globe éntendue.
Je vois l'être et la vie et leur source inconnue,
Dans les fleuves d'éther tous les mondes roulants.[10]

There is no reason to suppose that Erasmus Darwin must have had new scientific insights simply because he chose to write poetry about science. We cannot maintain that Darwin's writings presented an altogether new understanding of biology. He was pre-eminently a poet of botanical analogy, personifying flower parts to dramatize "The Loves of the Plants." The reaction of a typical eighteenth-century literary temperament to the idea of plant sensitivity appears in a letter from Hannah More to Thomas Percival. She found the notion "so pretty and poetical" that she would have written "the tragedy of Flora, with the dramatis personae from the parterre and

7. *The Natural History of Selborne* (1789), Letter 24 to Thomas Pennant, 29 May 1769.

8. Bk. 2, stanza 55.

9. *Natural History and Poetry*, p. 237.

10. *Poésies de André Chénier, édition critique* . . . (Paris: Charpentier, 1862), pp. 345–46. See Gode-von Aesch, *Science in German Romanticism* (1941), pp. 241–44 on Chénier and 39–52 on Christoph Martin Wieland's *Die Natur der Dinge* (1750).

the chorus from the shrubbery" had she not "renounced such idle company as the muses." [11]

We may note that in 1787 Erasmus Darwin expressed a notion of plant sensitivity very similar to Thomas Percival's:

> Vegetables are in truth an inferior order of animals, connected to the lower tribes of insects by many marine productions, whose faculties of motion and sensation are scarcely superior to those of the petals of many flowers, or to the leaves of the sensitive plant (Mimosa sensitiva), the moving plant (Hedysarum gyrans), and the fly-trap (Dionaea muscipula).[12]

Darwin had published two poems as an undergraduate but foreswore the muse until 1789.[13] He then set out to present the idea of botanical analogy and the Linnaean systematics as "diverse little pictures" festooned with "ribbons" for an audience of fashion.[14] Each poem, a liquid succession of tasteless couplets, was ballasted with "philosophical notes" and closely related to his bulky volumes of speculation: *Zoonomia* (1794 and 1796) and *Phytologia* (1800).

"The Loves of the Plants" contained versified descriptions of some eighty plants, each assigned to its proper class in the Linnaean system by mention of the number of stamens, personified as "brother swains," "suppliant beaux," and the like, except the asexual lower plants, which were acknowledged to practice "secret loves" or "clandestine rites." Most of the plants chosen have moving flower parts, whose purpose Darwin supposed to be self-fertilization or autogamy.[15] One might cite as a representative couplet his description of the pistil of

11. Letter of 8 Aug. 1785. *The Works . . . of Thomas Percival . . . , 3* (London: J. Johnson, 1807), cv.

12. Darwin, trans., *The Families of Plants, 1* (1787), xix.

13. Ritterbush, "Erasmus Darwin's Second Published Poem," *Rev. of English Studies, 13* (1962), 158–60.

14. "Proem.," "The Loves of the Plants" (1789). As the verses are numbered differently in successive editions of this poem, citations will be given as Roman numerals, referring to cantos. *The Botanic Garden* is the collective title for this poem and "The Economy of Vegetation" (1791).

15. Darwin was always careful to list the different degrees of sexual complication which he thought to parallel the scale of beings. The lowest creatures were generated spontaneously and were succeeded by asexual beings (parthenogenetic aphids and budding plants), hermaphrodite flowers (Darwin did not acknowledge the existence of monosexual flowers and thus denied the agency of insects in pollination), and finally monosexual beings ruled by "THE DEITIES OF SEXUAL LOVE." He supposed that evolution had taken place according to that sequence and that the Biblical account of the creation of Eve from Adam's rib was a hieroglyphic myth to explain the origin of monosexual from hermaphrodite forms. See *Phytologia,* pp. 79–81, 340, 365; *Zoonomia, 1* (1794), 514; and *The Temple of Nature* [1802], Canto II and Add. Note 9.

Collinsonia bending into successive contact with two stamens: "With sweet concern the pitying beauty mourns, / And soothes with smiles the jealous pair by turns." (I)

In a note on *Chrondrilla* Darwin cited dal Covolo's treatise on irritable flower parts and described periodic movements in numerous species. In the first edition of the poem Darwin hesitated to ascribe sensation to pendant flowers which come to an erect position after fertilization. "Is this a mechanical effect, or does it indicate a vegetable storge [i.e. natural affection] to preserve its offspring?" (I) In the second edition he declared that the erection of fertilized flowers indicated the presence of mother love and "cannot be explained by mere mechanism." [16]

Pollen carried by the wind struck him as analogous to winged insects; immobile female flowers, to wingless female insects. The *Anthoxanthum,* whose buds fall off to take direct root, was analogous to the aphid, which he described as viviparous in summer and oviparous in winter. The wind-borne seeds of some plants were analogous to spiders supported by long threads. Edible fungi had an animal taste and could survive without sunlight, which "would seem to show that they approach towards the animals, or make a kind of isthmus connecting the two mighty kingdoms of animal and of vegetable nature." (I)

The "Additional Notes" of "The Economy of Vegetation" (1791) presented one of the most extensive series of analogies ever entertained between plants and animals. We shall cite only a few of the more extreme instances, as examples of Darwin's uncritical delight in analogies. He ascribed heliotropism in plants to "the vegetable muscles of their leaf stalks": [17]

> This action of opening and closing the leaves or flowers does not appear to be produced simply by *irritation* on the muscles themselves, but by the connection of those muscles with a *sensitive* sensorium or brain existing in each individual bud or flower.[18]

He drew many analogies between buds in plants and the structure of polyzoa. "A tree is a congeries of many living buds and in this respect resembles the branches of corallines, which are a congeries of a multitude of animals." [19] Darwin proudly developed this notion about buds at great length in *Phytologia.* He attributed the sleep of plants to a

16. "The Loves of the Plants," (2d ed. 1791,) n. to I, 152, "Amaryllis."
17. N. to IV, 422.
18. Ibid., n. to III, 440.
19. *Zoonomia, 1,* p. 102.

voluntary faculty interposed between darkness (a negative stimulus incapable of mechanical effects) and the motions of the leaves. He pointed out in "The Loves of the Plants" that the motions might "be justly ascribed to a voluntary power; for without the faculty of volition, sleep would not have been necessary to them." [20] The apparent sensibility of flower parts led Darwin to this astonishing outburst of speculation:

> The anthers and stigmas are real animals, attached indeed to their parent tree like polyps or coral insects, but capable of spontaneous motion; that they are affected with the passion of love, and furnished with powers of reproducing their species, and are fed with honey like the moths and butterflies which plunder their nectaries.[21]

Most of these conjectures may be traced to Linnaeus: the notion that corals were half plant and half animal, the belief that the sleep of plants was accomplished through a voluntary faculty, analogies between flower parts and insects derived from the notion of metamorphosis, confusion about fungi and, finally, Darwin's versified account of prolepsis:

> Closed in the *Style* the tender pith shall end,
> The lengthening Wood in circling *Stamens* bend;
> The smoother Rind its soft embroidery spread
> In vaulted *Petals* o'er their fertile bed;
> While the rough Bark, in circling mazes roll'd,
> Forms the green *Cup* with many a wrinkled fold; [22]

The idea of botanical analogy constituted the central theme of Darwin's *Botanic Garden*, reflecting Linnaeus's poetic enthusiasm rather than the new insights of biological science.

We cannot claim Darwin as an exponent of the more rigorous scientific faculty which was to characterize early nineteenth-century natural science. He was inventive and filled his Commonplace Book, now in the library at Down House, with hastily scribbled designs.[23] He in-

20. "Loves of Plants," (1789), IV. Also "Economy of Vegetation," n. to IV, 456, 538.

21. *Zoonomia, I,* 105.

22. "Economy of Vegetation," IV, 469–74.

23. In the Hamilton and Greville Papers at the British Museum there is an amusing letter of 12 Dec. 1778 to C. F. Greville, with a duplicate written at the same time with a device Darwin invented for copying letters (f. 51). Darwin was a member of the Lunar Society of the Midland industrialists and was keenly interested in mechanical devices.

vestigated retinal impressions and meteorology with close attention and is said to have brought a shrewd and penetrating faculty of observation to his medical practice. But his philosophy of scientific method recalls early eighteenth-century beliefs about analogy as a refuge from empiricism. He thought natural philosophy the province of "philosophical analogy" as opposed to the loose "popular" analogies of poetry. "Since natural objects are allied to each other by many affinities, every kind of theoretic distribution of them adds to our knowledge by developing some of their analogies." [24] He argued that agriculture was still an underdeveloped art. Facts were isolated from each other for want of "a true theory to connect them, or to appreciate their analogy, at a time when many parts of knowledge of much inferior consequence have been nicely arranged and digested into sciences." [25]

In the preface to *Zoonomia* Darwin criticized the "idly ingenious" who had attempted to reduce organisms to mechanics. He hoped that a theory of medicine "deduced from such strict analogy" would "bind together" and "converge" scattered observations. His only essay on scientific method was an address he delivered to the philosophical society that he organized in Derby in 1784, wherein he repeated familiar arguments to show that the weaknesses of sense might be overcome by employing analogies.[26] James Keir, who had studied with Darwin at Edinburgh, wrote in 1802:

> Your father paid little regard to authority, and he quickly perceived the analogies on which a new theory could be founded. This penetration or sagacity by which he was able to discover very remote causes and distant effects, was the characteristic of his understanding.[27]

Erasmus Darwin's notion of evolution was in part an expression of a dynamic of nature utterly foreign to eighteenth-century thought, but in many other ways it was related to familiar abstractions of the time. In order for Darwin to hold a theory of evolution he need not have accepted ideas about an active energy of life. In 1744 Mark Akenside (1721–70) described a genius of nature who imparted to him

24. "Apology," "Economy of Vegetation." Also, the first dialogue between the poet and the bookseller in "Loves of Plants." (1789).

25. "Introduction," *Phytologia.*

26. Darwin MS, "Dr. Darwin's Address to the Philosophical Society of Derby on Their First Meeting. July 18 1784."

27. Letter to Robert Waring Darwin, quoted by Charles Darwin, "Preliminary Notice" to Krause, *Erasmus Darwin* (1879), pp. 49–50.

a "shining vision" of evolution. "The uncreated images of things" were ideas in God's mind which he realized by the exercise of his will upon creatures lower down along the scale of beings:

> . . . his parent-hand
> From the mute shell-fish gasping on the shore,
> To men, to angels, to coelestial minds,
> For ever leads the generations on
> To higher scenes of being; while supply'd
> From day to day by his inlivening breath,
> Inferior orders in succession rise
> To fill the void below.[28]

Because "all things which have life aspire to God" they "persevere / To climb th'ascent of being." [29] The infusion of divine will took place through the agency of subtle matter, "the energy of life / Kindling the mass with ever-active flame." [30] Akenside spoke of a "secret harmony which blends / Th'aetherial spirit with its mold of clay." [31] George Reuben Potter noticed that Akenside wrote a medical dissertation supposing that God might intervene at the moment of fertilization to cause the embryo to resemble higher forms.[32] While Akenside's explanation of evolution depended upon the plastic power of God's extended will, Lamettrie, d'Holbach, and Marmaduke Berdoe were to describe evolution as the inevitable elaboration of the active powers of matter into higher and higher forms of life.

28. *The Pleasures of Imagination, 2,* 343–50.
29. Ibid., 361–62.
30. Ibid., *1,* 518–19.
31. Ibid., *3,* 280–81. Visions incorporating "more than human" figures who impart truths from bright orbs or clouds seem to have been a characteristic device of Neoplatonic writers. Sir Humphry Davy and Shelley frequently employed the device (cf. Akenside, *2,* 220–41). Also Leibniz, *Theodicy: Essays on the Goodness of God the Freedom of Man and the Origin of Evil* [1710], trans. E. M. Huggard (London: Routledge and Kegan Paul, 1951), pp. 370–73, par. 414–17.
32. "Mark Akenside, Prophet of Evolution" (1926). Akenside wrote that the "enliven'd soul" might find "inexpressible semblance of himself" in nature (*3,* 284–85). Dr. John Gregory wrote in his *Comparative View* (1765) that the poets and scientists dealt with analogies in similar ways. "There is a correspondence between certain external forms of nature and certain affections of the mind that may be felt but cannot be explained" (pp. 143–44). I would suppose that the Romantic feeling for nature may be traced in part to such expressions of analogy. Coleridge seemed to acknowledge as much in supposing that the "soothing, love-kindling effect of rural nature" arose because "in natural objects we feel ourselves, or think of ourselves only by likenesses": *Anima Poetae* [1802–03], p. 25. Also, Wordsworth's "deep analogies by thought supplied" may have been based in part on eighteenth-century analogies: "Lines Written in Early Spring" (1798), lines 11–20. Also the *Prelude* (1805 version), III, 121–29.

In most respects Erasmus Darwin's idea of evolution did not differ from the other eighteenth-century ideas. We may observe the relation between analogies and evolution in his belief that flower parts evolved into insects:

> [Perhaps] the first insects were the anthers or stigmas of flowers, which had by some means loosed themselves from their parent plant, like the male flowers of Vallisneria, and that many other insects have gradually in long process of time been formed from these; some acquiring wings, others fins, and others claws, from their ceaseless efforts to procure their food, or to secure themselves from injury.[33]

Instead of intervention by God at the time of fertilization Darwin supposed the male imagination could impress vibrations on the embryo, causing the offspring to conform to the visual impression. It was in part to save this notion that Darwin maintained that thought or spirit could act upon matter. If the reader supposed, as Darwin often claimed, that animals possessed rudiments of reason, they would share in the idea of progress. Lower animals would conceive a better state for their progeny and direct their offspring toward higher forms at the moment of impregnation.[34] Darwin's belief that the course of evolution led from asexual to hermaphrodite and finally to monosexual forms was derived from familiar notions about different degrees of sexual elaboration along the scale of beings.

What was new in Darwin's theory of evolution was the way he related it to struggle in nature:

> Herb, shrub, and tree, with strong emotions rise
> For light and air, and battle in the skies;
> Whose roots diverging with opposing toil
> Contend below for moisture and for soil; [35]

He wrote that lust, hunger, and security were the "great objects of desire" among animals, "which have changed the forms of many animals by their exertion to gratify them." [36] He described the competition among males in mating periods and was led to an appreciation

33. "Economy of Vegetation," Add. Note 39. Coleridge indulged a similar "Darwinian flight": *Definitions of Life* [1830], p. 413. Also see "Darwinizing with a vengeance," "Notes on Stillingfleet," *Athenaeum,* no. 2474 (27 March 1875), 422–23.

34. *Zoonomia, I,* 509–24; cf. "Loves of Plants" (1789), I, note "Curcuma."

35. *Temple of Nature,* IV, 43–46.

36. *Zoonomia, I,* 503.

of sexual selection: "The final cause of this contest amongst the males seems to be, that the strongest and most active animals should propagate the species, which should thence become improved." [37] Such adaptations as the seed-cracking beaks of birds had "been gradually produced during many generations by the perpetual endeavor of the creatures to supply the want of food, and to have been delivered to their posterity with constant improvement of them for the purposes required." [38] In these instances Darwin referred the progress of organisms not to an abstract scale of beings or to analogies, but to their ecological relationships. We find references to mimicry, plant succession, protective resemblance, and adaptive devices in "The Loves of the Plants." We cannot dismiss Darwin's idea of evolution as altogether abstract and removed from nature because of its relation to ecological relationships and population dynamics.[39]

So far we have shown that the major themes of Erasmus Darwin's poetry and his philosophy of scientific method were characteristic of earlier beliefs. The reader of his poems may feel that he used the old abstractions with such enthusiasm that he meant to direct them toward other ends, but it is difficult to support such an appraisal by an analysis of Darwin's meaning.

We now turn to Darwin's theory of life. Although he accepted the idea of botanical analogy without qualification, we may note a degree of equivocation in his writings about the idea of immanence. His *Zoonomia* (1794) begins with a dualistic definition of matter and spirit foreign to eighteenth-century ideas of harmony between them. Spirit was capable of causing motion; matter, only of receiving it. Darwin denied that the spirit of animation was electrical. He described an experiment wherein twenty Leyden jars were suspended in a row by silk strings. If the jars were arranged alternately according to the charges of their outside surfaces, the whole line would draw together when the first and twentieth were connected by a conducting substance, "and thus shorten a line that might connect them, like a muscular

37. Ibid. Erasmus Darwin here describes the operation of a natural selection process which had served to eliminate weak or unfit individuals.

38. *Zoonomia, I,* 504.

39. Darwin described mimicry when he claimed that orchids resembled insects in keeping their honey from being plundered by other insects. His belief that flowers did not require insect pollination and thus sought to preserve nectar was erroneous, but indicates that he supposed mimicry was useful to the organism that displayed it. deVallemont had pointed out that orchids resembled insects: *Curiosities of Nature and Art* (1707), p. 288; but Darwin seems to have been the first writer to find in mimicry a principle of utility to the organism.

fiber." [40] This analogy might have seemed persuasive to an eighteenth-century reader had Darwin employed it to argue that muscular contraction was an electrical process. We can well imagine what Robert Turner, Richard Lovett, or Galvani would have made of this suggestive model. Darwin insisted that it was not "a philosophical analogy" but "an illustration or simile to facilitate the conception of a difficult subject." Electrical attraction diminished with distance, but a muscle contracted with the same force throughout. The laws of attraction did "not apply philosophically" to irritability: "We must conclude that animal contraction is governed by laws of its own, and not by those of mechanics, chemistry, magnetism, or electricity." [41]

The experiments of Galvani were not "conclusive": "The electric fluid may act only as a more potent stimulus exciting the muscular fibers into action, and not by supplying them with a new quantity of the spirit of life." [42] Electricity acted "only as a stimulus, and not by supplying any addition of sensorial power."

On other occasions Darwin seemed to subscribe to the idea of immanence:

> From earth's deep wastes *electric* torrents pour,
> Or shed from heaven the scintillating shower;
> Pierce the dull root, relax its fibre-trains,
> Thaw the thick blood, which lingers in its veins.[43]

He did not press his belief that there were "two essences or substances" in nature to the point of sundering the eighteenth-century unities. For one thing, he would have destroyed his mechanistic physiology, including suppositions about the mechanism whereby the parent could change the hereditary structure of the offspring. He concluded lamely that "as we are taught of spirits and of angels" the spirit of animation could sometimes take on the propensities of solidity and extension. The passage of light through transparent bodies, or "electric ether through metallic and aqueous bodies," and the phenomena of magnetism convinced Darwin that matter was an open latticework with interstices for subtle fluids: "The spirit of animation at the same time it communicates or receives motion from solid bodies, must itself possess some property of solidity." [44] The spirit of life was a subtle

40. *Zoonomia, I,* 65.
41. Ibid.
42. Ibid., p. 66.
43. "Economy of Vegetation," I, 463–66.
44. *Zoonomia, I,* 115.

fluid "acquired from the atmosphere" which caused irritability by flowing into the muscles.[45] He once wrote that some animal heat came from the subtle fluid of phlogiston in the atmosphere and the rest from "the chemical combinations produced in all the glands." [46] In other words, part of the energy of life came from external fluids and part was manufactured internally. This was not just a minor inconsistency but an attempt to have two definitions of life at once. He defined life on one occasion as the property of contraction in fibers; on another, as the motion of fluids; and yet again, as the capacity for reproduction. Darwin held conflicting opinions arising from two altogether different scientific outlooks. It could hardly be true, as one "celebrated professor of the medical art" supposed, that *Zoonomia* bid "fair to do for medicine what Sir Isaac Newton's *Principia* has done for natural philosophy." [47]

In a section on "Vegetable Generation" in *Phytologia,* Darwin denied that life could arise from chemical attraction or subtle fluids. Irritability and attraction did not bear a "philosophical analogy" and should only "popularly be compared." [48] In his poetry the vitality of lower forms was considered analogous to inorganic energies in a philosophical sense, but the life of higher animals was analogous to inorganic energies only in a popular sense. In the poems the cause of life and organic evolution appears to be a faculty of "love," which he compared to Newtonian attraction on the purely physical level in nature. This analogy, even if a popular one in Darwin's sense, makes it impossible for us to be sure to what extent he meant to distinguish organic from inorganic energies.

The first canto of "The Economy of Vegetation" (1791) presented a Herschelian narrative of the origin of the universe: "When LOVE DIVINE, with brooding wings unfurl'd, Called from the rude abyss the living world." [49] "Kindling Ether runs" through the "vast inane" and "the mass starts into a million suns." Ethereal fluids "rein the Planets in their swift careers," fuel the "comet-blaze," "Or give the sun's phlogistic orb to roll." In *The Temple of Nature,* Darwin wrote that by "firm immutable immortal laws" there arose "from elemental strife / Organic forms, and kindled into life." In higher forms love was an energy peculiar to organisms alone. In the descent of the scale of being love came to be more analogous to inorganic energies:

45. Ibid., p. 471.
46. "Economy of Vegetation," n. to I, 401.
47. Anon., *European Mag.,* 27 (1795), 77.
48. *Phytologia,* p. 125, 127; also 295.
49. "Economy of Vegetation," I, 101–02. Cf. *Paradise Lost, 1,* 19 ff.

IMMORTAL LOVE! who ere the morn of Time,
On wings outstretch'd, o'er Chaos hung sublime;
Warm'd into life the bursting egg of Night,
and gave young Nature to admiring Light!—

Or warm, descending on ethereal wing,
The Earth's cold bosom with the beams of spring;
Press drop to drop, to atom atom bind,
Link sex to sex, or rivet mind to mind; [50]

Early in the history of life on earth "The matter of heat . . . an ethereal fluid in which all things are immersed," penetrated to the bottom of shoreless seas: "Nurs'd by warm sun-beams in primeval caves / Organic Life began beneath the waves." [51] Matter was first activated with "strong repulsion." Then attraction "The ponderous atoms from the light divides." Matter "swells into spheres, and lengthens into lines" until it became irritable.

"CONTRACTION with ethereal flame / Lights into life the fibre-woven frame." This passage is a statement of the idea of immanence. In the note elaborating upon that couplet Darwin wrote that the power of contraction, which "distinguishes life from inanition, appears to consist of an ethereal fluid which resides in the brain and nerves of living bodies, and is expended in the act of shortening their fibers." [52] "Hence without parent by spontaneous birth / Arise the first specks of animated earth." [53] "Life's subtle woof in Nature's loom is wove" as ethereal fluids flow into organized matter. Points are "glued to points," then into "a living line," which "Touch'd by some goad" forms "rings and irritated tubes." "Urged by appetencies new" (more elaborate desires accompanying the ascent to higher forms), "the living web expands" with "Branching cones," and "convoluted glands." Finally, circulation and respiration arise: "Leaves, lungs, and gills, the vital ether breathe / On earth's green surface, or the waves beneath." [54]

The lower the organism, the more its life was analogous to the energies of subtle fluids. Darwin seems to have believed that such energies were eventually elaborated into irritability and the more complex properties of life which were not directly analogous to the simpler inorganic energies from which they had arisen.

50. *Temple of Nature, I,* 15–26.
51. Ibid., I, 233–34.
52. Ibid., n. to I, 245.
53. Ibid., I, 247–48.
54. Ibid., I, 263–64.

In the poems Darwin represents the evolution of life and love by three symbols. The first was the fable of Pluto and Persephone, representing the marriage of matter and spirit. The second was his comparison of the birth of organic life in the sea to the myth of Venus rising from the waves:

—So erst, as Egypt's rude designs explain,
Rose young DIONE from the shoreless main;
Type of organic nature! source of bliss!
Emerging Beauty from the vast abyss! [55]

The third was the Orphic symbol of the egg of night, which he used to denote the earth, hatching (like Réaumur's heat-incubated eggs) through the fires of love, as the "genial lustres" of spring inflamed the "mighty ball."

And the GREAT SEED evolves, disclosing ALL;
Life *buds* or *breathes* from Indus to the Poles,
And the vast surface kindles as it rolls! [56]

What does Darwin's use of these myths indicate of his opinion about vital energy? Was he alluding to the deep insights into natural fecundity expressed in ancient fertility myths? He cast *The Temple of Nature* in the form of the Eleusinian mysteries, which have often been supposed to contain enactments of ritual intercourse and agricultural rites invoking organic plenty.[57] But in the eighteenth century the light of rationalism shone brightly upon the shadows of chthonic deities and classical mysteries. Darwin subscribed to the allegorical theory of myth, believing that myths were coded expressions of chemical and biological knowledge similar to his own: [58]

55. Ibid., I, 371–74.

56. "Economy of Vegetation," IV, 406–08. For the sake of an analogy between the earth (wherein stratified rocks were produced) and a seed (wherein future plants were developed) Darwin accepted the preformation theory of Leeuwenhoek and Baker (see IV, 393–94). He disavowed the belief in *Zoonomia, 1,* 489–90. On the Orphic cosmology see Needham, *History of Embryology* (2d ed.) pp. 27, 54–55. Also see W. K. C. Guthrie, *Orpheus and Greek Religion* (London: Methuen, 1935).

57. But cf. George E. Mylonas, *Eleusis and the Eleusinian Mysteries* (Princeton Univ. Press, 1961), pp. 270–71, 275–76.

58. Perhaps no other aspect of Darwin's thought typifies his rationalism so well as this theory of allegorical interpretation of myths. For its history, see Andrew Lang, *Myth, Ritual, and Religion, 1* (London: Longmans, Green, 1887), 14–19; Plutarch, *Pausanius* ix. 31; Joseph Devey, ed., *The Physical and Metaphysical Works of Lord Bacon* (London: Henry G. Bohn, 1853), "On the Dignity and Advancement of Learning," Bk. 2, chap. viii, p. 98. It is worth noting that d'Holbach supposed Jupiter to have represented ethereal fire: "L'amour qui les anciens

> The Egyptians were possessed of many discoveries in philosophy and chemistry before the invention of letters; these were then expressed in hieroglyphic paintings of men and animals; which after the discovery of the alphabet were described and animated by the poets, and became first the deities of Egypt and afterwards of Greece and Rome.[59]

Darwin claimed that the Eleusinian mysteries involved ritual death and rebirth for the sake of moral purification. Just because he cast a poem in this form, we cannot argue that he meant to suggest a particular ritualistic meaning.[60]

Darwin used an illustration of the Diana of Ephesus cult figure as the frontispiece to *The Temple of Nature.* To modern readers the figure implies sexual fecundity. For Darwin, as for many other eighteenth-century writers who used it, the figure was a neutral image, a conventional representation of whatever he believed organic nature to be.[61]

---

attribuoient le débrouillement du Chaos, ne paroit être que l'attraction personnifiée," *Système de la nature, 1,* 36, 46. Also see Abraham Tucker, *The Light of Nature Pursued . . . , 3* (London: W. Oliver for T. Payne and Son, 1787), part 3, 33–48. Also Antoine Goguet, *The Origin of Laws, Arts, and Sciences, 1* (Edinburgh: Donaldson & Reid, 1761), 174; [James Burnet, Lord Monboddo] *Of the Origin and Progress of Language, 1* (Edinburgh: A. Kincaid and W. Creech, and T. Cadell of London, 1773), 305–12; and David Doig, *Two Letters on the Savage State . . .* (London: G., G., and J. Robinson, 1792), p. 17. Cf. Charles A. Lemmi, *The Classic Deities in Bacon; A Study in Mythological Symbolism* (Baltimore: Johns Hopkins Press, 1933).

59. "Advertisement," "Economy of Vegetation."

60. Ibid., II, 321–48 and Add. Note 22. Darwin was at pains to interpret the figures on the Portland vase as representing ritual death in the Eleusinian mysteries. For the eighteenth-century theory of the mysteries see Ephraim Chambers, *Cyclopaedia, 1* (7th ed. 1751), "Eleusinia." Also William Warburton, *The Divine Legation of Moses . . . , 1* (London: Fletcher Gyles, 1738), 133–231. Also [Edward Gibbon], *Critical Observations on the Sixth Book of the Æneid* (London: P. Elmsley, 1770). The notion that the mysteries embodied organic fertility seems to have begun with Thomas Taylor, *A Dissertation on the Eleusinian and Bacchic Mysteries* (Amsterdam: J. Weitstein, [1791], pp. 71–78 for "vivific," "prolific," and "fontal" deities; also pp. 93–134. Darwin did not mention the book in a later note (*Temple of Nature,* n. to I, 137).

61. The figure indicated the realm of nature as a whole and did not signify a single attribute such as fertility. See Hermann Thiersch, *Artemis Ephesis: eine archäologische Untersuchung,* Abh. der Ges. der Wissenschaften zu Göttingen, Philologisch-Historische Klasse, Dritte Folge, Nr. 12 (Berlin: Weidmannsche Buchhandlung, 1935). For eighteenth-century examples see deVallemont, *Curiositez de la nature et de l'art sur le vegetation, . . .* [1703], *1* (2d ed. Brussels: Jean Leonard, 1715), frontispiece. Also the translation of 1707. Also the frontispiece to *Nova Acta Physicomedica Academiae Caesareae Leopoldino-Carolinae Natvra Cvriosvm, 1* (Nuremberg: Wolfgang Schwarzkopf, 1757), and Linnaeus, *Fauna Svecica* (1746). Cf. the frontispiece to this study, and Gode-von Aesch, *Science in German Romanticism,* p. 248, n. 31.

We cannot claim that Darwin altogether discarded the idea of immanence in favor of a new conception of life. His poems show old interpretations swollen with the beginnings of a new intuition, elaborated as far as might be thought possible without seeking a new system. He might have been a loose and unpoetical thinker, but he is worthy of notice because he tried harder than anyone else we might cite to adapt eighteenth-century ideas to new intuitions which he made no explicit and unequivocal attempt to express.

We might take brief notice of the reaction to Darwin's writings. A whole host of writers condemned him for Jacobinism, sacrilege, philosophical and scientific confusion, and an outworn literary style. Norton Garfinkle has shown that anti-Jacobinism and a revival of religious feeling told heavily against Darwin's radicalism and skepticism.[62] Thomas A. Knight wrote to Sir Joseph Banks (1743–1820) in 1799 that Darwin's imagination was too strong for his judgment. Banks replied that *Phytologia* was like a punchbowl in which "truth and falsehood, ingenuity and perversity of opinions" were mixed.[63] Coleridge found that Darwin had confused poetry and science:

> O mercy! the blindness of the man! and it is imagination, forsooth! that misled him—too much poetry in his philosophy! this abject deadness of all that sense of the obscure and the indefinite.[64]

A parody by George Canning, John Frere, and George Ellis in the *Anti-Jacobin* in 1798, entitled "The Loves of the Triangles," attacked Darwin's poetic style and political beliefs: "Let Hydrostatics, simpering as they go / Lead the light Naiads on fantastic toe." [65]

Thomas Brown (1778–1820), who was to become professor of moral philosophy at Edinburgh, started writing his attack on *Zoonomia* at the age of only eighteen. He condemned the "slight analogies" on which the work was based. From a standpoint of Humean skepticism he argued that systems of materialism "owe their rise to the groundless belief that we are acquainted with the nature of causation." [66] He conceded that plants seemed to rise above "the common qualities of mat-

62. "Science, Religion, and Erasmus Darwin" (1955); also "T.T." on Darwin, *Methodist Mag.*, 27 (1804), esp. 261.

63. Knight, *Papers* (1841), p. 25, 29.

64. *Anima Poetae*, pp. 92–93.

65. *The Beauties of the Anti-Jacobin* (London: J. Plymsell, 1799), pp. 207–30.

66. Brown, *Observations on Zoonomia* (1798), p. xvi. He was not assisted by his teachers, although he did show the work to Dugald Stewart, who advised him to write to Darwin about it. In a letter to his mother in 1796 Brown wrote that the work was the product of his "own mind alone": quoted by Welsh, *Life of Brown* (1825), p. 33. For the correspondence with Darwin, see pp. 42–71.

ter" but denied that analogies with animals constituted an explanation at all: "There exists only an incomplete analogy, and the inference is, therefore, inadmissible. To reason by analogy is, in most cases, to mislead, rather than to guide the understanding." [67] The idea of evolution might surprise by its boldness, but it was supported by "only a few loose analogies." [68] He ridiculed Darwin's contention that negative stimuli such as cold or darkness brought on the sleep of plants through the agency of an interposed voluntary faculty. Why not regard sleep movements as the loss of turgescence caused by the removal of a positive stimulus? [69] Ideas that could be criticized with such effectiveness by an undergraduate could be expected to fall from favor. Such was indeed to be the case.

ii. Lamarck: The Rejection of Analogy

Jean Baptiste de Lamarck (1744–1829) became a member of the botanical department of the natural history museum in Paris after the publication of his flora of France in 1778. At the age of fifty he was appointed to one of the professorships of zoology created during the Revolution. He is of great interest at this point in our study because he continued to subscribe to the idea of immanence but rejected the idea of botanical analogy. He speculated on subtle fluids in *Recherches sur les causes des principaux faits physiques* in 1794, and in 1796 attempted a refutation of the pneumatic chemistry of Lavoisier.[1] He accepted the eighteenth-century belief that life arose from the collected energies of subtle fluids.

In the *Philosophie zoologique* (1809) he wrote that lower animals "live *only* by the help of excitations which they receive from the exterior. That is to say, subtle and ever-moving fluids contained in the environment incessantly penetrate these organized bodies and maintain life in them" [2] [italics added]. The movements of bodily fluids, impelled by ethereal fluids, "modify the cellular tissue in which they move . . . [to] create different organs." [3] Nervous action depended

67. Ibid., p. 247.
68. Ibid., p. 463.
69. Ibid., p. 253.
1. *Réfutation de la théorie pneumatique.*
2. Elliott trans. (1914), p. 5; also, 98–105. Cf. *Mémoires de physique* (1797), p. 101, 134, and table opp. p. 227.
3. Ibid., p. 2; also 292–303. The subtle fluid was the agent of evolutionary modification, which accounted for the acquisition of inheritable characteristics, a phrase wherein the emphasis more correctly represents Lamarck's views than the more usual phrase, "the inheritance of acquired characteristics." On the elabora-

on the circulation of electric matter through the medulla of nerves insulated from other tissues by "aponeurotic" sheaths. The electric fluid thrust out dendrites in its efforts to escape to the rest of the body. Lamarck supported this belief with an analogy between the outline of lightning flashes and the ramifications of nerves. The spontaneous generation of lower animals was accomplished by the impact of subtle fluids on pond scum. Perhaps the electricity was static in plants and lower animals, and electrochemical in higher ones.[4] Generation was effected by "a subtle penetrating vapor, which escapes into the gelatinous corpuscles capable of receiving it." Lamarck's notions of life as collected energy and of evolution as the function of such energies were correctly recognized by Charles Gillispie to be "no anticipation of Darwin, but a medley of dying echoes." [5]

Another idea which Lamarck acepted from the speculative naturalists was that of the scale of beings, "une sorte d'échelle ou de chaîne graduée parmi les corps doués de la vie." [6] In 1778 he published an essay "De l'ordre naturel" in which he argued for the superiority to artificial taxonomic systems of a natural method to be based upon the scale of beings and affinities from link to link on a linear scale.[7] The "distribution" of all known forms into such a simple linear sequence

---

tion of organs and subtle fluids see Gillispie, "The Formation of Lamarck's Evolutionary Theory" (1956), pp. 329–35. Lamarck had no particular interest in the study of heredity and admitted his ignorance of the mechanism whereby the offspring was "semblable à celui dans lequel il est formé": *Mémoires de physique* pp. 271–74.

The words "cellular tissue" denoted a high degree of organization in the tissues. Lamarck did not mean that tissue functions were performed by uniform components or that vital energies were derived from them. Hugh Elliott claimed that Lamarck's notion of cellular tissue "entirely anticipated" Schwann: Introduction to the Elliott translation, p. lxxiii. John H. Gerould remarked that he "could hardly believe his eyes" when he read Lamarck's words: "The Dawn of the Cell Theory" (1922). J. Walter Wilson, in "Cellular Tissue" (1944), p. 168, writes that Lamarck meant only what we would call connective tissue. Wilson has put too limited a construction on Lamarck's phrase in order to refute Elliott and Gerould. Along with other writers of the time, Lamarck knew about intricacy of texture in tissues, even though he did not use the phrase to describe functions performed by cells. Cf. Fontana, *Traite sur le vénin de la vipere, 2,* 234–38; see pp. 259–61 for analogies between the cellular tissues of plants and animals. Also Brisseau-Mirbel, "Hypothèse sur la formation et le développement du tissu cellulaire et du tissu tubulaire," *Traité d'anatomie, 1* (1801–02), 91–97.

4. *Philosophie zoologique,* trans. Elliott, p. 218.

5. Gillispie, "Lamarck and Charles Darwin" (1959), p. 276. Also see Simpson, "Lamarck, Charles Darwin, and Butler" (1961).

6. *Philosophie zoologique, 1* (1809), 7. Trans. Elliott, p. 12.

7. *Flore Françoise, 1* (1778), lxxxvii–cxvii, especially the scale of genera and the ascending series of "saillies particulières," pp. cxiv–cxvii.

was the first task of naturalists. "Classification" would be the arbitrary division of the scale into convenient units.[8] We have supposed that Linnaeus, before he became convinced that dual affinities prevented the arrangement of plants in linear series, also imagined that species could be arranged in this way. It would seem that Lamarck's "distribution" and Linnaeus's "natural method" indicate substantially identical ambitions for the development of systematics.

Lamarck was one of the earliest and most determined critics of the idea of botanical analogy. As early as 1789 he denied that the sensitive plant possessed true irritability, although he allowed that its motions might be compared to those of a muscle without its antagonist.[9] In 1797 he wrote that the movements of *Mimosa pudica* and *Biophytum sensitivum* "sont dûes à une cause mécanique, et non à l'irritabilité des parties."[10] In England Robert Townson offered similar arguments in his essay, "Objections against the Perceptivity of Plants" [1792].

Lamarck recognized that most plants performed autotrophic nutrition, whereby inorganic materials are converted to living matter. John Hunter had alluded to this faculty in an unpublished lecture in 1786. "Vegetables alone seem to have a power of immediately converting common matter into their own kind."[11] Lamarck wrote in 1794:

> Les végétaux diffèrent essentiellement des animaux, non-seulement par les caractères déjà reconnus par les naturalistes, mais en outre par la propriété très-remarquable de combiner ensemble des élémens libres, et d'être la cause première de tous les composés qui existent dans notre globe.[12]

In *Phytologia* Erasmus Darwin acknowledged that autotrophic nutrition was "an essential distinction between vegetable and animal

8. *Philosophie zoologique,* trans. Elliott, p. 34; also 28. For a detailed discussion of distribution (which Elliott translates as "arrangement") see pp. 56–67.

9. Lamarck, *Dictionnaire encyclopédique de botanique* (Paris: Hôtel de Thou, 1789), pp. 16–18.

10. *Mémoires de physique,* p. 288 n.

11. Hunter, "Lectures on the Principles of Surgery" [1786–87], *Works, 1* (1835), 214. Hitherto the assumption had been that plants, like animals, absorbed organic nutrients in a subtle form: plants, by root hairs, and animals, by digestive tissues. For a revealing exposition of changing ideas about plant nutrition, see Cullen, *Lectures on Vegetation and Agriculture* [1768] presenting the subtle-fluid physiology (republished in 1796 with annotations by George Pearson). Another exposition of the subtle-fluid physiology was Antoine Baumé, *Chymie expérimentale et raisonnée* (Paris: P. F. Didot le jeune, 1773), pp. 130–38.

12. Lamarck, *Recherches, 2,* 306.

nature."[13] Antoine de Fourcroy wrote to similar effect in 1800, as did Brisseau-Mirbel in 1802.[14] James Edward Smith, despite his liking for analogies between plants and animals, admitted the force of the distinction.[15] Rev. Patrick Keith, while claiming to find exceptions, acclaimed it as "the best ground of distinction that has hitherto been suggested."[16]

Lamarck took no notice of another important distinction, which was the release of oxygen by plants. Ingenhousz found in 1779 that plants give off oxygen in sunlight, which argued against the validity of analogies with animal respiration. Erasmus Darwin sought in vain to save the analogy by arguing that in the absence of sunlight plants gave off carbon dioxide just as animals did; he deemed the release of oxygen a type of perspiration:

> And thus in respect to the circumstance in which plants and animals seemed the furtherest removed from each other, I mean in their supposed mode of respiration, by which one was believed to purify the air which the other had injured, they seem to differ only in degree, and the analogy between them remains unbroken.[17]

The researches of Senebier and Theodore de Saussure established very plainly that plants bore no analogy with animals in this respect.[18]

Lamarck argued that the plant and animal kingdoms were fundamentally different:

> Je suis convaincu qu'il n'y a pas non plus de véritable nuance par aucun point entre ces deux règnes, et par conséquent qu'il n'y a point d'animaux-plantes, ce qu'exprime le mot zoophyte, ni de plantes-animales.[19]

In his *Histoire des animaux sans vertèbres* (1815) he observed that sensitive plants did not contract "suddenly and repeatedly" as animals

13. Darwin, *Phytologia* (1800), p. 239.

14. Fourcroy, *Systême des connoissances chimiques . . . , 4* (Paris: Baudouin, 1801), 29–30. Brisseau-Mirbel, *Traité, 1,* 19.

15. *Physiological Botany* (1807), p. 6.

16. *A System of Physiological Botany, 2* (London: Baldwin, Cradock, and Joy, 1816), 471. Both he and William McLeay supposed that there were autotrophic beetles. See McLeay, "On the Distinction of an Animal from a Vegetable," *Horae Entomologicae,* part 2 (1821), p. 193.

17. "Economy of Vegetation," Add. Note 34. Also *Phytologia,* pp. 39–56, 300.

18. For a history of these discoveries see Julius Wiesner, *Jan Ingen-Housz: sein Leben und sein Wirken als Naturforscher und Arzt* (1905), pp. 149–81.

19. *Philosophie zoologique, 1* (1809), 93. Trans. Elliot, p. 51.

did. No plant moved from the spot to which it was fixed. Their solid parts did not move to cause contractions, which were occasioned by fluid movements alone. Their sap did not circulate. They performed autotrophic nutrition. The growth of plants was an entirely automatic process motivated by caloric and electricity escaping from the earth.

> Conséquemment, les auteurs qui indiquent un passage insensible des animaux aux végétaux par les polypes et les infusoires qu'ils nomment zoophytes ou animaux-plantes, montrent qu'ils n'ont aucune idée juste de la nature animale, ni de la nature végétale; et, abusés eux-mêmes, ils exposent tous ceux qui n'ont de ces objets que des connaissances superficielles.[20]

As the idea of a linear chain of life forms lost its appeal, with the dissociation of lower animals from higher plants, some were attracted to the notion of a diverging "V" of life forms, in which the two great kingdoms followed diverging paths. Peter Simon Pallas had made this qualification to the idea of a linear series in *Elenchus Zoophytorum* (1766) wherein he represented the configuration of organisms as a branching tree: "This divides right at the root into a double trunk, namely the animal and the vegetable, although quite close together at some points—[namely] the simplest plants and animals." "Nothing of the sort sought by Bradley and Bonnet will ever be discovered." [21]

Brisseau-Mirbel repeated Pallas's branching metaphor:

> The conjunction of these two classes shows itself above all in the less perfect kinds, and in general the differences become more numerous and more marked in proportion as one moves away from their point of departure; so that the animals and the vegetables form two graduated series or, if you like, two ascending chains which, arising from a common point, diverge as they rise.[22]

Coleridge (1772–1834) wrote in 1818 that he had been critical of the idea of a linear series since "the first appearance of Dr. Darwin's Phytonomia [sic]": "The physiological botanists were hunting in a false direction; and sought for analogy where they should have looked

20. *1* (1815), 125. For the scale of beings see pp. 128–164; on subtle fluids impelling gross bodily fluids, pp. 165–212.

21. Pp. 23–24. See August Thienemann's illustration of Pallas's branching metaphor: "Die Stufenfolge der Dinge" (1910), p. 251.

22. *Elémens de physiologie végétale et de botanique, 1* (Paris: Magimel, 1815), 17–18.

for antithesis."[23] The plant and animal kingdoms might be conceived "as two streams from the same fountain indeed, but flowing the one due west, and the other direct east; and that consequently, the resemblance would be as the proximity, greatest in the first and rudimental products of vegetable and animal organization."[24]

iii. Sir Humphry Davy: The Rejection of Subtle Fluids and the Romantic Imagination in Science

Humphry Davy (1778–1829), who had subscribed to speculative Newtonian ideas in young manhood, became a determined and influential critic of notions about subtle fluids. His youthful essay, "In Defence of Materialism," had discussed thought and the energies of matter in the common terms of Priestley and Hartley. Can we doubt that he describes himself in an early poem, "The Sons of Genius"?

> To scan the laws of Nature, to explore
> The tranquil reign of mild Philosophy;
> Or on Newtonian wings sublime to soar
> Through the bright regions of the starry sky.[1]

From 1798 to 1801 he was employed as an assistant to Thomas Beddoes at his pneumatic institution in Bristol, where he formed associations particularly congenial to loose speculation. He then ventured the suggestion that light consisted of particles of matter in a state of "repulsive projection" and that light might be converted into electricity by "the subtraction of its repulsive powers."

> No more sublime idea can be formed of the motions of matter, than to conceive that the different species are continually changing into each other. The gravitative, the mechanical, and the repulsive motions, appear to be continually mutually producing each other, and from these changes all the phenomena of the mutation of matter probably arise.[2]

Davy proposed the name "phosoxygen" for a compound of light and oxygen which he supposed to condense into electricity at the tips of the nerves to cause sensation.

Later in the same year he repented of his early enthusiasm.

23. *The Friend, 3* (2d ed. 1818), 171–72.
24. Ibid., p. 172; also *Definitions of Life* [1885], pp. 410–11.
1. Lines 77–80: John Davy, *Memoirs* (1839), in *1, Works*, 24–26.
2. Quoted by John Davy, ed., 2, *Works,* 29 n.

> I was perhaps wrong, in publishing with such haste, a new theory of chemistry. My mind was ardent and enthusiastic. I believed that I had discovered the truth. Since that time my knowledge of facts is increased,—since that time I have become more skeptical.[3]

In 1800 he referred to the early essays as his "infant chemical speculations." [4] In 1802 he attacked "visionary and seductive theories" whose formulators had been "guided rather by the analogies of words than of facts." He had become thoroughly aware of the harmful influence of desires for total explanation:

> Instead of slowly endeavoring to lift up the veil concealing the wonderful phenomena of living nature; full of ardent imaginations, they have vainly and presumptuously attempted to tear it asunder.[5]

In 1810 he attacked notions about subtle fluids as a "Vulgar idea—like that of the peasant." [6]

Interrupting this account of Davy's writings, we may note other criticisms of the idea of immanence. Lavoisier's theory of combustion and oxidation had led chemists to impose limits upon their desires for explanation. Lavoisier (1743–94) was strongly critical of those who had failed to follow his lead along the path of reform:

> Les chimistes ont fait du phlogistique un principe vague qui n'est point rigoreusement défini, et qui en conséquence s'adapte à toutes les explications dans lesquelles on veut le faire entrer: tantôt ce principe est pesant, et tantôt il ne l'est pas; tantôt il est le feu libre, tantôt il est le feu combiné avec l'élément terreux; . . . il explique à la fois la causticité et la non-causticité, la diaphanéité et l'opacité, les couleurs et l'absence des couleurs. C'est un véritable protée qui change de forme à chaque instant.[7]

The exponents of the new chemistry, abandoning speculative overbeliefs that transcended experience, sought to "frame the human understanding anew." [8] Théodore de Saussure (1767–1845) wrote,

3. John Davy, *Memoirs* (1839), in *1, Works,* 54–55.
4. "An Account of Some Additional Experiments" [Dec. 1800] in *2, Works,* 169.
5. "Introductory Discourse" [1802], in *2, Works,* 314.
6. John Davy, *Memoirs, 1* (1836), 237.
7. "Réflexions sur le phlogistique" (1783), p. 523.
8. Lavoisier, *Elements of Chemistry . . . ,* trans. Robert Kerr (Edinburgh: William Creech, and G., G., and J. Robinson of London, 1790), p. xxxvi.

"J'aborde les questions qui peuvent être décidées par l'expérience, et j'abandonne celles qui ne peuvent donner lieu qu'à des conjectures." [9]

Once-favored beliefs about subtle fluids were subject to increasingly frequent criticism. Jan Ingenhousz, who repeated many of the experiments on plant electricity, denied that positive electricity forwarded and negative electricity retarded the growth of plants. He dismissed the illuminated nasturtium as chimerical.[10] Christoph Heinrich Pfaff pointed out that scrupulous experiments on sensitive and so-called illuminated plants had failed to disclose a trace of electricity.[11] Tiberius Cavallo was unable to excite motions in the sensitive plant with small electrochemical currents.[12] Spallanzani produced experimental proof that sperms, rather than subtle fluids, caused animal generation.[13] There were even those who doubted the highly constructive simplifications of Franklin's one-fluid theory of electricity.[14]

Davy, in his early essays, had also subscribed to the idea of botanical analogy. He wrote that plants possessed "an irritability so exquisite as to border on the sensibility of animals." He mentioned the Mimosa and Dionaea, praising Erasmus Darwin as "a most ingenious philosopher." [15] In his later *Elements of Agricultural Chemistry* he used these words to praise instead Thomas A. Knight, the experimentalist. Davy ridiculed eighteenth-century speculations on plant physiology as "a number of changes rung upon a string of technical terms . . . as if the science depended upon words rather than upon things." [16] He insisted that plants were physiological mechanisms altogether lacking in sensibility.[17] Irritability in animals and movement in plants "appear to depend upon entirely different causes." Analogies of cir-

9. *Recherches chimiques sur la végétation* (Paris: Nyon, 1804), p. iii.

10. "Electricity and Germination in Plants," [Rozier's] *Observations sur la physique, 28* (1786), 82; also *32* (1788), 324; also "De l'influence du fluide électrique sur les plantes prétendues lumineuses. . . ." *Nouvelles expériences, 2* (1789), 267–69.

11. *Über thierische Elektricität* (1795), p. 118.

12. "Of the Action of Electricity on the Vegetable Kingdom," (1795), p. 247.

13. "Generation of the Green Frog," *Dissertations, 2* (1784), 11–12. Also see J. F. P. Deleuze, *Histoire critique du magnétisme animale, 1* (Paris: Mame, 1813), 83–125, for another criticism of subtle fluids.

14. C. H. Wilkinson, *Essay on Electricity* (1799), pp. 1–88. John Bywater, *New Theory of the Leyden Phial* (1803).

15. "An Essay on the Generation of Phosoxygen and on the Cause of Colour of Organic Beings" [1799], in *2, Works,* 106. See his analogy between silica in plants and animal bones: ibid., pp. 133–38.

16. 4th ed. [1827], in *7, Works,* 195–96.

17. Ibid., p. 222.

culation were "too much insisted upon."[18] He aimed a lengthy rebuke at Erasmus Darwin:

> We must not suffer ourselves to be deluded by the very extensive application of the word life to conceive in the life of plants any power similar to that producing the life of animals. In calling forth the vegetable functions, common physical agents alone seem to operate; but in the animal system these agents are made subservient to a superior principle. To give the argument in plainer language; there are few philosophers who would be inclined to assert the existence of anything above common matter, anything immaterial in the vegetable economy. Such a doctrine is worthy only of a poetic form. The imagination may easily give Dryads to our trees, and Sylphs to our flowers; but neither Dryads nor Sylphs can be admitted in vegetable physiology; and for reasons nearly as strong, irritability and animation ought to be excluded.[19]

His attacks notwithstanding, Davy's views on evolution were similar to Darwin's. He wrote in a notebook in 1815, "Probably there is an analogy in all existence: the divided tail of the fish is linked in a long succession of like objects with the biped man."[20] In a sentence very reminiscent of Darwin, he wrote, "Beasts fight animated by the passion of love, and the strongest perpetuate the species."[21] Greatly interested in the speciation and possible evolution of fish, Davy wrote in an anonymous essay in 1828, "Particular character becomes hereditary and the effects of a particular food influence the appearance of the next generation."[22] "There is no doubt that in many successive generations animals may be fitted to bear changes which would have destroyed their progenitors."[23]

In the second edition of 1829 he revised his opinion somewhat and displayed considerable embarrassment at being compared with Darwin:

> I will not allow you to assimilate my views to those of an author who, however ingenious, is far too speculative; whose poetry has

18. Ibid., p. 374.
19. *Elements of Agricultural Chemistry* . . . (London: Longman, Hurst, Rees, Orme, and Brown, and A. Constable and Co. of Edinburgh, 1813), pp. 217–18. In the 4th ed. [1827], in *7, Works,* 374, the statement is much shorter.
20. *Memoirs* (1839), in *1, Works,* 217.
21. *Fragmentary Remains* (1858), p. 257.
22. *Salmonia* (1828), p. 42. Also pp. 60–61, 232–34.
23. Ibid., p. 170.

> always appeared to me weak philosophy, and his philosophy indifferent poetry; and to whom I have often been accustomed to apply Blumenbach's saying, that there were many things new, and many things true, in his doctrines; but that which was new was not true, and what was true, was not new.[24]

Davy's brilliant researches in electrochemistry, which led to the discovery of five elements in less than ten years, were only one concern of a successful and remarkably well-disciplined intelligence. He pondered the Boscovich force-atom as a hypothesis, altogether ignored subtle fluids, and endeavored to restrain conjecture.

> Seldom has physical investigation been pursued with greater ardor, and if new facts, by being sometimes insulated and incapable of application to established theories, have perplexed the public mind, yet they have at the same time been useful to it, by producing a habit of rational and active skepticism, which cannot fail to become at a future period the parent of truth.[25]

Davy's expositions on the subject of scientific method call to mind the familiar romantic literary emphasis on the intensely personal force and creative power of the imagination. We might recall Coleridge's celebrated concept of imagination as an "esemplastic" power forcing dissimilar phenomena into conjunction, which he contrasted to fancy, an "assembling, aggregating power" much like the complacent associative process whereby eighteenth-century naturalists employed analogies.[26]

> Newton was a mere materialist—*Mind* in his system is always *passive*—a lazy Looker-on on an external world . . . Any system built on the passiveness of the mind must be false as a system.[27]

Davy, too, denied "that the imagination ought to be passive in physical research." [28]

> The foundations of chemical philosophy are observation, experiment, and analogy. By observation, facts are distinctly and

24. *Salmonia,* 3d ed., in *9, Works,* 51, 53–54.

25. Davy, "Historical Introduction" to "Outlines of a View of Galvanism . . ." [1802], in *2, Works,* 190.

26. I. A. Richards, *Coleridge on Imagination* (London: Kegan Paul, Trench, Trubner, 1934), pp. 76–77.

27. Letter [of March 1801] to Thomas Poole: E. L. Griggs, ed., *Collected Letters of Samuel Taylor Coleridge, 2* (Oxford: Clarendon Press, 1956), no. 388.

28. Lecture of 1811, in *8, Works,* 317. Davy was a close friend of Coleridge between 1799 and 1809. See *Coleridge on Logic and Learning* (1929), p. 23.

> minutely impressed on the mind. By analogy, similar facts are connected. By experiment, new facts are discovered; and, in the progression of knowledge, observation, guided by analogy, leads to experiment, and analogy, confirmed by experiment, becomes scientific truth.[29]

Davy thought the creative process in the sciences quite similar to that in the arts. The imaginative scientist was "more fitted to enjoy the blaze of light of Milton, to pass into the proteus-forms of humanity with Shakespeare, and to move through the heavens with Newton." [30]

> Imagination, as well as reason, is necessary to perfection in the philosophical mind. A rapidity of combination, a power of perceiving analogies, and of comparing them by facts, is the creative source of discovery.[31]

Theories, not to be valued for conveying satisfaction alone, should instead be considered as mere "approximations to truth . . . the instruments that [the mind] employs for the purpose of gaining new ideas." [32] In Davy's presidential address to the Royal Society in 1820 he suggested that hypotheses were "part of the scaffolding of the building of science [rather] than as belonging either to its foundations, materials, or ornaments." [33] The role of hypothesis and analogy in leading to scientific discovery was too infrequently conceded:

> Too much has always been concealed in the methods of the sciences;—the true architect ought not only to be able to form the plan of his building, but likewise be acquainted with the scaffolding essential to the edifice.[34]

The technique of scientific discovery, as Davy described it, reflected the romantic notion of creative imagination, rather than the eighteenth-century concept of the association of ideas. This change was well in keeping with the more critical nineteenth-century scientific climate.

The critical use of analogies became a fruitful source of scientific progress. William Charles Wells' *Essay on Dew* (1814), which Sir John Herschel called "one of the most beautiful specimens of induc-

29. "Introduction," *Elements* [1812], in *4, Works,* 2.

30. Letter of 26 Aug. [1811] to Mrs. Apreece, his fiancée: *Fragmentary Remains,* p. 146.

31. "Parallels between Art and Science" [1807], in *8, Works,* 308.

32. "A Discourse Introductory to a Course of Lectures on Chemistry . . ." [1802], in *2, Works,* 324.

33. *Fragmentary Remains,* pp. 231–32.

34. Quoted by John Davy from a notebook of 1805, *Memoirs* (1839) in *1, Works,* 153. Cf. Arber, "Analogy in the History of Science" (1948), p. 229.

tive experimental inquiry," arrived at its conclusions by observing "analogous phenomena." Charles Lyell (1797–1875) wrote that the "immutable constancy" of natural phenomena, postulated by uniformitarian geology, "permits us to reason from analogy." [35] Certainly Davy's own discoveries of the elements bromine and iodine followed by analogy from his discovery of the elemental nature of chlorine.[36] The periodic table of the elements was an expression of analogies that led to more basic discoveries.

Morris Cohen writes that the modern scientist tests intuitions of analogy by experiment in order to transform them into clear assertions of identity or to isolate those properties which are not held in common.[37] Dr. Ernst Scharrer advances the argument that while homology has "largely disintegrated" as a useful concept in comparative anatomy, analogies might offer "great promise of a reorientation of comparative anatomy." [38] Davy's remarks on method fully described the changing role of analogies in the nineteenth-century scientific climate.

iv. John Hunter: The First of the Modern Biologists

In the work of John Hunter (1728–95) we may observe features destined to become more prominent in early nineteenth-century biology that may be said to have characterized the life sciences in the generation that followed him: pursuit of a theory of life, sophistication in experimental method, and the study of comparative anatomy. We shall discuss these developments in turn.

Notions of vital energy will not be discussed with reference to the mechanist-vitalist dispute; nor can we attempt a history of them in so short a space. Our brief summary of opinions about life between 1780 and 1830 will serve to show only that notions of passive vital processes dependent upon inorganic energies were abandoned. The rejection of the idea of immanence in its application to life meant an

35. *Principles of Geology . . . , I* (London: John Murray, 1830), 165; also 160.

36. Joshua C. Gregory, *The Scientific Achievements of Sir Humphry Davy* (1930), pp. 109–12.

37. *A Preface to Logic* (New York: Henry Holt, 1945), pp. 82–87. Also W. E. Hocking, "Analogy and Scientific Method in Philosophy," *J. Philos., Psychol. and Sci. Methods*, 7 (1910), 161.

38. Scharrer, "Anatomy and the Concept of Analogy" (1946), p. 579; also "The Concept of Analogy" (1956). Also Owsei Temkin, "Metaphors of Human Biology" (1949). Also J. W. L. Beament, ed., *Models and Analogues in Biology*, Symposia of the Society for Experimental Biology, no. 12 (Cambridge Univ. Press, 1960).

end to loose analogies between life and subtle fluids. There may well have been continuities in speculation about the nature of life, but the abandonment of the eighteenth-century idea of collected energy, significant in itself, brings to an end our central narrative.

John Gregory (1724–73) once sent a memoir cautioning against the use of subtle fluids in explaining life to William Cullen, who had expounded such views in his lectures at Edinburgh. We may gather Gregory's opinion from one of his own lectures published in 1770:

> Even Sir Isaac himself was led by analogy and the love of simplicity to conjecture, but with singular modesty and caution, that all the phenomena of the material world depended upon attracting and repelling powers in the particles of matter. But we have now reason to believe that he was deceived; for even in the unorganized kingdom, the powers by which salts . . . concrete into regular forms can never be accounted for by attraction and repulsion in the particles of matter; and in the vegetable and animal kingdom there are evident indications of powers of a different nature from those of unorganized bodies . . . [and] certain effects are produced which the laws of matter are not able to explain.[1]

After the manner of most abstractions which have figured in the history of scientific ideas, the idea of immanence in its application to life was accepted as long as it seemed to explain, and discarded when the light of greater sophistication disclosed complexities in the phenomena to which it did not conform. We may think of the rejection of subtle fluids as a stage in the refinement of explanatory techniques.

John Hunter told his students that physiologists had been so concerned with chemistry and mechanics that they had "entirely lost sight of life."[2] Hunter believed that a quality of life was a precondition for the manufacture of heat in an organism and the arrest of decay in its tissues. For example, he supposed that fertilized and unfertilized eggs each had the same composition and the same degree of organization. But the living egg decayed less rapidly and lost heat less rapidly in a cold liquid.[3] "Mere organization can do nothing even in mechanics; it must still have something corresponding to a living prin-

1. *Lectures* [1770], pp. 153–54.
2. "Lectures on the Principles of Surgery" [1786–87], in *Works, 1* (1835), 216.
3. "On the Heat of Animals" (1778), pp. 28–29; also *A Treatise on the Blood* (1794), p. 90.

ciple." [4] Hunter erred in supposing that fertilized eggs were no more "organized" than unfertilized ones, and was not precise about the qualities of the vital principle. He supposed that blood must be endowed with such a quality of life because it clotted (apparently increasing its degree of organization) outside the body. Despite these ambiguities, his attempt to define life as a "power of resisting heat, cold, and putrefaction" indicated a new approach to a central problem of physiology. He attempted to find the lowest common denominator of vital process rather than attempt a total explanation of its causes. His intention seems to have been to direct his students away from chemical and electrical theories of life and to interest them in its simplest processes and manifestations, a line of inquiry which has been pursued ever since. And one of the most important consequences of the newly suggested definitions of life was the discouragement of analogies to other kinds of energy. Hunter spoke of life in plants as "a power of action within the vegetable itself, independent of any mechanical power whatever." [5]

The reaction against analogies between life and other energies lacked the focus of a single persuasive definition. The search for a lowest common denominator led to the idea that life might be defined merely by its association with "organization," or structural elaboration in tissues.[6] Bichat (1771–1802) wrote that organic texture was the sole precondition for life and gave a noncommital definition of life as an anti-putrescent power which "consists in the sum of the functions by which death is resisted." [7] Such definitions aimed to isolate qualities and properties rather than to indicate causes. Cuvier (1769–1832) wrote that living things were ramified far beyond the

4. *A Treatise on the Blood,* p. 78. Also see James Gregory, *Philosophical and Literary Essays* (Edinburgh: W. Creech, and T. Cadell of London, 1792), p. 201, for the idea that life was "a different relation between the cause and the effect," "some further principle of change." Also Smellie, "Aether" (1773).

5. "Observations and Experiments on the Vegetable Economy" [after 1781], in *Essays, 1* (1861), 341.

6. See Girtanner, "Sur l'irritabilité, considéré comme principe de vie dans la nature organisée," [Rozier's] *Observations sur la physique, 37* (1790), 150 n.

7. *Physiological Researches on Life and Death* [1800], p. 21. He wrote that animals displayed some truly "vital" functions such as motion, communication, and sensibility, and some "organic" functions characteristic of all living things (including plants), such as irritability, growth, and reproduction (p. 107). This distinction, accepted by Cuvier and Lawrence, contradicted the idea of botanical analogy. Cf. the "obscur" and "manifeste" reactions described by Claude Perrault: Fearing, *Reflex Action* (1930), p. 33; also see pp. 102–10, describing early nineteenth-century physiology under the title, "The Reaction against a Mechanistic Physiology." Also Nordenskiold, *The History of Biology* (1929), pp. 301–51.

reach of sense; it would be foolish to seek proximate causes: "Nous ne pourrons en donner qu'une exposition empirique, et non un système raisonné; et tous nos travaux sur l'économie organique se réduiront a en faire l'histoire." [8]

Alexander von Humboldt (1769–1859) insisted that life was an active energy. He wrote in his chemical aphorisms on the physiology of plants in 1793: "That internal fire which breaks the bonds of chemical affinity and prevents the elements from being joined to one another at random, we call the vital force." [9] His tale, "Die Lebenskraft oder der Rhodische Genius" (1795) was an attempt to portray in mythological terms the notion that vital energy was more powerful than inorganic energies. He described a painting in which ranks of figures stretched out seeking to join together but were constrained by an emblem of Psyche surrounded by a blaze of light. The figure of Psyche symbolized the Bergsonian life energies which restrained physical forces. In the second picture Psyche had lost the power to constrain the ranks of figures and they were joined in joyous embraces. A sage was introduced to explain that Psyche represented a power of life that resisted the attracting force of common matter.

Richard Saumarez (1764–1835) insisted that life was an active power, "by the energy of which various species of matter are converted into one kind, under one system, so that the matter thus converted possesses the power of resisting the operation of external causes and of preserving itself from putrefaction and decay." [10] When life was no longer exerted, the substances of which an organism was composed became "amenable to the laws of physics in general." [11]

The change in attitudes toward the investigation of life may be seen to good advantage in a debate between John Abernethy (1764–1831) and William Lawrence (1783–1867). Abernethy identified Hunter's vital principle as "a subtle substance of a quickly and powerfully mobile nature [which] seems to pervade everything and appears to be the life of the world." [12] He cited Darwin's notion of a subtle fluid causing contractions in muscles. He sought to show that

8. *Leçons d'anatomie comparée, 1* (1799–1800), 5–6.

9. *Florae Fribergensis* (1793), p. 135; also "On the Chemical Process of Vitality" (1797). Also Hanno Beck, *Alexander von Humboldt, 1* (1769–1804) (Wiesbaden: Franz Steiner, 1959), 98–106, including the repudiation of analogies, 102.

10. *Generation and the Principle of Life* (1799), p. 325; also *A New System of Physiology, 1* (2d ed. 1799), 35, 42; also *The Principles of Physiological and Physical Science* (1812), p. 42; also p. 114 on the futility of speculation on causation.

11. *New System of Physiology, 2,* 522.

12. *Hunter's Theory of Life* (1814), p. 51.

Darwin and Hunter were both enthusiastic supporters of the idea of immanence. His description of scientific explanation recalls the most stultifying eighteenth-century doctrines. "Doubt and uncertainty are so fatiguing," he explains, that inquiry "must rest somewhere," preferably with a theory "inferred from analogy" which would derive its value from its "adequateness to account for all the vital phenomena." [13] Abernethy sneered at empiricists as "the modern skeptics." [14] He had no use for empiricism and did not shrink from writing that he would "confide more in the eye of reason than in that of sense, and would rather form opinions from analogy, than from the imperfect evidence of sight." [15]

William Lawrence subscribed to the opinions of Cuvier and Bichat. In a lecture on life in March of 1816 he scathingly attacked Abernethy. "There is no resemblance, no analogy, between electricity and life; the two orders of phenomena are completely distinct." [16] He ridiculed subtle fluids, calling them myths like the gods with which savages peopled the sky. He praised Hunter for having developed a technique for investigating life without a priori speculation or "illusory analogies of other sciences." Lawrence thought that ideas about subtle fluids and similar principles could be traced to ambitions to explain "the very essence of the vital properties and . . . their first causes." [17] Materialism was "the poetic ground of physiology." [18] Lawrence wrote a well-known essay on "Life" for Rees' *Cyclopaedia* in 1819, in which he maintained that physiology should seek "only an empirical exposition, instead of a rational system." [19]

> The soul of Stahl, the archaeus of van Helmont . . . with a long train of etceteras . . . [have] been successively destroyed and nothing has been preserved from their wrecks except the facts afforded by experiment . . . So narrow are the limits of the human understanding that the knowledge of first causes seem[s] placed forever beyond our reach. The thick veil which covers them envelops in its innumerable folds whoever attempts to break through it.[20]

13. Ibid., p. 95, and *Physiological Lectures* (1817), p. 26.
14. Ibid., p. 43, 51.
15. Ibid., p. 203; also 174–76, 327–31. Abernethy shared Lamarck's belief that lower animals would not survive without the support of external fluids.
16. Lawrence, *Comparative Anatomy and Physiology* (1816), p. 170.
17. Ibid., pp. 165–66; also 169.
18. *Lectures on Physiology* (1819), p. 83.
19. Sig. 4t4(a–b).
20. Ibid., sig. 4U4(b). Note the similarity of this comment to Davy's remarks on the veil of nature, p. 181 above.

In 1822 John Barclay (1758–1826) concluded that eighteenth-century theories had explained nothing.

> Without attempting to assign any particular cause, let us merely suppose that the cause of life is a subtle substance, of a quickly and powerfully mobile nature, that pervades everything. On this supposition, it may be not only the electric fluid, it may be the magnetic or the galvanic, it may be caloric, it may be the supposed ether of Newton, or it may be that incorporeal substance, that vegetative life, which Cudworth denominates the plastic nature. Yet take any or all of them separately or combined, and suppose the whole universally diffused. How is it explained? Or how can it be conceived that these unintelligent and unconscious materials may so vary their modes of operation, as to construct the almost innumerable species of organisms to be found in the animal and vegetable kingdoms? [21]

James Cowles Prichard (1786–1848) wrote in 1829 that life would one day be explained in terms of physical and chemical process, but the knotty problem should be "untied," not "cut at once." This metaphor perfectly expresses the principle of limited explanation. "How far the assigned cause affords a solution of the results which are ascribed to its operation" (recall Hartley's comparison between scientific explanation and the key to a cypher) was but one criterion for a scientific explanation of life. It was also necessary to know *"what degree of evidence* can be discovered, independently of this consideration, for establishing the existence of the supposed agent." Prichard found the electrical theory of life and other subtle fluid theories lacking by the second criterion and assumed the speculations to have arisen from ambitions for total explanation. "As to the hypothesis of an ethereal fluid, the medium of vibrations, we can determine nothing, and it is sufficient to say that it is destitute of proof." [22]

Charles Lyell criticized Lamarck's notion of subtle fluids as a fiction, "as ideal as the 'plastic virtue' and other phantoms of the middle ages." [23] Science would have to abandon "gratuitous assumption" and hasty theoretical systems based upon "any new and visionary doc-

21. Barclay, *An Inquiry into the Opinions, Ancient and Modern, Concerning Life and Organization* (1822), pp. 490–91.

22. *A Review of the Doctrine of a Vital Principle* (1829), p. 152; on electricity, see pp. 12–14. Cf. Thomas Rennell, *Remarks on Scepticism* (1819), pp. 86–102. Also Anon., *A Letter to the Reverend Thomas Rennell* [1819], p. 5, countering with Abernethy's notion that "more subtle and ethereal forms of matter" might explain life.

23. *Principles of Geology . . . ,* 2 (London: John Murray, 1832), 8.

trine."[24] Lawrence, Prichard, and Lyell condemned the speculative temper which had led to the excesses of the preceding century. In taking the first steps toward a modern appreciation of vital process, Hunter, Humboldt, Bichat, and Cuvier had at the least made it abundantly clear that life was not the collection of subtle fluids.

The history of experimental techniques in biology has yet to be written, and will not be attempted here even within the limited sphere of John Hunter's lifetime. It is already clear from brief mention of his careful measurement of organic temperatures in studying life that he was a determined experimentalist. The pages of his collected works are bright with flashes of experimental innovation. He disposed of the notion that sleep in plants was the relaxation of a voluntary faculty by turning a plant upside down and observing that the leaves rose against the influence of gravity to assume their sleep positions.[25] Hunter was the first to place seedlings on a rotating tub, seeking to show that the growth of the plumules was not determined simply by opposition to gravity.[26] The shameful destruction of Hunter's manuscripts by Sir Everard Home deprives us of exact knowledge of how far Hunter carried his experimental work on plants. He was not altogether successful in tracing the motions of Hedysarum or the tendrils of climbing plants to external stimuli, and seemed to allow plants a mediating reactive power akin to the irritability of animals.[27]

We might take brief notice of further developments in experimental study of plant sensitivity and tropisms. A remarkable sequence of experiments on the sensitive plant was sent to the Royal Society from Jamaica by John Lindsay in 1788 and 1790. The papers were not published and, except for a short description in 1827, cited by Sachs in 1875, they seem to have been forgotten.[28] The papers showed the sensitive plant being subjected to an array of ingenious experiments, including submersion, incisions, ligatures, hot irons, acids, and a great variety of chemical applications (Plate 6). If a leaf were scorched

24. Ibid., p. 20. Also see Coleridge's rejection of subtle fluid theories: *Definitions of Life*, p. 37.

25. "Croonian Lecture on Muscular Motion No. 1 for the year 1776," in *Works, 4* (1837), 206.

26. Abernethy, *Physiological Lectures*, p. 64. For a discussion of this experiment, which is not usually credited to Hunter, see C. A. Timiriazeff, *The Life of the Plant*, trans. from 7th ed. by A. Chérémételff (London: Longmans, Green, 1912), pp. 184–88.

27. "Observations and Experiments on the Vegetable Economy" [after 1781], in *Essays, 1* (1861), 341; also 356.

28. See Ritterbush, "John Lindsay and the Sensitive Plant," forthcoming in *Annals of Science*, for the text of part of the 1791 MS and a discussion of its authorship.

slowly, a pin pressed into some parts of the leaf stalk, or a portion of a leaf delicately removed, the plant did not react. These experiments conclusively showed that the plant did not sense injury and react after the manner of animals.[29] The irritability of animal tissues could be stilled with opium, but the plant would react in the usual way to a jarring blow after a solution of opium had been administered to it, providing experimental evidence against analogies with the irritability of animals.[30] Close observation also disclosed that fluid movements within the pulvini or effecting tissues were responsible for the motions of the leaves. The author supposed that exertions of the cellular tissue in the pulvinus accounted for the movements, but he would not speculate as to how the stimulus was transmitted after the initial blow to the plant. In the second portion of the manuscript, dealing with the sleep of plants, it was shown that sleeping plants would continue their motions in a darkened room. "[They] awake in the morning and go to sleep at night regularly untile their health is impaired by the confinement—." [31]

Thomas Andrew Knight (1759–1838) was a sound experimentalist of whose work on sap motions Humphry Davy wrote, "You have created almost all the science we possess on that interesting subject." [32] Knight treated the subject of plant "circulation" without speculation or analogies to the vascular system of animals. He was content merely to observe and record, without excessive concern for determining the cause of sap motions before he understood exactly what those motions were. Knight is remembered for the experiment whereby he placed the radicles of beans on a rotating surface, discovering that gravity was the chief agent in directing the growth of roots, although its effects could be offset by the presence of water or chemical concentrations in the soil. In his essay "On the Causes Which Influence the Direction of the Growth of Roots" (1811) he wrote:

> In all the preceding [experiments] the wisdom of nature and the admirable simplicity of the means which it employs, are conspicuously displayed; but I am wholly unable to trace the existence of anything like sensation or intellect in the plants; and

29. Lindsay MS, "An Inquiry into the nature of the motions of the Mimosa Pudica or Sensative Plant.—" (1788), p. 19.

30. Ibid., pp. 8–9.

31. Lindsay MS, "An Inquiry into the Nature of the motions of the Sens[i]tive, Sleeping & Moving Plants Jamaica, July 1790," pp. 38–39. Cf. du Fay, "Observations sur la sensitive" (1736), p. 88.

32. Quoted in Knight, *Papers* (1841), p. 22; letter of 3 Nov. 1810. Davy and Knight were close friends from 1804 until Davy's death in 1829.

> I therefore venture to conclude, that their roots are influenced by the immediate operation and contact of surrounding bodies and not by any degrees of sensation and passion analogous to those of animal life; and I reject the latter hypothesis, not only because it is founded upon assumptions which cannot be granted, but because it is insufficient to explain [my experiments].[33]

In his essay "On the Motions of the Tendrils of Plants" (1812) Knight found that the tendrils of many climbing plants "are made to recede from light, and to press against the opaque bodies which nature intended to support and protect them." [34] The motions were "the result of pure necessity only, uninfluenced by any degrees of sensation or intellectual powers." [35] Henri Dutrochet (1776–1847), in his *Recherches anatomiques* (1824), recommended that words such as "sensitivity" be replaced with neutral terms describing the motions without reference to causation.

Our investigation of one small development in the history of plant physiology, experiments upon the motions and tropisms of plants, shows the institution of the principle of limited explanation and a greater determination to resolve questions through experiment. In 1802 Charles François Brisseau-Mirbel (1776–1854) described the new science as follows. It was neither the most brilliant nor the easiest of exercises. It rejected generalizations for modest but lasting insights. It forsook knowledge of the whole for knowledge of the parts. "Notre raison calme et froide rejette tout ce que la passion ou l'enthousiasme suggère, et ne reconnoît pour vrai que ce qui est appuyé sur l'évidence." [36]

The third principal theme in the work of John Hunter, also foreshadowing nineteenth-century developments in the life sciences, was the study of comparative anatomy. The intricate network of relationships disclosed by the study of comparative anatomy forced the abandonment of the notion of a scale of beings with its parallel scale of functions. Hunter assembled a famous collection of anatomical preparations and housed them in a museum wherein different organs were arranged in series. Function was no longer to be seen as a corollary of an animal's location in the scale of beings, but was to be studied through analysis of organ systems.

In a dissertation "De Serie Corporum Naturalium Continua" (1772), C. J. Öhme observed that the scale of beings united dissimilar crea-

33. Ibid., pp. 163–64.
34. Ibid., p. 166.
35. Ibid., p. 168.
36. *Traité d'anatomie et de physiologie végétales, I,* 11–12.

tures too closely, was not in fact continuous, and would lead to different stations on the scale for males and females of the same species.[37] In 1774 Vicq d'Azyr published his "Table pour servir à l'histoire anatomique et naturelle des corps vivans ou organiques." The table showed that animals with the most complex respiratory system need not have the most complex circulatory or reproductive system. There were as many scales of beings as there were individual functions by which to arrange them.

The difficulties which beset the linear series may be seen in Johann Hermann's *Tabula Affinitatum Animalium* (1783). Hermann attempted to portray all relationships of affinity among animals in a single graphic scheme printed in small type on a large chart. He was unable to list the organisms in a simple linear series and showed them instead as a wide concourse of animal forms, with as many as twenty different kinds, of roughly equal complexity, on the same level. Man, for example, was linked by vertical lines of analogy to the orang-outang on the next lowest level, and then to the Cochin China monkey, the white-eyelid monkey, down through the lemur, flying maucauco, and bat, to the goatsucker among the birds! The marmot was linked to the amphibia, far down the scale, because it hibernated. The armadillo was linked by a vertical line to the turtle; the pangolin, to the crocodile; the whale, to the swordfish; and the hummingbird to the sphinx moth. The vertical lines of analogy were crossed by many horizontal lines between animals of equal rank, giving the effect of a net.[38] His chart was a reductio ad absurdum of the notion that all analogies and affinities might be presented by a simple scheme. Cuvier was to divide the animal kingdom into four great subkingdoms; in time the notion of linear series would be forgotten. Its fragmentation at the hands of comparative anatomists is yet another example of the refinement of explanatory techniques.

One consequence of the dissociation of the scale of functions from the scale of beings was the distinction between analogies, based on gross morphological likeness or similarity in function, and affinities,

37. Öhme, *De Serie Corporum* (1772), p. 11. On the difficulty of constructing a perfect series, see Bonnet, *Contemplation de la nature, 1* (1764), 59. Also Buffon, *Histoire naturelle des oiseaux, 1* (Paris: Imprimerie Royale, 1770), 394. Also [Voltaire], "Chaine des êtres créés," in *Questions sur l'encyclopédie, par des amateurs, 3* (1771), 284–87.

38. In *Tabula,* pp. 10–11 n., Hermann dismisses Bonnet's chain as being too simple. Also see Blumenbach, *A Manual of the Elements of Natural History,* trans. R. T. Gore from the 10th German ed. (London: W. Simpkin and R. Marshall, 1825), pp. 3–6. Also see Jean Guillaume Brouguière's criticisms of plant-animals: *Histoire naturelle des vers, Encyclopédie méthodique, 6* (Paris: Panckucke and Liege: Plomteux, 1789), 186, 445.

based on organs or structure. In 1815 Lamarck ridiculed the notion that aquatic mammals showed affinities to fish. They had the same habitat and their adaptations were bound to show a "certain analogy of form," but the total dissimilarity of their organs showed that there was no true affinity.[39]

William Stuart McLeay (1792–1865) developed an elaborate conjectural basis for systematics wherein he distinguished analogy from affinity. He imagined that each kingdom or order in nature might be divided into five segments, and set out to represent the organization of life as a circle divided into five segments, each with a circle containing five subdivisions represented in turn by circles similarly divided, until the end result was a highly ramified nest of circles. Within this system of "scholastische Nonsens" McLeay in fact distinguished between analogy and affinity. Analogies, such as aquatic form or the ability to fly, were represented by analogous geometrical locations in the same segment of all the circles, large or small. Organisms with close affinities were placed at tangent (not analogous) points of adjacent circles. McLeay credited Linnaeus, Pallas, and Desfontaines with having "mentioned certain analogies in nature as distinct from affinities," but he believed that his own essays were the best account of "the nature of the difference which exists in natural history between affinity and analogy."[40] Geometrically corresponding points on the circles showed relations of analogy for all life forms listed at those points, and tangent points in the nest of circles disclosed relations of analogy for the forms so listed.

William Swainson (1789–1855) distinguished between analogy and affinity in a similar way, but with less emphasis on nesting circles. By affinity he meant form, structure, habits, and "a strong similarity in the detail of the structure of two animals," while analogy meant superficial resemblance. A maned, slender-tailed colobus monkey was analogous to a maned, slender-tailed lion, but there was no affinity. A lion and a tiger, while lacking in external resemblance, displayed close affinity. "The student will readily perceive that there are relations of analogy as well as relations of affinity; and he will plainly see the theoretical difference between them."[41]

In 1825 Geoffroy St. Hilaire used the word "homology" to indicate all sense organs, which he felt to be physiologically similar. In 1843

39. *Histoire naturelle des animaux sans vertèbres, 1* (1815), 374.

40. "Identity of Certain General Laws" (1822), p. 49; also *Horae Entomologicae* (1821), part 2, p. 162, and diagrams at pp. 212, 318, 390, 395, 439.

41. Swainson, *A Preliminary Discourse on the Study of Natural History* (1834), p. 186.

Richard Owen defined analogue as "A part or organ in one animal which has the same function as another part or organ in another animal."[42] A homologue was "the same organ in different animals under every variety of form and function."[43] Homologous organs showed relationships of affinity; analogous organs, of analogy only. This distinction, a very important contribution to the development of comparative anatomy, split up the Aristotelian synthesis between beings and functional capacities. The scale of beings, as Bradley, Linnaeus, Bonnet, and others had conceived it, was a naive notion ignored by nineteenth-century biologists in their attempts to deal with a multitude of newly discovered species and fossil forms.

John Hunter was not alone responsible for these developments, but they may all be traced to his writings. It must be noted that Hunter's theory of life was never carefully presented or made explicit. Abernethy was able to claim him as an exponent of the eighteenth-century notion of life, based upon the idea of immanence. Hunter's experiments on plants did not lead him to repudiate all analogies between plants and animals. His studies in comparative anatomy did not result in a repudiation of the scale of beings. A portrait by Sir Joshua Reynolds in 1787 shows an open sketchbook with six skulls drawn in descending order.[44] He continued to believe that "The more imperfect animals are the more they approach towards a vegetable in many circumstances, if not all."[45] It would, however, be incorrect to overlook the prominence in Hunter's work of new approaches to vital energy and comparative anatomy and better-developed experimental techniques. These features of his work foreshadowed nineteenth-century developments in the life sciences.

v. The Romantic Protest

The writings of the eighteenth-century naturalists reveal their exaltation over the broad understanding of nature they thought they had

42. *Lectures on the Comparative Anatomy and Physiology of the Invertebrate Animals . . . , I* (London: Longman, Brown, Green, and Longmans, 1843), 374.

43. Ibid., p. 379. Also see Charles Darwin, *On the Origin of Species . . .* (London: John Murray, 1859), p. 427. For the later history of the concept of homology see Hans Spemann, "Zur Geschichte und Kritik des Begriffs der Homologie" (1915).

44. The portrait hangs at the Royal College of Surgeons and is reproduced as the frontispiece to S. Roodhouse Gloyne, *John Hunter* (Edinburgh: E. & S. Livingstone, 1950). For a description of the Hunterian Museum see Abernethy, *The Hunterian Oration for the Year 1819*, pp. 61–66, 294. Also Everard Home's introduction to Hunter, *A Treatise on the Blood* (1794), pp. xxxviii–xlv.

45. Hunter, "Observations on Natural History" [1784], in *Essays, I* (1861), 23.

achieved. Their appetite for knowledge was fulfilled in a world that seemed to stand at one with reason.[1] What was to be the reaction to the abandonment of their cherished ideas? An accurate and detailed premonition of this thought, expressed in religious terms but nevertheless adaptable to the ideas of the naturalists, appears in some verses written by Benjamin Stillingfleet:

all becomes
Without thy ray divine, one dreary gloom;
Where lurk the monsters of phantastic brains;
Order bereft of thought, uncaused effects,
Fate freely acting, and unerring Chance.
Where meanless matter to a chaos sinks
Or something lower still, for without thee
It crumbles into atoms void of force,
Void of resistance—it eludes our thought
Where laws eternal to the varying code
Of self-love dwindle. Interest, passion, whim
Take place of right, and wrong, the golden chain
Of beings melts away, and the mind's eye
Sees nothing but the present. All beyond
Is visionary guess—is dream—is death.[2]

The complex sorrow of the Romantic generation and the religious yearning of many of the poets may credibly be ascribed to the loss of the eighteenth-century satisfactions in unity, order, and design. It is that loss of certainty, the dissociation of energy from matter, and the melting away of the chain of beings that we have described in this chapter. But there were those who continued to seek the satisfaction of total understanding. It may appear that some of the champions of the discredited philosophy were nineteenth-century poets and writers who doubted that inquiry had to be limited in order to achieve scientific objectives, or that the basis for the cosmic unity had disappeared.

Joseph Priestley's later attempts to uphold the phlogiston theory and the facile speculations of Edward Peart (1756?–1824) and Robert Harrington (fl. 1780–1815) showed the persistence of desires for total

1. See T. E. Hulme, "A Critique of Satisfaction" (1924); L. S. Feuer, "Psychoanalysis and Discovery" (1959); and George Gaylord Simpson, "Biology and the Nature of Science" in *Science, 139* (11 Jan. 1963), 83.

2. Stillingfleet, *Miscellaneous Tracts* (4th ed. 1791), pp. 128–29.

explanation.[3] We may note several attempts to maintain the idea of immanence in its application to life.

Andrew Crosse (1784–1855), an electrician and experimentalist, stated that electricity was a universal proximate cause:

> Electricity is no longer the paltry confined science which it was once fancied to be . . . but it is even now, though in its infancy, proved to be connected most intimately with all operations in chemistry,—with magnetism, with light and caloric, apparently a property belonging to all matter, and perhaps ranging through all space, from sun to sun, from planet to planet, and not improbably the secondary cause of every change in the animal, mineral, vegetable, and gaseous systems.[4]

These reflections seem out of place in 1837; they were occasioned by a grotesque misinterpretation of his observation of water mites in his electrical apparatus. Crosse announced that he had caused their appearance with electric currents! "A swarm of Acari" also appeared in the apparatus of W. H. Weekes.[5] Charles Gillispie notes the incident: "Mr. Crosse's claims created quite a stir, until it turned out that his creation was a common parasitic mite which had come off his fingers while he mixed his electrolyte." [6]

In *Vestiges of the Natural History of Creation* (1844), Robert Chambers (1802–71) propounded a speculative natural philosophy. He wrote about Newtonian attraction and the Herschelian "universal fire mist" from which the planets were formed. He claimed that "globules" of organized matter could be created by electrical discharges in albumen. He observed that crystallizing metals formed dendrites

3. *Heads of Lectures on a Course of Experimental Philosophy* . . . (London: J. Johnson, 1794), pp. 127–44; also *Experimental Observations* . . . (London: J. Johnson, 1796); also *The Doctrine of Phlogiston Established, and That of the Composition of Water Refuted* (Northumberland, Pa.: by A. Kennedy for the author, 1800); also 2d ed. (by A. Kennedy for P. Byrne of Philadelphia, 1803), pp. 27–33, 55–57. Also see Peart, *Animal Heat* (1788), *On Electricity* (1791), and *Properties of Matter* (1792). Also [Harrington], *Fire and Planetary Life* (1796), Harrington, *Volta's Electrical Pile* (1801), and *The Death-Warrant of the French Theory of Chemistry* (1804).

4. Crosse, "Experiments" [1837], p. 10. For electricity and vegetation, see *Memorials, Scientific and Literary, of Andrew Crosse, the Electrician* (London: Longman, Brown, Green, Longmans, & Roberts, 1857), pp. 225–37.

5. "Details of an Experiment" (1843).

6. *Genesis and Geology* (1951), pp. 155–56. Also Rupert T. Gould, "Crosse's Acari," *Oddities: A Book of Unexplained Facts* (London: Philip Allan, 1928), pp. 181–90. Also Rev. Richard Owen, *The Life of Richard Owen, 1* (London: John Murray, 1894), 250.

and that plant growth followed a path resembling "the most ordinary appearances of the electric fluid." He called plant forms "the *brush* realized." [7] "The first step in the creation of life upon this planet was *a chemico-electric operation, by which simple germinal vesicles were produced.*" [8] He believed that evolution had occurred through stages whereby life "presses in" to higher stations on the scale of beings. Chambers' book is very similar in conception to Lamettrie's *L'Homme-plante* and Lamarck's *Philosophie zoologique,* with ambitions for total explanation, frequent references to electrical appetency in life forms, and delight in analogies between man and other organisms.

We may characterize the establishment of empiricism in early nineteenth-century biology as the dissociation of poetry from science, provoking that strain of criticism which has ever since belittled the scientific enterprise as drawing upon something less than the full scope of human powers. Caution in investigation and the rejection of grand synthetic schemes were condemned as degrading, unimaginative, and false to the scale of human intuition. This was the charge brought against contemporary natural science by Blake, Wordsworth, and Keats.

In his insistent visionary lyrics William Blake (1757–1827) mounted a sweeping attack on rationalism, including the sciences, which he described as "experience" corroding "innocence" as disease blights a rose. He did not realize that the idea of immanence had led some scientific writers to attempt "To see a World in a Grain of Sand," or that the idea of botanical analogy supported intimations of "a Heaven in a Wild Flower." [9] There was irony in the poet's condemnation of science when natural scientists were still struggling to discipline their innocence. Had he not characterized science in this way, Blake might have thought more generously of it.

A bald statement that the Romantic poets were opposed to science, whatever it might mean, would oversimplify their reactions and neglect their indebtedness to the naturalists for beliefs about external nature. The appearance of eighteenth-century speculative concepts in

7. Pp. 166–67.

8. Ibid., pp. 204–05. The persistence of the speculative ideas through the nineteenth century might be investigated in the following writers, whose works are listed in the bibliography: Gustav Theodor Fechner, Sir Jagadis Bose, and Pierre Teilhard de Chardin. For a comment on Bose and Lamettrie see Francis L. Rougier, ed., *Offray de la Mettrie: L'Homme-plante* (Columbia Univ., Institute of French Studies, 1936), pp. 108–09, 123. Cf. Nordenskiold, *The History of Biology* (1929), pp. 505–27 on monism in Haeckel, Avenarius, and Mach.

9. On Blake and science see Bernard Blackstone, *English Blake* (Cambridge Univ. Press, 1949), pp. 213–49.

Romantic nature poetry has been noticed by scholars, although there is no comprehensive study that makes this plain for all the poets, or one that relates the poets' ambitions to their inheritance of cosmic speculation. It was as though the poets sought to perpetuate concepts of speculative natural philosophy relinquished by the scientists.

As a schoolboy of fifteen Wordsworth (1770–1850) wrote of "Elysian plains / Where throned in gold, immortal science reigns," and truth teaches "the curious soul / To search the mystic cause of things / And follow Nature to her secret springs." Walter Garstang supposes that Wordsworth might have become a biologist had he found a Henslow at Cambridge as Charles Darwin did, or had there been a "biological synthesis to attract his imagination." [10] He longed for the speculative unity which underlay eighteenth-century materialism and resolved to make his "office upon earth" that of a poet, at least partly because Hartleyan psychology and Godwinian social science seemed to be in need of his advocacy.

S. G. Dunn, Joseph Warren Beach, and Newton P. Stallknecht have noticed the affinities between Newton's ether and Wordsworth's ethereal force of nature. William K. Wimsatt, Jr., relates Newton's ether to the unseen forces of "Tintern Abbey" and the *Prelude,* wherein the ether found "a poetic counterpart." Moonlit mists and shadows, indicating a universally diffused subtle presence, were invested with a complexity of metaphor and multiplicity of meanings not attained by eighteenth-century poets.[11] Wordsworth depended upon the idea of immanence for:

> a sense sublime
> Of something far more deeply interfused,
> Whose dwelling is the light of setting suns,
> And the round ocean, and the living air,
> And the blue sky, and in the mind of man
> A motion and a spirit, that impels
> All thinking things, all objects of all thought,
> And rolls through all things.[12]

The wanderer of *The Excursion* (1814), explicitly refusing to be bound by the limitations of his senses, asserted:

10. "Wordsworth's Interpretation of Nature" (1926), p. 1.

11. See Wimsatt, "The Structure of Romantic Nature Imagery" [1949].

12. "Tintern Abbey" (1798), lines 96–103; also see "Influence of Natural Objects in Calling Forth and Strengthening the Imagination . . ." [1798], lines 3–4.

"To every Form of being is assigned,"
Thus calmly spake the venerable Sage,
"An *active* principle:—howe'er removed
From sense and observation, it subsists
In all things, in all natures . . .
Spirit that knows no insulated spot,
No chasm, no solitude; from link to link
It circulates, the Soul of all the worlds." [IX, 1–15]

In the second preface added to *Lyrical Ballads* in 1802 Wordsworth wrote that "if the time should ever come" when "the remotest discoveries" of natural science become familiar, they "will be as proper objects of the poet's art as any upon which it can be employed." He seems to have thought that science stripped of its speculative dimension was no longer a fit subject for poetry. He acknowledged that the poet "converses with general nature with affections akin to those, which, through labor and length of time, the man of science has raised up in himself, by conversing with those particular parts of nature which are the objects of his studies." Such affections were part of the emotional endowment of many biologists when Wordsworth wrote this passage but they were increasingly denied any influence upon the program of science or the interpretation of observed phenomena. "Poetry is the breath and finer spirit of all knowledge; it is the impassioned expression which is in the countenance of all science." And was not science denying its imaginative dimension for the sake of sound knowledge?

Oh! there is laughter at their work in heaven!
Inquire of ancient Wisdom; go, demand
Of mighty Nature, if 'twas ever meant
That we should pry far off yet be unraised;
That we should pore, and dwindle as we pore,
Viewing all objects unremittingly
In disconnection dead and spiritless;
But still dividing, and dividing still,
Break down all grandeur, still unsatisfied
With the perverse attempt, while littleness
May yet become more little; waging thus
An impious warfare with the very life
Of our own souls! [13]

13. *The Excursion* (1814), IV, 956–68. Also see Knight, *The Starlit Dome* (1959), p. 16, and Stallknecht, *Strange Seas of Thought* (1945), pp. 64–71.

The wanderer of *The Excursion* described the spirit as carried, like Lamettrie's ethereal energy, from link to link without chasms. There are few suggestions of the chain of being in Wordsworth's poems, but we might cite one passage that reveals an indebtedness to the idea of botanical analogy:

> And 'tis my faith that every flower
> Enjoys the air it breathes. . . .
> The budding twigs spread out their fan;
> To catch the breezy air;
> And I must think, do all I can,
> That there was pleasure there.[14]

In an article entitled, "Is Wordsworth's Nature-Poetry Antiquated?" Ernst Bernbaum endeavors to show that Wordsworth's notion of natural harmony anticipated the conclusions of modern science. Such a contention overlooks its relationships with eighteenth-century speculation. Nor should Wordsworth's verses on plant sensitivity be cited as foretelling the modern awareness that the mechanisms and processes of plant life are complex, because the idea manifestly arose from notions of botanical analogy.[15] The Romantic protest against the establishment of empiricism in biology was in great measure due to the awareness that the ideas of immanence and botanical analogy were doomed to decline.

The eighteenth-century system of ideas exercised a lifelong influence over Shelley (1792–1822), who apparently sought to preserve the cosmic synthesis even in the face of his own skepticism. Whitehead may have startled his readers in 1926 by insisting that Shelley's interest in science was not "a casual oddity" but "in fact, part of the main structure of his mind, permeating his poetry through and through." [16] But Carl Grabo's studies of Shelley's poetry in relation to the ideas of Newton, Herschel, Erasmus Darwin, and Davy have established the origins of "fire that is not brightness"—the "azure mist / Of ele-

14. "Lines Written in Early Spring" (1798), lines 11–20; also see *Prelude* (1805 version), III, 121–29, and VIII, 624–31.

15. Bernbaum (1940). He offers a similar argument in T. M. Raysor, ed., *The English Romantic Poets* (1956), pp. 53–54.

16. *Science and the Modern World* (1926), p. 118. His statement was a necessary corrective to nineteenth-century studies of Shelley, such as Mathilde Blind's "Shelley's View of Nature Contrasted with Darwin's," *The Shelley Society's Papers* (1888), part 1, pp. 36–49; Edgar Pelham, *A Study of Shelley with Special Reference to His Nature Poetry* (Toronto: William Briggs, 1899); and Henry Sweet, *Shelley's Nature Poetry* (London: Richard Clay and Sons, [1888]).

mental subtlety."[17] It is very widely recognized that Shelley was influenced by the lectures of Adam Walker (1730?–1821), which he heard at Syon House School and later at Eton. Walker wrote in 1799:

> The identity of fire, light, heat, caloric, phlogiston, and electricity, or rather their being but modifications of one and the same principle . . . The theory was not sought, but has obtruded itself through an experience of near forty years.[18]

Shelley performed electrical experiments in his rooms at University College, Oxford, and tried to cure his little sister's chilblains with electric shocks.[19] In *A Refutation of Deism* (1814) Eusebes, the theist, spoke as follows:

> Matter, such as we behold it, is not inert. It is infinitely active and subtle. Light, electricity, and magnetism are fluids not surpassed by thought itself in tenuity and activity: like thought they are sometimes the cause and sometimes the effect of motion; and, distinct as they are from every other class of substances, with which we are acquainted, seem to possess equal claims with thought to the unmeaning distinction of immateriality.[20]

In *Queen Mab* (1812) the poet exulted in Godwinian necessity and materialism akin to that of Lamettrie and d'Holbach. G. Wilson Knight, in his study of thematic imagery in Romantic poetry, writes that "Shelley's precise scientific and atmospheric interests are at one with his spiritual intuitions."[21] Queen Mab, a figure rather like the hierophant of Darwin's *Temple of Nature* or the didactic apparitions of Leibniz and Akenside, tells an inquiring spirit:

> "Throughout these infinite orbs of mingling light,
> Of which yon earth is one, is wide diffused
> A Spirit of activity and life,
> That knows no term, cessation, or decay;

17. *Prometheus Unbound* (1820), IV, 230, 254–55. Also see John "Walking" Stewart, *The Revelation of Nature* (n.d.), p. xii, 81–83. "Bodies around a wide effluvia moves / And every atom has its atmosphere" (p. 7).

18. *A System of Familiar Philosophy* (1799), p. xi. Also see Desmond King-Hele, *Shelley: His Thought and Work* (London: Macmillan, 1960), p. 159.

19. Grabo, *A Newton among Poets* (1930), p. 135.

20. Roger Ingpen and Walter E. Peck, ed., *The Complete Works of Percy Bysshe Shelley, 6* (London: Ernest Benn, for Julian Editions, 1929), p. 50.

21. *The Starlit Dome* (1959), p. 209; also 220–24. Beach, in *The Concept of Nature* (1936), wondered how Shelley could be lyrical about scientific concepts despite "the strict sobriety of scientific method" (p. 239). But, as we have seen, the idea of immanence was the poetic ground of physics in the eighteenth century.

That fades not when the lamp of earthly life,
Extinguished in the dampness of the grave,
Awhile there slumbers . . .
No atom of this turbulence fulfils
A vague and unnecessitated task,
Or acts but as it must and ought to act." [VI, 146–73]

As had been assumed by Richard Watson and others, not an atom of earth existed that had not once been enlivened (II, 212). Each "fragile blade of grass" (II, 227) was "an unbounded world" (II, 230). Queen Mab disclosed an effluvium of "viewless beings" who "Think, feel, and live like men" (II, 234), in obedience to strict laws of necessity.

Shelley often employed electrical metaphors to describe the moving force. In the first act of *Prometheus Unbound* (1820) a chorus of spirits asks, "Hast thou beheld the form of Love?" (763). A spirit replies:

As over wide dominions
I sped, like some swift cloud that wings the wide air's wildernesses,
That planet-crested shape swept by on lightning-braided pinions,
Scattering the liquid joy of life from his ambrosial tresses:
His footsteps paved the world with light.[22] [763–67]

The conflict between cosmic aims and empiricism became apparent to Shelley after he finished *Queen Mab* (1812). C. E. Pulos, in a study of what he styles Shelley's skepticism, identifies as the central tenet of his materialism the idea that "spirit can be explained in terms of matter and motion." Shelley became doubtful about this belief as he came increasingly to be influenced by Humean skepticism. Pulos correctly notes that Hume's principles strengthened the application of the scientific method at the same time that speculative concepts were being discredited.[23] In "Mont Blanc" (July 1816) Shelley spoke of the same powers, but they had become "Remote, serene, and inaccessible" (97), a "secret Strength of things" (139). Doubts about the validity of his speculations had succeeded the certainty of *Queen Mab:*

The wilderness has a mysterious tongue
Which teaches awful doubt, or faith so mild,
So solemn, so serene, that man may be
[In such a] faith, with nature reconciled.[24] [76–79]

22. Cf. Grabo, *A Newton among Poets* (1930), pp. 118–38.

23. *The Deep Truth* (1954), p. 39. On Shelley's materialism, see White, *Shelley, I* (1947), 276–78, 293; for his opinions by 1818, see pp. 558–59; on skepticism, 424–25.

24. Words in brackets from *Boscombe MS.*

The poem ends on a note of anguish: "And what were thou, and earth, and stars, and sea, / If to the human mind's imagining / Silence and solitude were vacancy?" Shelley wrote in his essay on life, variously dated between 1815 and 1819: "We are on that verge where words abandon us and what wonder if we grow dizzy to look down into the dark abyss of how little we know."

In Shelley's poetry between 1812 and 1820 the idea of immanence became increasingly less certain and concrete. The intensity of his poetic drive increased over the same years, sublimating the idea in an intense platonism.[25] Shelley's mature works speak of a principle of cosmic love, which we may relate to Newtonian attraction and Darwin's appetencies of matter. Love, "penetrating me with living light," is a force of "magnetic might." [26]

One of Shelley's most important mature poems, "The Sensitive Plant" (1820) shows a poetic sublimation of the idea of botanical analogy. The line from "Adonais": "All baser things pant with sacred thirst" (169), is an expression of the notion of vegetable life that Shelley derived from Darwin.[27] But he did not present a botanical description; the eighteenth-century idea was given less exact, more poetically intense expression. The plant was employed as an emblem of all organisms aflame with love: "And it opened its fan-like leaves to the light, / And closed them beneath the kisses of Night." (I, 3–4)

Other plants were represented as struggling upward from the turf to open their sexual organs to the sky. He mentioned sleeping plants "drooping as day drooped too," that "Fell into pavilions" at night. Shelley reminds us of Hales' notion of subtle fertilizing vapors in writing that each flowering plant "was interpenetrated / With the light and odour its neighbour shed, / Like young lovers whom youth

25. Grabo notes Shelley's indebtedness to Davy for ideas about physics and chemistry: *A Newton among Poets*, pp. 114–17. But he remarks, p. 116, that Davy had avoided the "platonic mysticism" of Shelley. This is entirely untrue, and that such an outstanding scholar could have supposed it is a compelling argument for a thorough study of Davy's life and thought. See his poems, visions, and dreams, indicating that after 1815 Davy lapsed into an intense platonic mysticism: John Davy, *Memoirs*, *2* (1836), 77, 95–96, 377–80; *Memoirs* (1839), in *1*, *Works*, 114–15, 286, 439–40; and *Fragmentary Remains* (1858), pp. 258–59; also see his very remarkable *Consolations in Travel* (1829) in *9*, *Works*. Note especially pp. 345–46 and cf. Feuer, "Psychoanalysis and Discovery" (1959), p. 324, for their possible significance in understanding the decline of Davy's scientific career.

26. "Epipsychidion" (1821), lines 342, 348.

27. In a letter to Hogg on 16 June 1811 Shelley wrote that plants enjoyed sensation. On 28 July 1811 he wrote that he had been spending his time in Wales "reading Darwin": Ingpen and Peck, ed., *Complete Works of Shelley*, *8*, 106, 135. For respiration in plants see *Prometheus Unbound*, II, ii, 70–82; on electricity and plant growth, I, 53–58.

and love make dear / Wrapped and filled by their mutual atmosphere" (I, 66–69). Insects, "Laden with light and odour" (I, 84), also fertilized the flowers. Although the sensitive plant did not survive the winter, for the spirit of nature which it represented "There is no death nor change" (III, 135). Carlos Baker interprets the poem as a commentary on the sensitive poetic mind, in which the moral and aesthetic dimensions of the parable are far more important than any concrete description of the plant.[28] Harold Bloom finds that the "visions of innocence which fade under the impact of experience" constitute the poem's central meaning.[29] The eighteenth-century conception of the plant barely appears at all.

Eighteenth-century concerns continue to appear in Shelley's poetry, although in greatly changed forms better suited to the headlong, impassioned rush of his poetic drive. Monistic interpretations of fire, electricity, light, and life, affirmed in *Queen Mab,* were subject to doubt in "Mont Blanc" and appear in *Prometheus Unbound* and "The Sensitive Plant" only as the concentrated poetic essence of Shelley's early confident materialism. The eighteenth-century cosmic philosophy was like a "dome of many-coloured glass," a wonderful vision which "Stains the white radiance of Eternity," until the critical faculty of experience "Tramples it to fragments." [30]

The final stage in the passage of eighteenth-century ideas from scientific speculation to poetic expression appears in the poetry of Keats (1795–1821), which Whitehead once mentioned as "an example of literature untouched by science." The poetry of Keats sublimates, but does not neglect, the eighteenth-century synthesis of love in man and nature. G. Wilson Knight finds in Keats' botanical imagery "some almost human vitality in vegetable and earthy life." Bernard Blackstone, in his study of Keats' indebtedness to Erasmus Darwin's sense of appetencies and abundant energies, emphasizes the poet's "medical education which certainly included more than the elements of physiology and morphology." The ultimate destiny of the eighteenth-century sense of the community of a life principle was a poetic one. Without love, Keats asked, who could tell:

That flowers would bloom, or that green fruit would swell
To melting pulp, that fish would have bright mail,
The earth its dower of river wood and vale.[31]

28. *Shelley's Major Poetry: The Fabric of a Vision* (Princeton Univ. Press, 1948), pp. 195–201.

29. *Shelley's Mythmaking,* Yale Studies in English, 141 (Yale Univ. Press, 1959), 157.

30. "Adonais" (1821), 462–64.

31. *Endymion* (1817), II, 833–38.

The poet describes: "the moist earth fed / So plenteously all weed-hidden roots / Into o'erhanging boughs, and precious fruits." [32] Blackstone points to the divine analogy between the urn, the human artifact produced by aesthetic passion, and the fruit swollen by solar rays. This was Keats' "vast idea," "his 'sensation' of the principle of analogy." [33] Blackstone senses that Keats and Darwin "trod a common road," and that Darwin gave him clues to the vast idea; their road was "adorned with flowers and fruits and corn and branching trees, haunted by spirits of the four elements: it passes over caves bright with crystals and veins of gold and silver ore." [34]

There are important differences between the meaning of Darwin and that of Keats. For the latter, life was an active, fecund energy. The analogies he described were impressed upon a diversity of experience by an active poetic faculty, and were not merely perceived and recorded. With Keats the poetic description of nature lost all touch with the sciences. Above all, Keats was profoundly aware that the complexities of life cannot be disciplined for the human understanding. He wrote John Reynolds in May 1818 that further study of medicine "would not make the least difference in my poetry," because the scope of human knowledge is too broad to permit the poet any specialized bias.[35] The Romantic poets sought to maintain the speculative, even poetic, dimension forsaken by science. In the course of the Romantic protest the ideas of immanence and botanical analogy came to serve the moral and aesthetic ends of poetry and were no longer held to explain or interpret objective reality. Thus it is also true that, with Keats, the sciences lost all touch with the poetic description of nature.

Another element of the Romantic protest was the German *Naturphilosophie,* an antiempirical devotion to eighteenth-century motives in opposition to mechanistic physiology. Grandiose notions of morphology or comparative anatomy and florid treatises on physical and organic energies were characteristic products of its insistent perception of unity. Goethe's central concept in interpreting nature was the *Urphänomen,* a primal type to be apprehended from the multiplicity

32. Ibid., I, 64–66.

33. *The Consecrated Urn* (1959), p. xiii.

34. Ibid., p. 337; also "To Autumn" (1819), 1–11, and the opening lines of "I Stood Tip-Toe upon a Little Hill" [1816].

35. Keats criticized Coleridge for being content with half-knowledge and reaching irritably after reason. Walter J. Bate, *John Keats* (Harvard Univ., 1963), p. 249. It is some indication of the rapid change in literary sensibility which marked this period that Coleridge had criticized Darwin on almost exactly the same grounds only in 1804.

of natural forms. He presented a *Darstellung,* a representation of nature, not a scientific *Erklärung.* He insistently characterized his activities as scientific, even as the life sciences became steadily more hostile to such thinking. Goethe (1749–1832) sought an "organismal" view of life, deploring the analysis of biological facts by chemistry and specialized anatomical studies. He supposed that all leaves and flowers were modifications of the same Ur-organ, an idea that came to him during his Italian tour in 1796. He always imagined that the genius who had achieved a proper degree of spiritual intensity could arrive at true scientific theories by direct perception of nature.

In his first soliloquy Faust lamented the failure of a lifetime of science to lead him to the ultimate springs of truth: "Dass ich erkenne, was die Welt / Im Innersten zusammenhält." Faust's desires amply characterize the ambitions for total explanation which underlay eighteenth-century speculation. Faust tells the student Wagner that man is sadly lacking in powers of perception, with regret that science must plod. His words constitute a poignant aspiration toward totality of scientific explanation:

> Ach! zu des Geistes Flügeln wird so leicht
> Kein körperlicher Flügel sich gesellen.
> Doch ist es jedem eingeboren,
> Dass sein Gefühl hinauf und vorwärts dringt,
> Wenn über uns, im blauen Raum verloren,
> Ihr schmetternd Lied die Lerche singt,
> Wenn über schroffen Fichtenhöhen
> Der Adler ausgebreitet schwebt,
> Und über Flächen, über Seen
> Der Kranich nach der Heimat strebt.

Goethe's flight imagery, like that of Chénier's "Hermes," Beattie's *Minstrel,* or Davy's "Sons of Genius," symbolizes the endeavor of eighteenth-century naturalists. There is a breadth to their insights, which for scope and daring may bear comparison even with those of modern science. We have dismantled the scaffolding of surmise where the more solid structure of scientific knowledge now stands, but should not deny that the scaffolding was as great an achievement for its time as the building is for our own. This is not to overlook the errors, contentment with doctrine, and extravagance of speculation which figured in the writings of eighteenth-century naturalists. We have not tried to understand these failings in order to excuse them although, having understood, we may find them equally difficult to condemn. We may only hope that the materials presented and this history of general ideas may lend to the writings of the eighteenth-century naturalists some part of the interest they must have had for their original audience.

Illustrations

From an engraving dated 1778 (courtesy of the Burndy Library, Norwalk, Connecticut). The original painting, now in the White House, depicts Franklin as crowned with a laurel wreath and expressing intense anger. The bolt of lightning in the background recalls the descriptive imagery of Shelley's poems on tyranny.

YOU led your FRANKLIN to your glazed retreats,
Your air-built castles, and your silken seats;
Bade his bold arm invade the lowering sky,
And seize the tiptoe lightnings, ere they fly;
O'er the young Sage your mystic mantle spread,
And wreath'd the crown electric round his head—
—Erasmus Darwin, address to the Nymphs of Fire in "The Economy of Vegetation" (1791), *I*, 383–88.

Plate 1. Allegorical portrait of Benjamin Franklin by Jean Honoré Fragonard. 

The Leyden Jar "f" receives the charge accumulated by the prime conductor "Y–Z" and may be discharged across the patient's arm with the two glass-handled applicators. Frontispiece from George Adams [the younger], *An Essay on Electricity* (4th ed., 1792), pp. 327–28: "The stream of the electric fluid may, without a shock, be made to pass through any part of the body; it may also be thrown upon, or extracted from any part, and its action in each case varied, by causing the fluid to pass through materials which resist its passage in different degrees; it may be applied to the naked integuments, or to the skin . . . and its power may be rarefied or condensed, confined to one spot, or applied in a more diffusive manner, at the discretion of the operator." (From the collections of the Library of Congress.)

—Starts the quick Ether through the fibre-trains
Of dancing arteries, and of tingling veins,
Goads each fine nerve, with new sensation thrill'd,
Bends the reluctant limbs with power unwill'd;
Palsy's cold hands the fierce concussion own,
And Life clings trembling on her tottering throne.
—Erasmus Darwin, address to the Nymphs of Fire in "The Economy of Vegetation" (1791), *I*, 363–68.

Plate 2. The grand desideratum in physick.

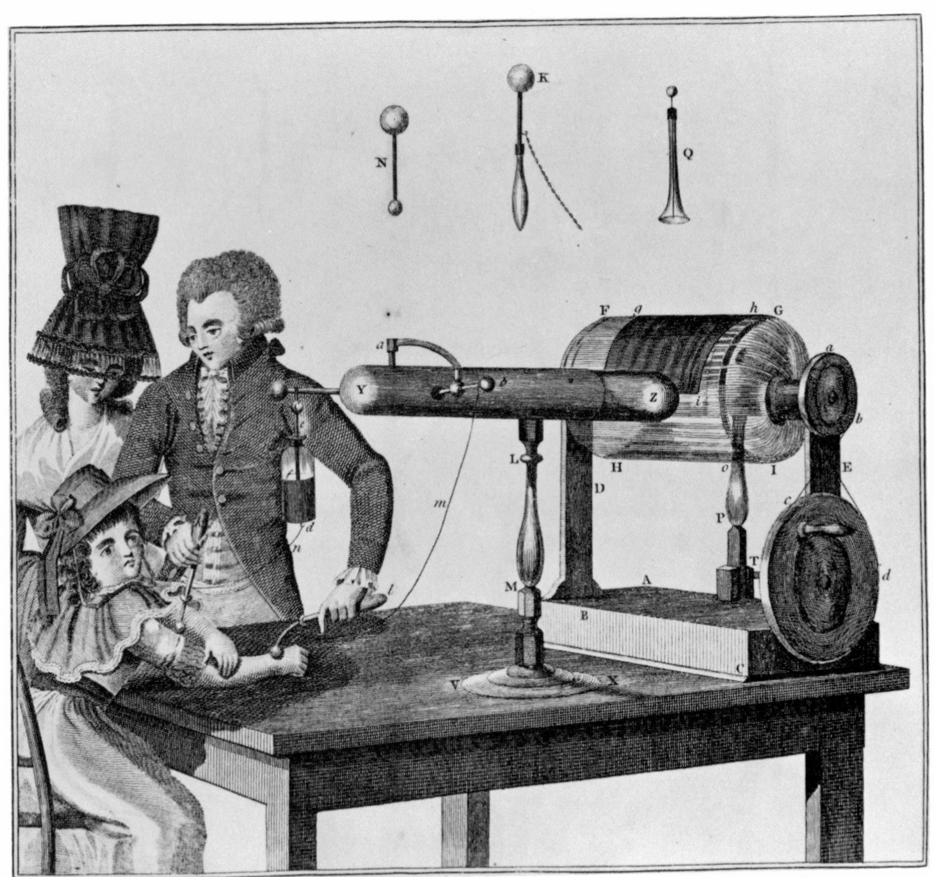

From [Linnaeus], "Sponsalia Plantarum" [1746], plate opp. p. 108. (From the collections of the Library of Congress.)

> *"Les vents, ces messagers de l'amour végétal, qui portent aux plants fémelles le sperme des mâles."*
>
> —Lamettrie, "L'Homme-plante" [1748], in *Œuvres,* 2 (1764), 20.

Plate 3. The wind pollination of Mercurialis; the egg-seed analogy.

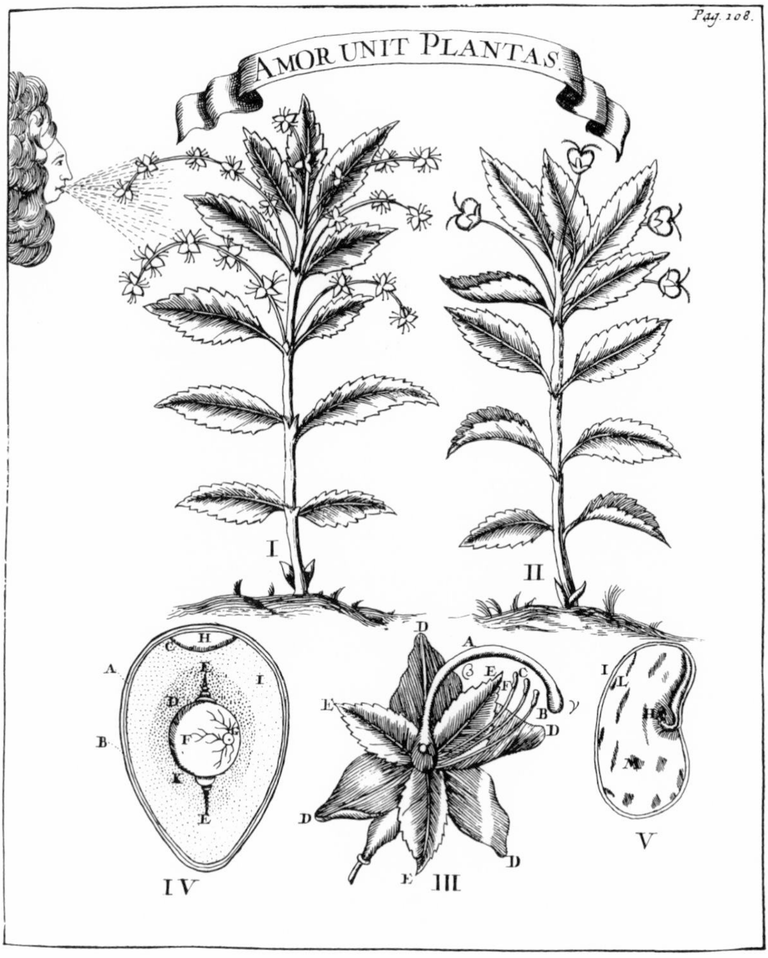

Pag. 108.

AMOR UNIT PLANTAS.

a, The parent. b, Mature buds. c, Young buds. d, "Swelled organizations" growing into new ramifications. From Parsons, *Philosophical Observations on the Analogy between the Propagation of Vegetables and That of Animals* (1752), plate opp. p. xvi. (From the collections of the Library of Congress.)

> *The chain of my arguments, through this little work, shall be carried on link by link, in search of the mystery of propagation by analogy.*
>
> —Parsons, *Philosophical Observations,* pp. 67–68.

Plate 4. Analogies in regeneration and budding.

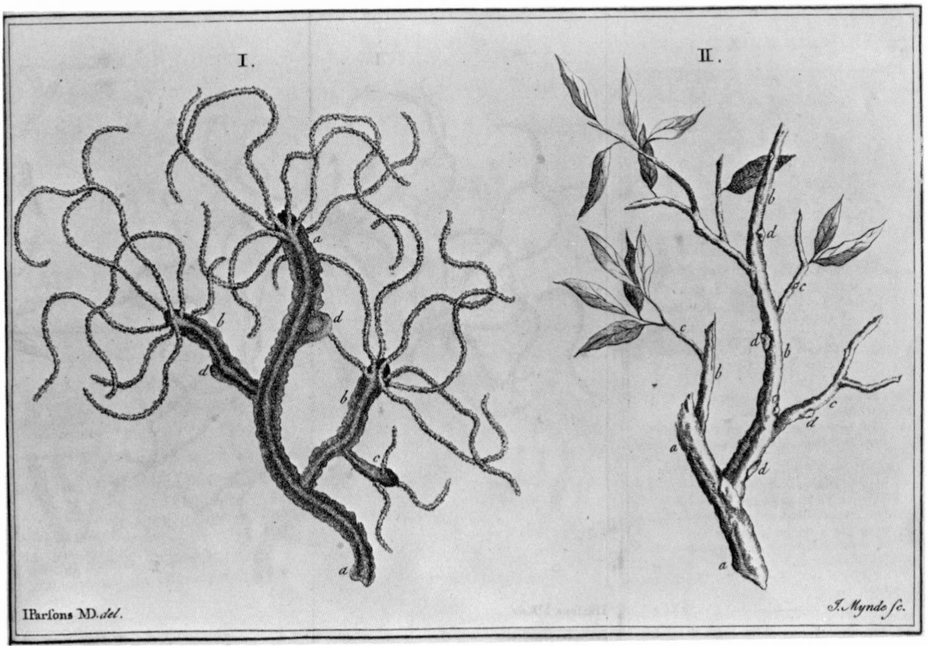

The manner in which the Sea Polypes call'd Corallines produce their Young

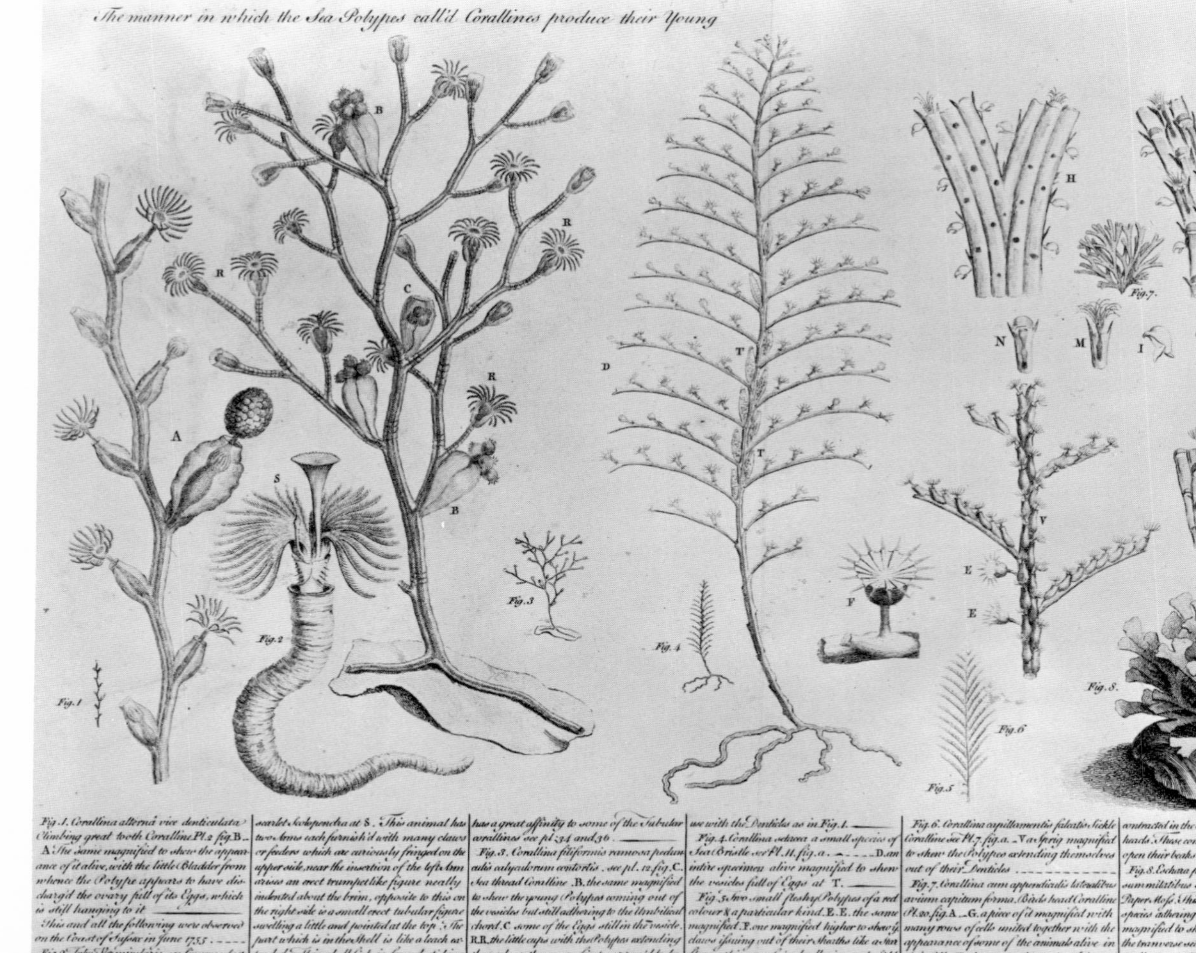

Fig. 1. Corallina alterna vice denticulata Climbing great tooth Coralline Pl. 2 fig. B. — A. The same magnified to shew the appearance of it alive, with the little Bladder from whence the Polype appears to have discharg'd the ovary full of its Eggs, which is still hanging to it ———

This and all the following were observed on the Coast of Sussex in June 1755 ----

scarlet Scolopendra at S. This animal has two Arms each furnish'd with many claws or feeders which are curiously fringed on the upper side, near the insertion of the left Arm arises an erect trumpetlike figure neatly indented about the brim, opposite to this on the right side is a small erect tubular figure swelling a little and pointed at the top; The part which is in the Shell is like a leach ex-tended;

has a great affinity to some of the Tubular corallines see pl. 34 and 36. ———

Fig. 3. Corallina filiformis ramosa pedunculis calyculorum contortis, see pl. 12 fig. C. Sea thread Coralline. B. the same magnified to shew the young Polypes coming out of the vesicles but still adhering to the Umbilical chord. C some of the Eggs still in the vesicle. R.R. the little cups with the Polypes extending

use with the Denticles as in Fig. 1. ———

Fig. 4. Corallina setacea a small species of Sea Bristle see Pl. 11. fig. a. ------ D. an intire specimen alive magnified to shew the vesicles full of Eggs at T. ———

Fig. 5. Two small fleshy Polypes of a red colour & a particular kind. E. E. the same magnified. F. one magnified higher to shew ye claws issuing out of their sheaths like a Sun

Fig. 6. Corallina capillamentis falcatis. Sickle Coralline see Pl. 7. fig. a. — V a Sprig magnified to shew the Polypes extending themselves out of their Denticles ----------------

Fig. 7. Corallina cum appendiculis lateralibus avium capitum forma. Birds head Coralline Pl. 20. fig. A. — G. a piece of it magnified with many rows of cells united together with the appearance of some of the animals alive in

contracted in the Cells. I.K.L. three views of the Birds heads. These continued to move up & down and open their beaks during the time of Observation.

Fig. 8. Eschara papyracea utrinque cellifera; summitatibus spatis acici instar truncatis. Paper Moss. This is the natural size of this new species adhering to a cockleshell. O. a piece of it magnified to shew the animals in the cells. P. the transverse section of the lower part contrived

Fig. 4: "Sea Bristle" *Plumularia setacea* (Pall.) Natural size. A colonial hydroid. The "vesicles full of eggs" at T are gonothecae containing immature stages or medusae. *Fig. 5:* "Sickle Coralline" *Plumularia falcata* (L.) Natural size. *Fig. 6:* The same, magnified. V, a polyp. E, E, F, gonothecae, "ye claws issuing out of their sheaths like a star flower." *Fig. 7:* "Birds Head Coralline" Natural size. One of the polyzoa. *Bugula avicularia* (Pall.) G, H, the same, magnified. I, K, L, "Three views of the birds heads. These continued to move up and down and open their beaks during the time of observation." *Fig. 8:* "Paper Moss" *Flustra papyracea* (Ellis and Solander) Natural size. One of the polyzoa. O, P, the same, magnified. "Animals in their cells." From Ellis, *Essay on Corallines* (1755), Pl. XXXVIII, opp. p. 102. (From the collections of the Yale University Library.)

Involved in sea-wrack, here you find a race,
Which science, doubting, knows not where to place;
On shell or stone is dropp'd the embryo-seed,
And quickly vegetates a vital breed.

—George Crabbe, "The Borough" (1810), 91–94.

Cf. a description of coral by James Montgomery, *The Pelican Island and Other Poems* (2d ed., London: Longmans, Green and Co., 1828), p. 18:

And nameless tribes, half-plant, half-animal,
Rooted and slumbering through a dream of life.

Explanation of the Motions:

A. The collapse of a "whole leaf" and its four "partial petioli."

D4. The order in which the "pinnulae" collapse on a "partial petiolus."

Cl. The terminal pinnulae are collapsed as the result of a stimulus. The other pinnulae then collapse pair by pair up the partial petiole to point 2. Then the pinnulae of the next two partial petioli begin to collapse from point 2 out to the terminus of each subpetiole. Finally, the whole leaf falls from the "joint of the common petiolus" at point 4. After pronounced stimulus the entire leaf responds before its parts.

Lindsay's Experiments:

3–4. Cuts in the stem, if sufficiently deep to cut the longitudinal fibers, cause the collapse of leaves A or B, sometimes both. The incision does not affect a leaf below unless closer than one-half inch. A cut at point 4 would not affect C, although it might affect leaves as much as 3 inches above.

D. Incisions in common petiole D, whether "o" at the pulvinus or "i" on the common petiole itself, cause the pinnulae to collapse on the side of the cut. A shallow incision at "o" or "i" affects only points 2 or 3; when deepened, the pinnulae of 4 close; and if very deep, then all partial petioli close.

1. A single ligature limits the excitation, thus apparently something material flows to transmit the stimulus.

2. A double ligature has a greater effect. A cut at point 4, below the double ligature, does not affect A or B. A ligature on D interrupts the transmission of stimuli even when the rest of the leaf is removed.

E. A deep incision at "o" causes the whole leaf to rise, whereas it would usually fall if stimulated.

F. A deep incision at "o", on the lower side of the pulvinus, causes the leaf to fall. It remains in this position even when the pinnulae reopen.

G. "View of a longitudinal section of the joint of the common petiolus [pulvinus], such as may be obtained with the assistance of a small magnifier" (p. 21, 1788 MS).
"ss" are "longitudinal fibres" uniting into "one bundle or cord" at point 2, and separating again at the stem. The rest is "cellular substance."

Plate 6. *The sensitive plant.*

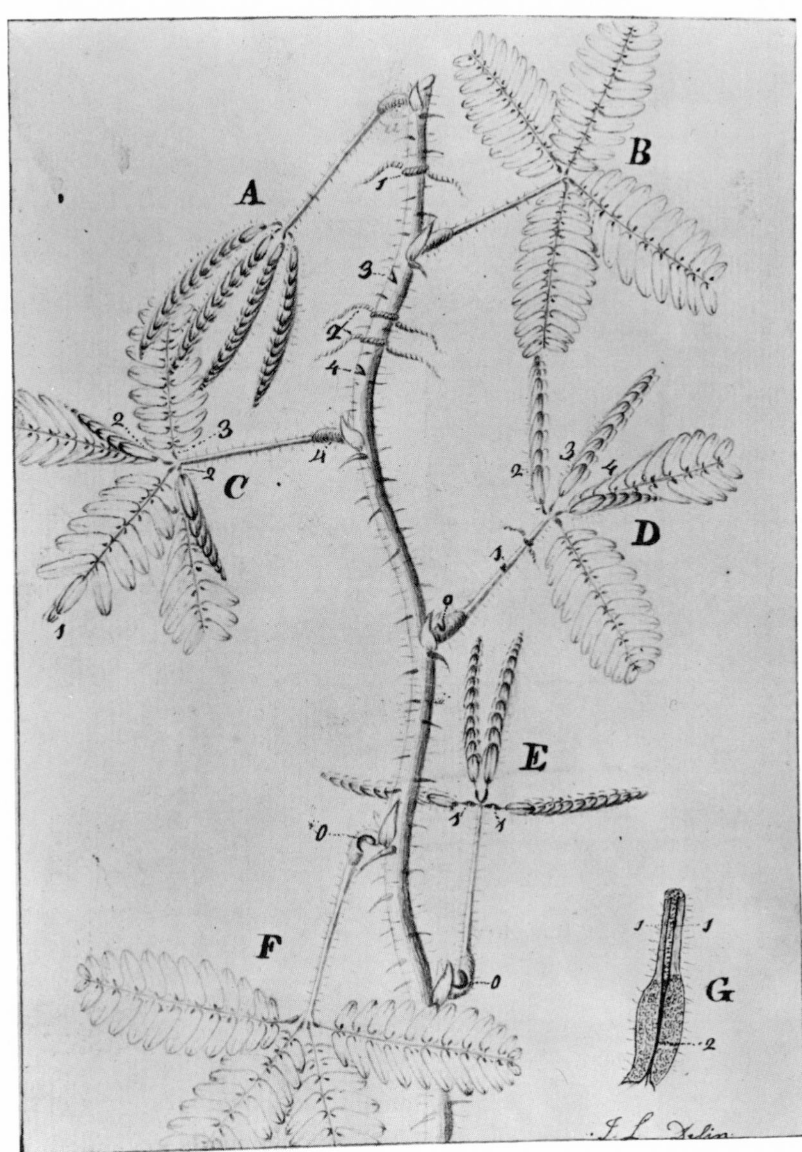

From Lindsay MSS, 1788. (Reproduced with Permission of the Council from the Collections of the Royal Society.)

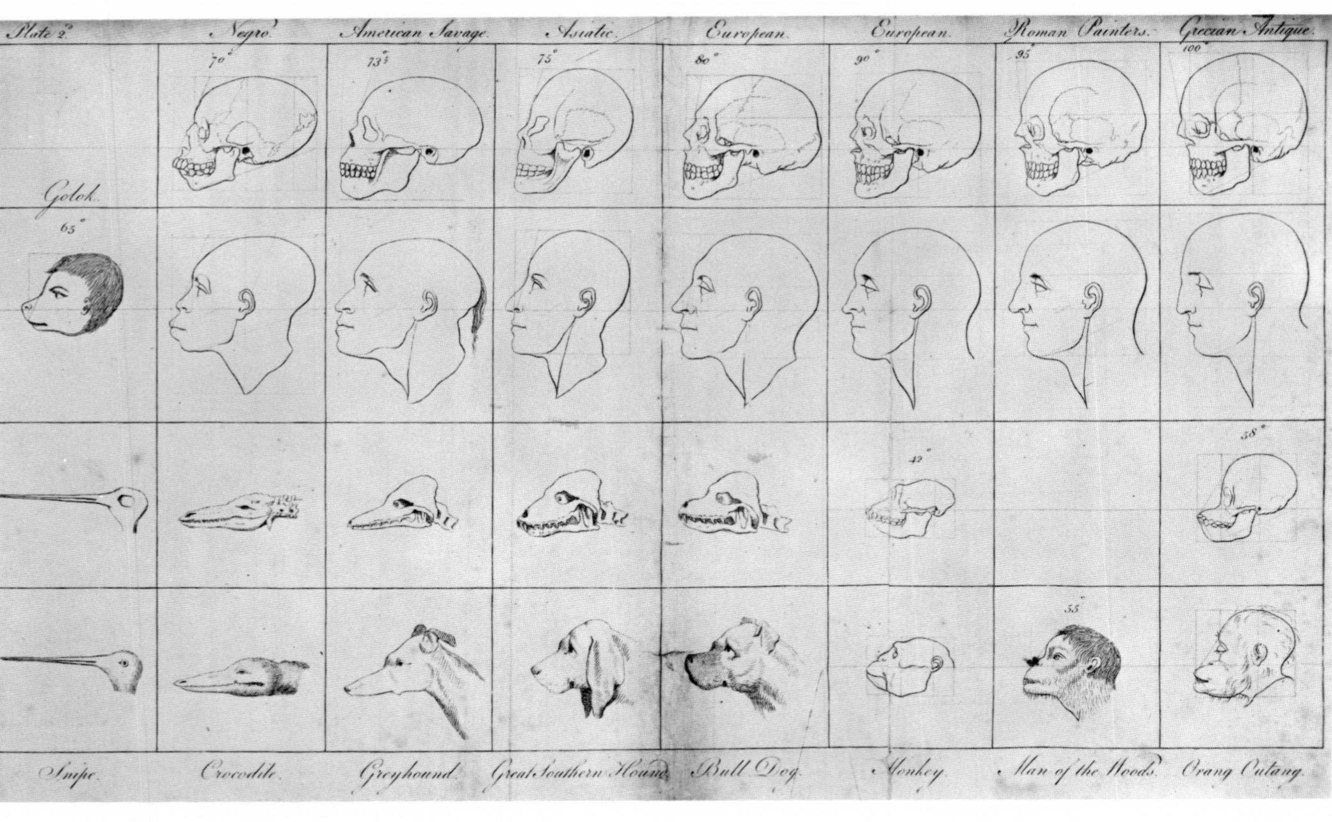
Plate 2.
Negro.
American Savage.
Asiatic.
European.
European.
Roman Painters.
Grecian Antique.
70°
73½
75°
80°
90°
95
100°
Golok.
65°
42°
58°
55
Snipe.
Crocodile.
Greyhound.
Great Southern Hound.
Bull Dog.
Monkey.
Man of the Woods.
Orang Outang.

Plate 7. Gradation in man, and in different animals.

From Charles White, *An Account of Gradation* (1799), Pl. II. In preparing his plate White was influenced by Peter Camper, *Dissertation physique . . . sur les différences réelles que présentent les traits du visage chez les hommes de différents pays et de différents ages* . . . (Utrecht: B. Wild and J. Altheer, 1791), Pl. I, II and pp. 34–44. (From the collections of the Library of Congress.)

Bibliography

Anonymous. "Two letters from a gentleman in the country, relating to Mr Leuwenhoeck's letter in Transaction, No. 283. Communicated by Mr. C.," *Phil. Trans.*, no. 288 (1703), 1494–1501 and Fig. i–iv of plate opp. title page.

——— "Part of a letter from —— of Cambridge, to a friend of the Royal Society, occasioned by what has lately been reported concerning the insect mentioned in page 218 of this transaction," ibid., no. 466 (1742), 227–34.

——— A philosophical enquiry into the properties of electricity. In which is contain'd a confutation of the solutions which have hitherto been given of it, and the most probable reason of the late surprizing experiments. In a letter to a friend. London: M. Cooper, 1746.

——— "A particular account of the death of Mr Professor Richmann, of the Imperial Academy of Sciences at Petersburgh, who was killed whilst he was making an electrical experiment," *Gentleman's Mag.*, 25 (July 1755), 312–13.

——— A letter to Benjamin Franklin, LL.D. Fellow of the Royal Society. In which his pretensions to the title of natural philosopher are considered. London: J. Bew, and Fletcher, Parker, and Prince of Oxford, 1777.

——— Entwurf einer nach der mutmasslichen Stufen-Folge eingerichteten allgemeinen Naturgeschichte 1780. Printed by Thienemann, in "Die Stufenfolge der Dinge" (1910), pp. 190–230.

——— A letter to the Reverend Thomas Rennell, concerning his remarks on scepticism; from a graduate in medicine of the University of Oxford. London: Thomas and George Underwood [1819].

Abernethy, John. An enquiry into the probability and rationality of Mr. Hunter's theory of life; being the subject of the first two anatomical lectures delivered before the Royal College of Surgeons, of London. London: Longman, Hurst, Rees, Orme, and Brown, 1814.

Abernethy, John. Physiological lectures, exhibiting a general view of Mr. Hunter's physiology, and of his researches in comparative anatomy. Delivered before the Royal College of Surgeons in the year 1817. London: Longman, Hurst, Rees, Orme, and Brown, 1817.

——— The Hunterian Oration for the year 1819. Delivered before the Royal College of Surgeons, in London; by John Abernethy, F.R.S. &c. London: Longman, Hurst, Rees, Orme, and Brown, 1819.

Adams, George. Micrographia Illustrata, or, the knowledge of the microscope explain'd: together with an account of a new invented universal, single or double, microscope. . . . The whole being, as it were, a natural history of a multitude of aerial, terrestrial, and aquatick animals, seeds, plants, &c. To which is added . . . a very particular account of that surprising phænomenon, the fresh water polype, translated from the French treatise of Mr. Trembley. . . . London: for the author, 1746.

Adams, George [the younger]. An essay on electricity, explaining the theory and practice of that useful science; and the mode of applying it to medical purposes. With an essay on magnetism. 2d ed., London: for the author, 1785.

——— Essays on the microscope; containing a practical description of the most improved microscopes: a general history of insects, their transformations, peculiar habits, and oeconomy: an account of the various species and singular properties of the Hydrae and Vorticellae; a description of three hundred and seventy-nine animalcula, with a concise catalogue of interesting objects: a view of the organization of timber, and the configuration of salts when under the microscope. London: for the author, 1787.

Adams, George. The Living Plant and the Science of Physical and Ethereal Spaces / a study of the "Metamorphosis of Plants" in the light of modern geometry and morphology. Clent, Stourbridge, Worcestershire: Goethean Science Foundation, 1949.

Adanson, Michel. "Voyage au Sénégal." Histoire naturelle du Sénégal. Coquillages. Paris: Claude-Jean-Baptiste Bauche, 1757.

Agassiz, Louis. Bibliographia zoologiae et geologiae. A general catalogue of books, tracts, and memoirs on zoology and geology. Corrected, enlarged, and edited by H. E. Strickland. 4 vols., London: Ray Society, 1848–54.

Aikin, John. An essay on the application of natural history to poetry. Warrington: by W. Eyres for J. Johnson of London, 1777.

——— "An essay on the plan and character of Thomson's Seasons," in The Seasons, by James Thomson . . . (London: J. Murray, 1778), pp. iii–xlv.

Akenside, Mark. The Pleasures of Imagination. A poem in three books. London: R. Dodsley, 1744.

Bibliography

Aldini, Giovanni. General Views on the Application of Galvanism to Medical Purposes; principally in cases of suspended animation. London: J. Callow, and Burgess and Hill; A. Constable and Co. of Edinburgh; and Smith and Son of Glasgow, 1819.

Allamand, J. N. S. "Kort verhaal van de uitwerkzelen, welke een Americaanse vis veroorzaakt op de geenen, die hem aanraaken; door J. N. S. Allamand," Verhandelingen uitgegeeven door de Hollandse Maatschappy der Weetenschappen, te Haarlem, 2 (publ. 1758), 372–79.

Almquist, E. "Linné und das natürliche Pflanzensystem," *Beiblatt zu den Botanischen Jahrbüchern,* no. 128, *58* (1922), 1–16.

Alston, Charles. "A dissertation on the sexes of plants . . . ," Essays an[d] observations, physical and literary. Read before the Philosophical Society in Edinburgh, and published by them, *1* [1754], 2d ed. (1771), 228–318.

Amici, Giovanni Battista. "Note sur le mode d'action du pollen sur le stigmate; extrait d'une lettre de M. Amici à M. Mirbel," *Annales Sci. Naturelles,* par MM. Audoin, ad Brongniart et Dumas . . . , *21* (Paris: Crochard, 1830), 329–32.

Arber, Agnes. "The interpretation of the flower: a study of some aspects of morphological thought," *Biol. Rev. Cambridge Phil. Soc., 12* (1937), 157–84.

——— "Goethe's Botany: *The metamorphosis of plants* (1790) and Tobler's *Ode to Nature* (1782) with an introduction and translations," *Chronica Botanica, 10* (1946), 63–126.

——— "Analogy in the history of science," M. F. Ashley Montagu, ed., Studies and Essays in the History of Science and Learning Offered in Homage to George Sarton . . . (New York: Henry Schuman, 1948), pp. 221–33.

——— The Natural Philosophy of Plant Form. Cambridge Univ. Press, 1950.

Aromatariis, Joseph de. "An epistle writ by Josephus de Aromatariis, concerning the seeds of plants, and generation of animals" [1625], *Phil. Trans.* no. 211 (1694), 150–52.

Ayscough, Samuel. A general index to the Monthly Review, from its commencement, to the end of the seventieth volume . . . 2 vols., London: for Ralph Griffiths, and sold by T. Becket and T. Longman, 1786.

——— A continuation of the general index to the Monthly Review; commencing at the seventy-first, and ending with the eighty-first, volume: completing the first series of that work . . . London: for Ralph Griffiths, and sold by T. Becket and T. Longman, 1796.

d'Azyr, Felix Vicq. "Table pour servir à l'Histoire anatomique & naturelle des Corps vivans ou organiques, publiée le 12 Novembre 1774, à la Séance publique de l'Académie Royale des Sciences," [Rozier's] *Observ. sur la Physique . . . , 4* (1774), opp. p. 479.

Bacon, Francis. Sylva Sylvarum: or a naturall historie. In ten centuries. London: J. H. for William Lee, 1626.

Baker, Henry. "The discovery of a perfect plant in semine," *Phil. Trans.,* no. 457 (1740), 448–55 and Pl. II, Fig. 2–4.

——— An attempt towards a natural history of the polype: in a letter to Martin Folkes, Esq; president of the Royal Society. Describing their different species; the places where to seek and how to find them; their wonderful production and increase; the form, structure and use of their several parts; and the manner they catch their prey: with an account of their diseases and cures; of their amazing reproduction after being cut in pieces . . . intermixt throughout with variety of observations and experiments. London: R. Dodsley, 1743.

——— The Microscope Made Easy . . . The second edition: with . . . some farther accounts of the polype. London: R. Dodsley, 1743.

——— "Some observations on a polype dried," *Phil. Trans.,* no. 471 (1743), 616–19 and Fig. 5 of Pl. III, opp. title page.

——— "A letter from Henry Baker, F.R.S. to the president, concerning several medical experiments of electricity," ibid., no. 486 (1748), 270–75.

——— Employment for the Microscope . . . Also occasional considerations on gems, poisons, the vegetation of metals, the resuscitation of plants, the formation of amber, corals, and many other subjects. II, An account of various animalcules never before described. . . . London: R. Dodsley, 1753.

Baker, James Volant. The Sacred River / Coleridge's theory of the imagination. Louisiana State Univ. Press, 1957.

Baker, John R. Abraham Trembley of Geneva / scientist and philosopher 1710–1784. London: Edward Arnold, 1952.

Bancroft, Edward. An essay on the natural history of Guiana, in South America. Containing a description of many curious productions in the animal and vegetable systems of that country. Together with an account of the religion, manners, and customs of several tribes of its Indian inhabitants. . . . London: T. Becket and P. A. deMondt, 1769.

Banks, Sir Joseph. The Banks Letters / a catalogue of the manuscript correspondence of Sir Joseph Banks preserved in the British Museum, the British Museum (Natural History) and other collections in Great Britain, ed. Warren R. Dawson. London: Trustees of the British Museum, 1958.

Barclay, John. An Inquiry into the Opinions, Ancient and Modern, Concerning Life and Organization. Edinburgh: Bell & Bradfute, and Waugh and Innes; and G. and W. B. Whittaker of London, 1822.

Barfield, Owen. Saving the Appearances; a study in idolatry. London: Faber and Faber, 1957.

Barrell, Joseph. Shelley and the Thought of his Time / a study in the history of ideas. Yale Studies in English, 106, Yale Univ. Press, 1947.

Barton, Richard. The Analogy of Divine Wisdom, in the material, sensitive, moral, civil, and spiritual system of things, in eight parts. Dublin: for the author, 1750.

Baster, Job. "Observationes de corallinis, iisque insidentibus polypis, aliisque animalculis marinis: quas Regiae Societati Londinensi offert Job Baster, Med. Doct. Acad. Caesar. Reg. Societ. Lond. & Scient. Holland. Socius," *Phil. Trans., 50* (1757), 258–80.

——— "Dissertationem hanc de zoophytis, Regiae Societati Scientiarum Angliae legendam et judicandam praebet Job Baster, Med. Doctor. Acad. Caes. Reg. Soc. Angl. et Holland. Socius," ibid., *52* (1761), 108–18 and Pl. IV, opp. p. 117.

Bate, Walter Jackson. From Classic to Romantic / premises of taste in eighteenth-century England. Harvard Univ. Press, 1946.

Bazin, Gilles Augustin. Observations sur les plantes et leur analogie avec les insectes, precedées de deux discours . . . Strasbourg: Jean Renaud Doulssecker, 1741.

Beach, Joseph Warren. The Concept of Nature in Nineteenth-Century English Poetry. New York: Macmillan, 1936.

Beale, John. "Instances promised in numb. 42. and intended to shew the correspondence of the pith and timber, with the seed of the plant; and that of the bark or sap in the bark, with the pulp of the fruit, or some encompassing coat, or cod, containing the seed," *Phil. Trans.,* no. 46 (1669), 919–22.

——— "Some considerations upon Mr. Reed's letter; printed in N. 70. shewing, in what sense the sap may be said to descend, and to circulate in plants; . . . all by Dr. John Beal, in a letter to the publisher of May 13, 1671," ibid., no. 71 (1671), 2144–49.

Beardsley, E. Edwards. Life and Correspondence of Samuel Johnson, D.D. Missionary of the Church of England in Connecticut, and first president of King's College, New York. New York: Hurd and Houghton, and London: Rivington, 1874.

Beatty, Arthur. William Wordsworth / his doctrine and art in their historical relations. University of Wisconsin Studies in Language and Literature, no. 24, 2d ed., Madison, Wis.: 1927.

Beaumont, John. "Two letters written by Mr. John Beaumont Junior of Stony-Euston in Somerset-shire, concerning rock-plants and their growth," *Phil. Trans.,* no. 129 (1676), 724–42.

Beccaria, Giambattista. A treatise upon artificial electricity, in which are given solutions of a number of interesting electric phoenomena, hitherto unexplained. To which is added, an essay on the mild and slow electricity which prevails in the atmosphere during serene weather. London: J. Nourse, 1776.

Becket, John Brice. An essay on electricity, containing a series of experiments introductory to the study of that science, in which are included some of the latest discoveries; intended chiefly with a view of facilitating its application, and extending its utility in medical purposes. Bristol: for the author; T. Becket and G. Robinson of London; D. Prince of Oxford; and W. Frederick of Bath; and E. Score and B. Thorn of Exeter, 1773.

deBeer, [Sir] Gavin R. "The correspondence between Linnaeus and Johann Gesner," *Proc. Linnaean Soc., London,* Session 161 (1948–49), part 2 (30 Dec. 1949), pp. 225–41.

deBeer, Sir Gavin R. "Jean-Jacques Rousseau: botanist," *Annals of Sci. 10* (1954), 189–223.

Bell, Charles G. "Mechanistic replacement of purpose in biology," *Philos. of Sci., 15* (1948), 47–51.

Bell, George. "A translation of Dr. Bell's thesis, de physiologia plantarum. By James Currie, M.D. Read March 30, 1785," [1777]. *Mem. Lit. and Philos. Soc., Manchester, 2* (1785), 394–419.

Bell, P. R. "The movement of plants in response to light," in P. R. Bell, ed., Darwin's Biological Work / some aspects reconsidered (Cambridge Univ. Press, 1959), pp. 1–49.

Benjamin, Park. The Intellectual Rise in Electricity, a history. London: Longmans, Green, 1895.

Bennet, Richard Henry Alexander. New Experiments on Electricity, wherein the causes of thunder and lightning as well as the constant state of positive or negative electricity in the air or clouds, are explained; with experiments on clouds of powders and vapours artificially diffused in the air. Also a description of a doubler of electricity, and of the most sensible electrometer yet constructed. With other new experiments and discoveries in the science, illustrated by explanatory plates. Derby: John Drewry, 1789.

Bentinck, William. See Trembley (1743).

Berdoe, Marmaduke. An enquiry into the influence of the electric-fluid, in the structure and formation of animated beings. Bath: for the author, 1771.

[*Berington, Joseph*] Letters on materialism and Hartley's theory of the human mind, addressed to Dr. Priestley, F.R.S. London: G. Robinson, 1776.

[*Berkeley, George*] Alciphron: or, the minute philosopher. In seven dialogues. Containing an apology for the Christian religion, against those who are called free-thinkers. 2 vols., London: J. Tonson, 1732.

——— Siris: a chain of philosophical reflexions and inquiries concerning the virtues of tar water, and divers other subjects connected together and arising from one another. By G. L. B. O. C. Dublin: R. Gunne, 1744.

Bernbaum, Ernest. "Is Wordsworth's nature poetry antiquated?" *ELH, 7* (1940), 333–40.

——— Guide Through the Romantic Movement. 2d ed., New York: Ronald Press, 1949.

Bertholon, Abbé Pierre. De l'électricité du corps humain dans l'état de santé et de maladie. Ouvrage couronné par l'Académie de Lyon, dans lequel on traite de l'électricité de l'atmosphere, de son influence & de ses effets sur l'économie animale. &c. &c. Lyon: Burnuset, 1780.

——— De l'électricité de végétaux. Ouvrage dans lequel on traite de l'électricité de l'atmosphere sur les plantes, de ses effets sur l'économie des végétaux, de leurs vertus médico & nutrivo-électriques, & principalement des moyens de pratique de l'appliquer utilement à l'agriculture, avec l'invention d'un électro-végétometre. Paris: P. F. Didot jeune, 1783.

——— "Nouvelles expériences sur les effets de l'electricité artificielle & naturelle, appliquée aux végétaux," [Rozier's] *Observ. sur la Physique . . . , 35* (1789), 401–23.

Bichat, Marie François Xavier. Physiological Researches on Life and Death. Trans. F. Gold. London: Longman, Hurst, Rees, Orme, and Brown [1815].

Bicheno, J. E. "On systems and methods in natural history," *Trans. Linnaean Soc., London, 15* (1827), 479–96.

Birch, John. Considerations on the Efficacy of Electricity in Removing Female Obstructions. To which is now added a description of the manner of applying it. 2d ed., London: T. Cadell, 1780.

——— "A letter to Mr. George Adams, on the subject of medical electricity; from Mr. John Birch, Surgeon," [1792] George Adams [the younger], An essay on electricity . . . , [4th or] 5th ed. (London: by J. Dillon and Co. for W. and S. Jones, 1799), pp. 507–58.

Blackstone, Bernard. The Consecrated Urn: an interpretation of Keats in terms of growth and form. London: Longmans, Green, 1959.

Blair, Patrick. Botanick Essays. In two parts. The first containing, the structure of flowers, and the fructification of plants, with their various distributions into method: and the second, the generation of plants, with their sexes and manner of impregnating the seed: also concerning the animalcule in semine masculino. Together with the nourishment of plants, and circulation of the sap in all seasons, analogous to that of the blood in animals. With many curious remarks, and several discoveries and improvements. Adorn'd with figures. London: William and John Innys, 1720.

——— "Observations upon the generation of plants, in a letter to Sir Hans Sloane, Bart. Pr. Coll. Med. By Patrick Blair, M.D.F.R.S.," *Phil. Trans.,* no. 369 (1721), 216–21.

——— Rawlinson MS, Commercium Epistolicum: Botanicum or a Collection of letters and other curious observations in Botany and other parts of Natural History past betwixt Dr Patrick Blair fellow the Royal Society and others his ingenious Correspondents.

MS bound with Bradley's *Philosophical account . . .* (1721) of 92 leaves 281 mm × 230 mm [150 written pages] + 7 leaves [12 written sides] + 76 blank leaves.

Copies of letters by John Martyn 1724–25, Sir Hans Sloane 1724, Philip Miller 1724–25, R. Mead 1720, James Douglas 1724, Alexander Airth 1724, and Patrick Blair 1724–25. Also a letter of 16 June 1754 from John Martyn to Bishop Richard Rawlinson, 151 mm × 324 mm. One sheet folded.

In references to this MS I have counted the title page as [1] and numbered both sides, blank and script pages, to [162].

Bodleian Library, "4 to Rawl. 323" or Western MS. 16,068.

Blair, Patrick. "The Preface" [to an unwritten pamphlet] July 1724. Rawlinson MS, [pp. 79–106].

Blake, William. The writings of William Blake. Ed. Geoffrey Keynes. 3 vols., London: Nonesuch Press, 1925.

Boas, Marie. "The establishment of the mechanical philosophy," *Osiris, 10* (1952), 412–541.

——— and *Hall, Rupert,* "Newton's 'mechanical principles,'" *J. Hist. Ideas, 20* (1959), 167–78.

Boerhaave, Hermann. A New Method of Chemistry; including the history, theory, and practice of the art: translated from the original Latin of Dr. Boerhaave's Elementa Chymiae, as published by himself. To which are added, notes; and an appendix, shewing the necessity and utility of enlarging the bounds of chemistry. With sculptures. By Peter Shaw, M.D. 2d ed., 2 vols., London: T. Longman, 1741.

"Boerhaave, Hermann." An essay on the virtue and efficient cause of magnetical cures. To which is added a new method for curing wounds without pains, and without the application of remedies. Hitherto kept a secret in private families. Written originally in Latin, by the famous Dr. Herman Boerhaave, Professor at the University of Leyden in Holland, but never published till now. London: 1748.

Boerman, A. J. "Carolus Linnaeus / a psychological study," *Taxon* (Utrecht), 2 (1953), 145–56.

Bonnet, Charles. Contemplation de la nature. 2 vols., Amsterdam: Marc-Michel Rey, 1764.

——— "Idées sur la fécondation des plantes," [Rozier's] *Observ. sur la Physique . . . , 4* (1774), 261–83.

Boscovich, Rogerio Josephus. A Theory of Natural Philosophy, ed. and trans. J. M. Child. Chicago: Open Court, 1922.

An introduction by J. M. Child and a brief life by Branislav Petronievič. Translated from the 1763 Vienna edition; Latin text facing translation on alternate pages.

Bose, George Mathias. Die Elektricität nach ihrer Entdeckung und Fortgang mit poetischer Feder entworffen von George Mathias Bose. Wittenberge: J. J. Ahlfelben, 1744.

Bose, M. Caspar, and *Bose, George Matthias.* Dissertatio botanico-philosophica de motu plantarum sensus aemulo quam consensu et autoritate amplissimi philosophorum ordinis in Academia Lipsiensi add. VII. Febr. a. MDCCXXIIX. . . . Leipzig: Breitkopf [1728?].

Bose, Jagadis. Response in the Living and Non-living. London: Longmans, Green, 1902.

——— Researches on Irritability of Plants. London: Longmans, Green, 1913.

——— Life movement in plants. *Trans. Bose Inst., 3–4* (1920–21). Bombay: Longmans, Green, 1923.

——— The Nervous Mechanism of Plants. London: Longmans, Green, 1926.

Bostock, John. "Outline of the history of galvanism: with a theory of the action of the galvanic apparatus," [Nicholson's] *J. Natural Philos., Chem., Arts,* N.S., 2 (1802), 296–304.

——— An Account of the History and Present State of Galvanism. London: Baldwin, Cradock, and Joy, 1818.

Bourde, André J. The Influence of England on the French Agronomes 1750–89. Cambridge Univ. Press, 1953.

Bourguet, Louis. Lettres philosophiques sur la formation des sels et des crystaux. Et sur la génération & le mechanisme organique des plantes et des animaux; a l'occasion de la pierre belemnite et de la pierre lenticulaire. Avec une memoire sur la theorie de la terre. Amsterdam: François l'Honoré, 1729.

Bowra, C. M. The Romantic Imagination. Oxford Univ. Press, 1950.

Boyle, Robert. "Experiments and notes about the mechanical origin or production of electricity" [1675]. The works of the Honourable Robert Boyle . . . , *4* (London: W. Johnston and others, 1772), pp. 345–54.

Bradley, Richard. "Observations and experiments relating to the motion of the sap in vegetables," *Phil. Trans.,* no. 349 (1716), 486–90 and plate opp. title page.

——— New Improvements of Planting and Gardening, both philosophical and practical. Explaining the motion of the sap and generation of plants: with other discoveries never before made publick, for the improvement of forrest-trees, flower-gardens, or parterres; with a new invention whereby more designs of garden platts may be made in an hour, than can be found in all the books now extant. Likewise several rare secrets for the improvement of fruit-trees, kitchen-gardens, and green-house plants. 3 vols., London: W. Mears, 1717–18.

——— A Philosophical Account of the Works of Nature. Endeavouring to set forth the several gradations remarkable in the mineral, vegetable, and animal parts of the creation. Tending to the composition of a scale of life. To which is added, an account of the state of gardening, as it is now in Great Britain, and other parts of Europe: together with several new experiments relating to the improvement of barren ground, and the propagating of timber-trees, fruit-trees, &c. With many curious cutts. London: W. Mears, 1721.

——— New experiments and observations, relating to the generation of plants: occasion'd by a letter lately publish'd in the Philosophical Transactions, by Patrick Blair, M.D.F.R.S. . . . London: T. Corbett, 1724.

——— Ten practical discourses concerning earth and water, fire and air, as they relate to the growth of plants. With a collection of new discoveries for the improvement of land, either in the farm or garden. Westminster: by J. Cluer and A. Campbell for B. Creake, 1727.

Brady, T. "An account of some remarkable insects of the polype kind, found in the waters near Brussels in Flanders. In a letter to Thomas Birch, D.D. Secret.R.S. from T. Brady, M.D. Physician to his Highness Prince Charles of Lorraine," *Phil. Trans., 49* (1755), 248–51, and Pl. VII, opp. p. 248.

Bremekamp, C. E. B. "Linné's views on the hierarchy of taxonomic groups," *Acta Botanica Neerlandica, 2* (1953), 242–53.

Brisseau-Mirbel, C. F. Traité d'anatomie et de physiologie végétales, suivi de la nomenclature méthodique ou raisonnée des parties extérieures des plantes, et un exposé succinct des systêmes de botanique plus généralement adoptés. Ouvrage servant d'introduction a l'étude de la botanique. 2 vols., Paris: F. Dufart [1801–1802].

Brook, Abraham. Miscellaneous Experiments and Remarks on Electricity, the Air Pump, and the Barometer: with the description of an electrometer of a new construction. Norwich: by Crouse and Stevenson for J. Johnson of London, 1789.

Broussonet, Pierre Marie Auguste. "Mémoire sur le trembleur, espèce peu connue de poisson électrique," *Mém. Acad. Roy. des Sci.* (for 1782), pp. 692–98.

——— "Essai de comparaison entre les mouvemens des animaux et ceux des plantes. Et description d'une espèce de Sainfoin [Hedysarum], dont les feuilles sont dans un mouvement continuel," ibid. (for 1784), pp. 609–21.

Brown, Harcourt. "Buffon and the Royal Society of London" [1944], in M. F. Ashley Montagu, ed., in Studies and Essays in the History of Science and Learning Offered in Homage to George Sarton . . . (New York: Henry Schuman, 1948), pp. 141–65.

Brown, Thomas. Observations on the Zoonomia of Erasmus Darwin, M.D. Edinburgh: Mundell & Son; J. Mundell of Glasgow; and J. Johnson, and J. Wright of London, 1798.

Browne, Peter. A letter in answer to a book entituled Christianity not mysterious. As also to all those who set up for reason and evidence in opposition to revelation and mysteries. London: Robert Clavell, 1697.

[*Browne, Peter*] The Procedure, Extent, and Limits of Human Understanding. London: William Innys, 1728.

——— Things Divine and Supernatural Conceived by Analogy with Things Natural and Human. London: William Innys and Richard Manby, 1733.

Browning, John. "Part of a letter from Mr. John Browning, of Bristol, to Mr. Henry Baker, F.R.S. dated Dec. 11. 1746. concerning the effect of electricity on vegetables," *Phil. Trans.*, no. 482 (1747), 373–75.

Bruce, Robert. "An account of the sensitive quality of the tree Averrhoa carambola. In a letter from Robert Bruce, M.D. to Sir Joseph Banks, Bart. P.R.S.," ibid., *75* (1785), 356–60.

Bryant, William. "Account of an electrical eel, or the torpedo of Surinam, by William Bryant, Esquire," *Trans. Am. Phil. Soc.,* 2 (1786), 166–69.

Buchanan, James. Analogy, considered as a guide to truth, and applied as an aid to faith. Edinburgh: Johnstone, Hunter, 1864.

Bush, Douglas. Science and English Poetry / a historical sketch, 1590–1950. The Patten Lectures, Indiana Univ., 1949. New York: Oxford Univ. Press, 1950.

Butler, Joseph. The Analogy of Religion, natural and revealed, to the constitution and course of nature. To which are added two brief dissertations: I. Of personal identity. II. Of the nature of virtue. London: James, John, and Paul Knapton, 1736.

Butler, Samuel. Evolution, Old and New; or, the theories of Buffon, Dr. Erasmus Darwin, and Lamarck, as compared with that of Mr. Charles Darwin. London: Hardwicke and Bogue, 1879.

Bywater, John. New Theory of the Leyden Phial. Founded on experiments, and not dependent on the mysterious powers of electrical attraction & repulsion. "2d ed.," Nottingham: J. Dunn for E. B. Robinson, B. Crosby and Co., and T. Hurst of London, 1803.

——— An essay on the history, practice, and theory of electricity. London: for the author, 1810.

C., J. A general index to the Monthly Review, from the commencement of the new series, in Jan. 1790 to the end of the eighty-first volume, completed in Dec. 1816. 2 vols., London: John Porter, and Longman, Hurst, Rees, Orme, and Brown, 1818.

Cain, Arthur J. "Logic and memory in Linnaeus's system of taxonomy," *Proc. Linnaean Soc., London,* Session 169, parts 1 and 2 (April 1958), pp. 144–63.

——— "Taxonomic concepts," *Ibis, 101* (1959), 302–18.

——— "Function and taxonomic importance," *Systematics Assoc., Publ.* 3 (Nov. 1959), pp. 5–19.

Cajori, Florian. See Newton (1934).

Camerarius, Rudolph Jacob. Academiae Caesario Leopold. N. C. Hectoria II. Rudolphi Jacobi Camerarii, Professoris Tubingensis, ad Thessalum, D. Mich. Bernardum Valentini, Professorum Giessensem excellentissimum, de sexu plantarum epistola. Tübingen: Typis Viduae Rommeii, 1694.

——— *See* Mikan (1797).

Cameron, Kenneth Neill. The Young Shelley; genesis of a radical. London: Victor Gallancz, 1951.

Camper, Pieter. Oratio de analogia inter animalia et stirpes. Habita d. IX Maji a. MDCCLXIV cum medicinae theoriae anatomes chirurgiae et botanices professionem in Academia Groningae et Omlandiae solemni ritu auspicaretur. Groningen: Haionem Spandaw, 1764.

Candolle, Augustin Pyrame de. Physiologie végétale, ou exposition des forces et des fonctions vitales des végétaux, pour servir de suite a l'organographie végétale, et d'introduction a la botanique géographique et agricole. 3 vols., Paris: Béchet jeune, 1832.

——— *See* Sprengel, K. (1821).

Canton, John and William. The Canton Papers, collected by John Canton, M.A.F.R.S., and his son, William Canton, and given by their descendant Edwin Canton, to the Royal Society. London: 1870. Royal Society General MSS 598, vol. 2, Correspondence.

Carpue, John Constantine. An Introduction to Electricity and Galvanism; with cases, shewing their effects in the cure of diseases: to which is added, a description of Mr. Cuthbertson's plate electrical machine. London: A. Phillips, Longman and Rees, Cadell and Davies, 1803.

Cavallo, Tiberius. A Complete Treatise of Electricity in Theory and Practice; with original experiments. London: Edward and Charles Dilly, 1777.

——— An essay on the theory and practice of medical electricity. London: for the author, 1780.

——— "Of the electric properties of the torpedo, Gymnotus electricus, and Silurus electricus," in A Complete Treatise of Electricity . . . , 3d ed., 2 (London: C. Dilly, 1786), 287–313.

——— "Of the action of electricity on the vegetable kingdom," in ibid., 4th ed., *3* (London: C. Dilly, 1795), 240–50.

——— "An account of the discoveries concerning muscular motion which have been lately made, and are commonly known under the name of animal electricity," in ibid., *3*, 1–75 and Fig. 1, 2 of Pl. I.

——— Cavallo MSS. Vol. 1, 64 letters dated 1782–91, BM. Add. MSS 22,897; Vol. 2, 51 letters dated 1792–1809, BM Add. MSS 22,898.

Cavendish, Henry. "An account of some attempts to imitate the effects of the torpedo by electricity," *Phil. Trans., 66* (1776), 196–225.

Cesalpino, Andrea. De Plantis libri xvi. Andreae Cesalpini aretini, medici clarissimi, doctissimiq; atque philosophi celeberrimi, ac. subtilissimi. Florence: Giorgio Marescotti, 1583.

Chambers, Ephraim. "Circulation of the sap," Cyclopaedia: or, an universal dictionary of arts and sciences . . . , *1* (London: James and John Knapton etc., 1728), 225.

——— "Sensitive plant," in Cyclopaedia, *4* (8th ed. 1783), no. 323.

[*Chambers, Robert*] Vestiges of the Natural History of Creation. London: John Churchill, 1844.

Clark-Kennedy, A. E. Stephen Hales, D.D., F.R.S., an eighteenth century biography. Cambridge Univ. Press, 1929.

Cohen, I. Bernard. *See* Franklin (1941).

——— "Prejudice against the introduction of lightning rods," *J. Franklin Inst., 253* (1952), 393–440.

——— Franklin and Newton / an inquiry into speculative Newtonian experimental science and Franklin's work in electricity as an example thereof. "Memoirs of the American Philosophical Society . . . ," *43* (Philadelphia: American Philosophical Soc., 1956).

——— *See* Newton (1958).

Colden, Cadwallader. An Explication of the First Causes of Action in Matter and of the Cause of Gravitation. New York: James Parker, 1745.

——— The Principles of Action in Matter, the gravitation of bodies, and the motion of planets, explained from those principles. London: R. Dodsley 1751.

——— ["A paper intended to be transmitted to the readers of the Monthly Review"], *Monthly Review, 21* (Nov. 1759), 397–403.

——— The Cadwallader Colden Letter Books. Ed. New-York Historical Society, The Publication Fund Series, nos. IX–X. 2 vols., New York: for the Society, 1877–78.

——— The Cadwallader Colden Papers. Ed. New-York Historical Society. 7 vols., New York: published as *Collections of the New-York Historical Society,* 1918–23. [Appendix II of Vol. 7, pp. 358–76, "Calendar of unprinted scientific and political papers of Cadwallader Colden."]

Cole, Francis J. Early Theories of Sexual Generation. Oxford: Clarendon Press, 1930.

——— A History of Comparative Anatomy from Aristotle to the Eighteenth Century. London: Methuen, 1944.

Coleridge, Samuel Taylor. Biographia Literaria; or biographical sketches of my literary life and opinions. 2 vols., London: Rest Fenner, 1817.

——— The Friend: a series of essays, in three volumes, to aid in the formation of fixed principles in politics, morals, and religion, with literary amusements interspersed. 2d ed., 3 vols., London: Rest Fenner, 1818.

——— Aids to Reflection in the formation of a manly character on the several grounds of prudence, morality, and religion: illustrated by select passages from our elder divines, especially from Archbishop Leighton. London: Taylor and Hessey, 1825.

——— "On the definitions of life hitherto received. Hints toward a more comprehensive theory" [1848]. With a preface by Dr. Seth B. Watson, in Miscellanies, aesthetic and literary: to which is added the theory of life (London: George Bell and Sons, 1885), pp. 349–430.

——— Anima Poetae / from the unpublished note-books of Samuel Taylor Coleridge, ed. Ernest Hartley Coleridge. London: William Heinemann, 1895.

Coleridge, Samuel Taylor. Coleridge on Logic and Learning, with selections from the unpublished manuscripts, ed. Alice D. Snyder. New Haven: Yale Univ. Press, 1929.

Cook, John. An anatomical and mechanical essay on the whole animal oeconomy; in one view. Wherein is shewn the most wonderful conduct of nature in all the phaenomena attending human bodies, with many curious subjects not commonly treated of . . . 2 vols., London: W. Meadows, 1730.

C.[ooper], T.[homas] "On vegetable life," *Port Folio* (Philadelphia), ser. III [IV], *4* (1814), 59–74, 176–91; and *5* (1815), 428–38.

——— "On the analogy between animal and vegetable physiology," ibid., *6* (1815), 27–32.

Coxe, Daniel. "A way of extracting a volatil salt and spirit out of vegetables; intimated in numb. 100. p. 7002; experimented, and compacted by the learned and intelligent Dr. Daniel Coxe, Fellow of the R. Society," *Phil. Trans.* no. 101 (1674), 4–8.

——— "A discourse denying the pre-existence of alcalizate or fixed salt in any subject, before it were exposed to the action of the fire: to which is added a confirmation of an assertion, deliver'd in numb. 101. p. 5. §6. of these tracts, viz. that alcalizate or fixed salts extracted out of the ashes of vegetables, do not differ from each other: the same likewise affirm'd of volatil salts and vinous spirits; by the learned Dr. Daniel Coxe," ibid., no. 107 (1674), 150–58.

——— "A continuation of Dr. Daniel Coxe's discourse, begun in numb. 107. touching the identity of all volatil salts, and vinous spirits; together with two surprizing experiments concerning vegetable salts, perfectly resembling the shape of the plants, whence they had been obtained," ibid., no. 108 (1674), 169–78.

Crawford, Adair. Experiments and Observations on Animal Heat, and the Inflammation of Combustible Bodies. Being an attempt to resolve these phaenomena into a general law of nature. London: J. Murray and J. Sewell, 1779. [Also 2d ed. London: J. Johnson, 1788]

Crombie, Alistair C. "Some reflections on the history of science and its conception of nature," *Annals of Sci.*, *6* (1948), 54–75.

Crosse, Andrew. "On the production of insects by voltaic electricity. By Andrew Crosse, Esq., &c., &c. Communicated in a letter from Sir Richard Phillips to William Sturgeon, Esq., &c., &c." [Sturgeon's] *Annals of Electricity, Magnetism, and Chemistry; and Guardian of Experimental Science, 1* (1837), 242–44. *Reprinted:* [Silliman's] *Am. J. Sci. and Arts, 32* (1837), 374–77.

——— "Description of some experiments made with the voltaic battery, by Andrew Crosse, Esq. of Broomfield, near Taunton, for the purpose of producing crystals; in the process of which experiments certain insects constantly appeared. Communicated in a letter dated 27th December, 1837, addressed to the secretary of the London Electrical Society," *Trans. and Proc. London Electrical Soc., 1837–40* (1841), pp. 10–16 and Pl. I.

Reprinted: [Sturgeon's] *Annals of Electricity,* 2 (1838), 246–57 and Pl. VIII, Figs. 56–59. *Reprinted:* [Silliman's] *Am. J. Sci. and Arts, 35* (1839), 125–37.

Cullen, William. "The substance of nine lectures on vegetation and agriculture, delivered to a private audience in the year 1768, by the late William Cullen, M.D. professor of medicine in the University of Edinburgh; with a few notes by George Pearson, M.D.F.R.S." Additional appendix to the outlines of the fifteenth chapter of the proposed general report from the Board of Agriculture (London: W. Bulmer and Co., 1796), Paper 2.

Cushing, Harvey. See Fulton (1936).

Cuthbertson, John. Practical Electricity, and Galvanism, containing a series of experiments calculated for the use of those who are desirous of becoming acquainted with that branch of science. London: J. Callow, 1807.

Cuvier, Georges Léopold Chrétien Frédéric Dagobert. Leçons d'anatomie comparée. 2 vols., Paris: Baudouin [1799–1800].

Translated: Lectures on comparative anatomy. Trans. William Ross. 2 vols., London: T. N. Longman and O. Rees, 1802.

——— Rapport historique sur les progrès des sciences naturelles depuis 1789, et sur leur état actuel. . . . Paris: Imprimerie Royale, 1810.

dal Covolo, Count Giambattista. A discourse concerning the irritability of some flowers [1764]. A new discovery. Trans. from the Italian [by Benjamin Stillingfleet]. London: J. Dodsley, S. Baker and G. Leigh, and T. Payne [1767?]. [The date was written in Joseph Banks's copy, which is now at the British Museum.] *Reprinted:* W. Coxe, ed., Literary Life and Select Works of Benjamin Stillingfleet . . . , 2 (London: Longman, Hurst, Rees, Orme, and Brown, 1811), part 2, 209–26.

Darwin, Charles. The Movements and Habits of Climbing Plants. 2d ed., London: John Murray, 1875.

——— *see* Krause (1879).

——— assisted by Darwin, Francis. The Power of Movement in Plants. London: John Murray, 1880.

Darwin, Erasmus. Lecture notes 1752–53. In shorthand, presumably the Gurney system of brachygraphy. The Wellcome Historical Medical Library, MS 2485. 8vo.

pp. 1–177—lectures by [Sir] George Baker (1722–1809) on mineralogy. King's College, Cambridge.

pp. 179–187—lectures by [Sir] Noah Thomas (1720–1792) on the method of salivation.

pp. 189–227.—lectures by [Sir] Noah Thomas (1720–1792) on poisons.

14 leaves 8vo written one side—lectures by William Heberden (1710–1801), an introduction to medicine. Also lectures on the materia medica and causes of error by Charles Alston (1683–1760) of the Edinburgh Botanic Garden.

Darwin, Erasmus. "Remarks on the opinion of Henry Eeles, Esq; concerning the ascent of vapour, published in the Philosoph. Transact. Vol. xlix, part i. p. 124. By Erasmus Darwin, M.D. communicated by M. William Watson, F.R.S.," *Phil. Trans., 50* (1757), 240–54.

——— *The Hamilton and Greville Papers,* BM Add. MSS 42,071.

I. Letter of 4 pp. on one folded sheet to C. F. Greville; dated Lichfield, 12 Dec. 1778. Also a duplicate of this letter written at the same time on Darwin's polygrapher, ff. 48–52.

II. Letter of 18 pp. on four folded sheets to C. F. Greville; 7 Jan. 1779 [on the polygrapher with drawings and an explanation of its use in drawing landscapes and profiles], ff. 53–62.

III. Letter of 3 pp. on one folded sheet to C. F. Greville; 10 May 1779 [the polygrapher is now back from the instrument maker but is too bulky to send. Invites Greville to Lichfield to see "all the new experiments upon *airs,* or gas's"], ff. 63–64.

——— translator. A System of Vegetables, according to their classes / orders / genera / species / with their characters and differences. Translated from the thirteenth edition (as published by Dr. Murray) of the Systema vegetabilium of the late professor Linneus; and from the Supplementum plantarum of the present professor Linneus. By a botanical society at Lichfield. 2 vols., Lichfield: J. Jackson for Leigh and Sotheby of London, 1782–83.

——— "Dr. Darwin's address to the Philosophical Society of Derby on their first meeting. July 18 1784," MS, 12 pp. Down House, Downe, Kent. [Lady Nora Barlow owns a photostat of this address in printed form, with numerous changes in punctuation. It may be a copy of the pamphlet in the Derby Borough Library cited by Robinson (1953).]

Darwin, Erasmus, translator. The Families of Plants, with their natural characters, according to the number, figure, situation, and proportion of all the parts of fructification. Translated from the last edition, (as published by Dr. Reichard) of the Genera plantarum, and of the Mantissae plantarum of the elder Linneus; and from the Supplementum plantarum of the younger Linneus, with all the new families of plants, from Thunberg and l'Heritier . . . 2 vols., Lichfield: John Jackson for Joseph Johnson of London, T. Byrne of Dublin, and J. Balfour of Edinburgh, 1787.

——— The Botanic Garden, Part II. Containing the loves of the plants, a poem. With philosophical notes. Volume the second. Lichfield: J. Jackson for J. Johnson of London, 1789.

——— The Botanic Garden, Part I. Containing the economy of vegetation. A poem. With philosophical notes. London: J. Johnson, 1791.

——— Zoonomia; or, the laws of organic life. 2 vols., London: J. Johnson, 1794–96.

——— Phytologia; or the philosophy of agriculture and gardening. With the theory of draining morasses, and with an improved construction of the drill plough. London; J. Johnson, 1800.

——— The Temple of Nature; or, the origin of society: a poem, with philosophical notes. London: J. Johnson, 1803.

Darwin, Robert Waring. Principia Botanica: or, a concise and easy introduction to the sexual botany of Linnaeus. Containing the genera; their mode of growth (as tree, shrub, or herb); the known number of species to each genus; where principally native; and the number indigenous to the British Isles; arranged in a tabular form, under each class and order; and digested alphabetically under several generic distinctions. Together with three indices . . . 3d ed., Newark: M. Hage, 1810.

Daudin, Henri. De Linné a Lamarck / méthodes de la classification et idée de série en botanique et en zoologie (1740–1790). Paris: Félix Alcan [1926].

——— Cuvier et Lamarck / les classes zoologiques et l'idée de série animale (1790–1830). 2 vols., Paris: Félix Alcan, 1926.

[*Davy, Sir Humphry*] Salmonia: or days of fly fishing. In a series of conversations. With some account of the habits of fishes belonging to the genus Salmo. By an angler. London: John Murray, 1828.

Davy, Sir Humphry. The collected works of Sir Humphry Davy, Bart. LL.D.F.R.S. . . . edited by his brother, John Davy, M.D.F.R.S. 9 vols., London: Smith, Elder, 1839–40. [includes 2d ed. lectures on chemistry, 4th ed. lectures on agriculture, and 3d ed. *Salmonia*]

——— Fragmentary remains, literary and scientific, of Sir Humphry Davy, Bart., late president of the Royal Society, etc. with a sketch of his life and selections from his correspondence. Edited by his brother, John Davy, M.D., F.R.S. London: John Churchill, 1858.

Davy, John. Memoirs of the Life of Sir Humphry Davy, Bart. . . . 2 vols., London: Longman, Rees, Orme, Brown, Green, & Longman, 1836.

——— Memoirs of the Life of Sir Humphry Davy, Bart. . . . *Works,* Vol. 1 (London: Smith, Elder, 1839).

Dawson, Warren R. See Banks (1958).

Deane, C. V. Aspects of Eighteenth Century Nature Poetry. Oxford: Basil Blackwell, 1935.

Dedu, N. De l'ame des plantes. Deu leur naissance, de leur nourriture & de leur progrez. Essay de physique. Bound with Nehemiah Grew, Anatomie des plantes . . . (Leyden: Pieter van der Aa, 1685), pp. 247–310.

Delille, Jacques. Les trois règnes de la nature . . . avec des notes par M. Cuvier, de l'Institut, et autres savants. 2 vols., Paris: H. Nicolle and Giguet et Michaud, 1808.

Demainbray, Stephen Charles Triboudet. "An application of electricity towards the improvement of vegetation," *Scots Mag., 9* (Jan. 1747), 40.

——— "Mr. Demainbray's experiment in electricity, p. 40. repeated," ibid. (Feb. 1747), p. 93.

Dickson, Adam. A Treatise of Agriculture [1762] 2d ed., Edinburgh: A. Kincaid and J. Bell, 1765.

Digby, Sir Kenelm. "A discourse concerning the vegetation of plants. Spoken by Sir Kenelme Digby, at Gresham-Colledge, on the 23d. of January 1660. At a meeting of the society for promoting philosophical knowledge by experiments," Of bodies, and of mans soul. To discover the immortality of reasonable souls. With two discourses of the powder of sympathy, and of the vegetation of plants. (London: John Williams, 1669), part 2, pp. 210–31.

D'Israeli, Isaac. "Sir John Hill with the Royal Society, Fielding, Smart, &c.," Quarrels of Authors; or, some memoirs for our literary history . . . , 2 (London: John Murray, 1814), 81–124.

Donati, Vitaliano. Della storia naturale marina dell'Adriatico. Saggio del Signor Dottore Vitaliano Donati giuntavi una lettera del Signor Dottore Lionardo Sesler intorno ad un nuovo genere di pianti terrestri. Venice: Francesco Storti, 1750.

——— "New discoveries relating to the history of coral, by Dr. Vitaliano Donati. Translated from the French, by Tho. Stack, M.D.F.R.S.," *Phil. Trans., 47* (1751), 95–108.

——— Letters between the years 1751 and 1758, in Antonio Roncetti, ed., Lettere inedite scientifico-letterarie di Ludovico Muratori—Vitaliano Donati—Gio. Maria Lancisi—Daniele le Clerc. (Milan: Giorgio Silvestri, 1845), pp. 119–58.

Donovan, Michael. Essay on the origin, progress, and present state of galvanism: containing investigations experimental and speculative of the principal doctrines offered for the explanation of its phenomena; and a statement of a new hypothesis. Dublin: Hodges and McArthur, 1816.

Dove, John. Strictures on Agriculture. Wherein a discovery of the physical cause of vegetation, of the food of plants, and the rudiments of tillage, is attempted. London: for the author, 1770.

Driesch, Hans. The History and Theory of Vitalism. Trans. C. K. Ogden [1905]. London: Macmillan, 1914.

Dryander, Jonas. Catalogus bibliothecae historico-naturalis Josephi Banks . . . 5 vols., London: William Bulmer, 1798–1800.

DuBois-Reymond, Emil. On Animal Electricity: being an abstract of the discoveries of Emil duBois-Reymond. Ed. H. Bence Jones. London: John Churchill, 1852.

Dudley, Paul. "Observations on some of the plants in New-England, with remarkable instances of the nature and power of vegetation . . . ," *Phil. Trans.*, no. 385 (1724), 194–200.

Du Fay, Charles François de Cisternay. "Observations sur la sensitive," *Mém. Acad. Royale des Sci.* (for 1736), pp. 87–110.

Duhamel du Monceau, Henri Louis. La physique des arbres; où il est traité de l'anatomie des plantes et de l'économie végétale: pour servir d'introduction au traité complet des bois & des forests . . . Paris: H. L. Guerin and L. F. Delatour, 1758.

Duncan, Carson S. "The scientist as a comic type," *Modern Philol., 14* (1916), 89–99.

Duncan, J. S. Analogies of Organized Beings. Oxford: J. Parker and J. G. and F. Rivington of London, 1831.

Dutrochet, Henri Joachim. Recherches anatomiques et physiologiques sur la structure intime des animaux et des végétaux et sur leur motilité. Paris: J. B. Ballière, 1824.

——— "Recherches sur la cause et sur le mecanisme de l'irritabilité végétale," Nouvelle recherches sur l'endosmose et l'exosmose . . . (Paris: J. B. Ballière, 1828), pp. 55–84.

Eeles, Henry. "A letter from Mr. Henry Eeles to the Royal Society concerning the cause of thunder," *Phil. Trans., 47* (1752), 524–29.

——— Philosophical Essays: in several letters to the Royal Society, containing a discovery of the cause of thunder, with a subsequent explanation and demonstration of the same. The cause of the ascent, station, and descent of vapours and exhalations: the cause of winds; and, an explanation of the general phaenomena of the weather, barometer, &c. The true rudiments and theory of electricity and magnetism. An attempt to shew that the electrical powers are the cause of the reflection and refraction of light. Some mention of the wonderful medicinal effects of electricity on a great number of patients, whom the author has cured of palsies, and many other disorders. With other useful matters, which may be deduced from these essays. London: G. Robinson and J. Roberts, 1771.

"Eirionnach" "Aurea catena Homeri," *Notes and Queries,* 2d ser., *3* (1857), 63–65, 81–84, 104–07; *12* (1861), 161–63, 181–83.

Ellicott, John. "Several essays towards discovering the laws of electricity, communicated to the Royal Society by Mr. John Ellicott F.R.S. and read on the 25th of Feb. 1747. and at two meetings soon after," *Phil. Trans.,* no. 486 (1748), 195–224.

Ellis, John. Letter to Philip Carteret Webb. Dated 18 June 1752; read to the Royal Society on the same day. *Letters and Papers of the Royal Society, 15* (Decade II, no. 317), 3 pp.

——— "Observations on a remarkable coralline, in a letter from Mr. John Ellis to the Rev. Thomas Birch, D.D. Secret. R.S." *Phil. Trans., 48* (1753), 115–17.

——— "A letter from Mr. John Ellis to Mr. Peter Collinson, F.R.S. concerning a cluster-polype, found in the sea near the coast of Greenland," ibid., pp. 305–08.

——— "A letter to Mr. Peter Collinson, F.R.S. concerning a particular species of coralline. By Mr. John Ellis, F.R.S.," ibid. (1754), pp. 504–07.

——— "A letter from Mr. John Ellis, F.R.S. to Mr. Peter Collinson, F.R.S. concerning the animal life of those corallines, that look like minute trees, and grow upon oysters and fucus's all around the seacoast of this kingdom," ibid., pp. 627–33.

——— An essay towards a natural history of the corallines, and other marine productions of the like kind, commonly found on the coasts of Great

Britain and Ireland. To which is added the description of a large marine polype taken near the North Pole, by the whale-fishers, in the summer 1753. London: for the author, 1755.

Ellis, John. "An account of a curious, fleshy, coral-like substance; in a letter to Mr. Peter Collinson, F.R.S. from Dr. John Albert Schlosser, M.D.F.R.S. with some observations on it communicated to Mr. Collinson by Mr. John Ellis, F.R.S.," *Phil. Trans., 49* (1756), 449–52.

——— "An account of a red coral from the East-Indies, of a very singular kind: in a letter from Mr. John Ellis, F.R.S. to Mr. Peter Collinson, F.R.S.," ibid., *50* (1757), 188–94.

——— "Remarks on Dr. Job Baster's observationes de corallinis, &c. printed above, p. 258. In a letter to the Right Honourable George Earl of Macclesfield, President of the R.S. from Mr. John Ellis, F.R.S.," ibid., pp. 280–87.

——— "An account of the sea pen, or Pennatula phosphorea of Linnaeus; likewise a description of a new species of sea pen, found on the coast of South-Carolina, with observations on sea-pens in general. In a letter to the Honourable Coote Molesworth, Esq; M.D. and F.R.S. from John Ellis, Esq; F.R.S. and member of the Royal Academy at Upsal," ibid., *53* (1763), 419–35.

——— "On the nature and formation of sponges: in a letter from John Ellis, Esquire, F.R.S. to Dr. Solander, F.R.S.," ibid., *55* (1765), 280–89.

——— "Extract of a letter from John Ellis, Esquire, F.R.S. to Dr. Linnaeus, of Upsal, F.R.S. on the animal nature of the genus of zoophytes, called Corallina," ibid., *57* (1767), 404–27.

——— "An account of the Actinia sociata, or clustered animal-flower, lately found on the sea-coasts of new-ceded islands: in a letter from John Ellis, Esquire, F.R.S. to the Right Honourable the Earl of Hillsborough, F.R.S.," ibid., pp. 428–37.

E.[llis], J.[ohn] Comments on a paper sent to Linnaeus by Baron "Munkhausen," *St. James's Chronicle;* or, *British Evening Post,* no. 1012 (25–27 Aug. 1767).

——— Observations on mushroom spores, *St. James's Chronicle;* or, the *British Evening Post,* no. 1023 (19–22 Sept. 1767).

Ellis, John. "A botanical description of the Dionaea muscipula, or Venus's fly trap. A newly-discovered sensitive plant: in a letter to Sir Charles Linnaeus . . . ," Directions for bringing over seeds and plants from the East-Indies and other distant countries, in a state of vegetation: together with a catalogue of such foreign plants as are worthy of being encouraged in our American colonies, for the purposes of medicine, agriculture, and commerce. To which is added, the figure and botanical description of a new sensitive plant, called Dionaea muscipula or, Venus's fly-trap. (London: L. Davis, 1770), pp. 35–41 [letter dated 23 Sept. 1769].

——— "On the nature of the Gorgonia; that it is a real marine animal, and not of a mixed nature, between animal and vegetable. By John Ellis, Esq.

F.R.S. in a letter to Daniel Solander, M.D.F.R.S." [June, 1775], *Phil. Trans., 66* (1776), 1–17.

——— and *Solander, Daniel.* The natural history of many curious and uncommon zoophytes, collected from various parts of the globe by the late John Ellis, Esq. F.R.S. Soc. Reg. Upsal. Soc. author of the natural history of English corallines, and other works. Systematically arranged and described by the late Daniel Solander, M.D.F.R.S. &c. London: Benjamin White and Son, 1786.

——— "Calendar of the Ellis Manuscripts (The correspondence and miscellaneous papers of John Ellis, F.R.S.)," Catalogue of the manuscripts in the library of the Linnaean Society of London, part 4 (1948). Ed. Spencer Savage. London: for the Linnaean Society, 1948.

Emery, Clark. "Scientific theory in Erasmus Darwin's *The Botanic Garden,*" *Isis, 33* (1941), 315–25.

——— " "Sir" John Hill versus the Royal Society," *Isis, 34* (1942), 16–20.

Engelmann, Wilhelm. Index librorum historiam naturalem spectantium ab anno mdcc ad mdcccxlvi in Germania, Scandinavia, Anglia, Gallia, Belgio, Italia atque Hispania . . . Leipzig: Wilhelm Engelmann, 1846.

Fairchild, Thomas. "An account of some new experiments, relating to the different, and sometimes contrary motion of the sap in plants and trees, made by Thomas Fairchild, Gardener at Hoxton," *Phil. Trans.,* no. 384 (1724), 127–29.

Fallén, Carl Friederich. Dissertatio de irritabilitate motus caussa in plantis . . . XXIV Octobr., MDCCXCVIII. Lund: Litteris Berlingianis [1798?].

Fearing, Franklin. Reflex Action / a study in the history of physiological research. London: Baillière, Tindall & Cox, 1930.

Fechner, Gustav Theodor. Nanna oder über das Seelenleben der Pflanzen [1848]. 3d ed., Hamburg and Leipzig: Leopold Voss, 1903.

——— Religion of a Scientist: selections from Gustav Th. Fechner. Ed. and trans. by Walter Lowrie. New York: Pantheon Books, 1946.

Ferguson, James. An Introduction to Electricity. In six sections . . . London: W. Strahan and T. Cadell, 1770.

Ferriar, John. "Observations concerning the vital principle" [1787], *Mem. Lit. and Philos. Soc. Manchester, 3* (1790), 216–41.

Feuer, L. S. "The bearing of psychoanalysis upon philosophy," *Philosophy and Phenomenol. Res., 19* (1959), 323–40.

Field, George. Outlines of Analogical Philosophy: being a primary view of the principles, relations and purposes of nature, science, and art. 2 vols., London: Charles Tilt, 1839.

[*Fielding, Henry*] Some papers proper to be read before the R——L SOCIETY, concerning the terrestrial chrysipus, golden-foot or guinea; an insect, or vegetable, resembling the polypus, which hath this surprising property, that being cut into several pieces, each piece becomes a perfect animal, or vegetable, as complete as that of which it was originally only a part. London: J. Roberts, 1743.

Flagg, Henry Collins. "Observations on the numb fish, or torporific eel . . . ," *Trans. the Am. Phil. Soc., 2* (1786), 170–73.

Folkes, Martin. "Some account of the insect called the fresh-water polypus, before-mentioned in these transactions, as the same was delivered at a meeting of the Royal Society, by the president, on Thursday, March 24. 1742–3," *Phil. Trans.,* no. 469 (1743), 422–36.

Fontana, Felix. Traite sur le vénin de la vipere / sur les poisons americains / sur le laurier-cerise et sur quelques autres poisons végetaux. On y a joint des observations sur la structure primitive du corps animal. Différentes expériences sur la reproduction des nerfs et la description d'un nouveau canal de l'œil. 2 vols., Florence: 1781.

Fothergill, Charles. An essay on the philosophy, study, and use of natural history. London: White, Cochrane, 1813.

Fowler, Richard. Experiments and observations relative to the influence lately discovered by M. Galvani and commonly called animal electricity. Edinburgh: T. Duncan, P. Hill, Robertson & Berry, G. Mudie, and J. Johnson of London, 1793.

Franklin, Benjamin. Benjamin Franklin's Experiments / a new edition of Franklin's experiments and observations on electricity. Ed. I. Bernard Cohen. Harvard Univ. Press, 1941.

Freke, John. An essay to shew the cause of electricity; and why some things are non-electricable, in which is also consider'd its influence in the blasts on human bodies, in the blights on trees, in the damps in mines; and as it may affect the sensitive plant, &c. In a letter to Mr. William Watson, F.R.S. London: W. Innys, 1746.

——— "Appendix," in ibid., 2d. ed. (1746), pp. 53–64.

——— A treatise on the nature and property of fire. In three essays. I. Shewing the cause of vitality, and muscular motion; with many other phaenomena. II. On electricity. III. Shewing the mechanical cause of magnetism; and why the compass varies in the manner it does. London: W. Innys and J. Richardson, 1752.

Fries, T. M. See Jackson (1923).

Fulton, John Farquhar. Muscular Contraction and the Reflex Control of Movement. Baltimore: Williams & Wilkins, 1926.

——— and *Cushing, Harvey.* "A bibliographical study of the Galvani and the Aldini writings on animal electricity," *Annals of Sci., 1* (1936), 239–68.

——— "Medicine in the eighteenth century." Logan Clendening Lectures on the history and philosophy of medicine (Univ. of Kansas Press, 1950), pp. 25–49.

——— "The Principles of Bibliographic Citation / an informal discourse addressed to writers of scientific papers," *Internat. Record of Medicine and General Practice Clinics, 169* (1956), 710–22.

Fussell, G. E. "Crop nutrition in the late Stuart Age (1660–1714)," *Annals of Sci., 14* (1958), 173–84.

Gallesio, Count Giorgio. Theorie der vegetablischen Reprodukzion, oder: Untersuchungen über die Natur und die Ursachen der Abarten und Missgebilde. Trans. [from Gallesio's essay on citrus, 1811] by George Jan. Vienna: F. Stöckholzer von Hirschfeld, 1814.

Galvani, Luigi. Commentary on the effects of electricity on muscular motion. With notes and a critical introduction by I. Bernard Cohen / together with a facsimile of Galvani's De viribus electricitatis in motu musculari commentarius (1791) and a bibliography of the editions and translations of Galvani's book prepared by John Farquhar Fulton and Madeline E. Stanton. Trans. Margaret Glover Foley. Norwalk, Conn.: Burndy Library, 1953.

——— De viribus electricitatis in motu musculari commentarius [1791], trans. Robert Montraville Green. Cambridge, Mass.: Elizabeth Licht, 1953.

——— Dell'uso e dell'attività dell'arco conduttore nelle contrazione dei muscoli [1794], trans. as "Later experiments of Galvani" in Bern Dibner, Galvani-Volta . . . (Burndy Library: 1952), pp. 50–51.

Garden, Alexander. "An account of the Gymnotus electricus or electrical eel. In a letter from Alexander Garden, M.D.F.R.S. to John Ellis, Esq. F.R.S.," *Phil. Trans., 65* (1775), 102–10.

Garden, George. "A discourse concerning the modern theory of generation . . . ," ibid., no. 192 (1691 N.S.), 474–83.

Garfinkle, Norton. "Science and religion in England, 1790–1800: the critical response to the work of Erasmus Darwin," *J. Hist. Ideas, 16* (1955), 376–88.

Garstang, Walter. "Wordsworth's interpretation of nature," *Nature,* Supp. to no. 2933 (16 Jan. 1926).

Geddes, Patrick. The Life and Work of Sir Jagadis C. Bose . . . London: Longmans, Green, 1920.

Geoffroy, E. F. "Observations sur les analyses du corail & de quelques autres plantes pierreuses, faites par M. le Comte Marsigli," *Mém. Acad. Roy. des Sci.* (for 1708), pp. 102–05.

——— "Observations sur la structure et l'usage des principales parties des fleurs," ibid. (for 1711), pp. 210–34.

Gerould, John H. "The dawn of the cell theory," *Sci. Monthly, 14* (1922), 268–77.

Gesner, Johann. "De fructificatione," Dissertationes physicae de vegetabilibus . . . in quibus elementa botanica celeb. Linnaei dilucide explicantur. Contained in Examen epicriseos in systema plantarum sexuale Cl. Linnaei . . . (Leyden: Cornelius Haak, 1743), pp. 79–108.

Gill, H. V. Roger Boscovich, S.J. (1711–1787): forerunner of modern physical theories. Dublin: M. H. Gill and Son, 1941.

Gillispie, Charles Coulston. Genesis and Geology: a study in the relations of scientific thought, natural theology, and social opinion in Great Britain, 1790–1850. Harvard Univ. Press, 1951.

——— "The foundation of Lamarck's evolutionary theory," *Arch. Internat. Histoire des Sci.*, 9th year (1956), pp. 232–338.

——— "Lamarck and [Charles] Darwin in the history of science," in Bentley Glass, ed., Forerunners of Darwin: 1745–1859 (Johns Hopkins Univ. Press, 1959), pp. 265–91.

——— The Edge of Objectivity / an essay in the history of scientific ideas. Princeton Univ. Press, 1960.

Gingerich, S. F. "From necessity to transcendentalism in Coleridge," *Publ., Modern Language Assoc., 25* (1920), 1–59.

Girod-Chantrans, Justin. Recherches chimiques et microscopiques sur les conferves, bisses, tremelles, etc. Paris: Bernard, 1802.

Gleichen genannt Russworm, Wilhelm Friederich Freiherrn von. Decouvertes les plus nouvelles dans le regne vegetal ou observations microscopiques sur les parties de la generation des plantes renfermées dans leurs fleurs, & sur les insectes, qui s'y trouvent, avec quelques essais sur la germe, un supplement d'observations melees . . . Trans. J. F. Isenflamm. Paris: Chretien de Launoy, 1770.

——— Mikroskopische Untersuchungen und Beobachtungen der geheimen Zeugungstheile der Pflanzen in ihren Blüten, und der in denselben befindlichen Insekten; nebst einigen Versuchen über dem Keim, und einem Anhang vermischter Beobachtungen . . . Nuremberg: Kaspische Buchhandlung, 1790.

Gmelin, Johann Friederich. Irritabilitatem vegetabilivm, in singvlis plantarvm partibvs exploratam, vlterioribvsqve experimentis . . . praeside . . . Ferdin. Christoph. Oetinger . . . D. Octobr. MDCCLXVIII . . . Tübingen: Sigismund [1768?].

Reprinted: Christian Friederich Ludwig, Delectvs opvscvlorvm ad scientiam natvralem spectantivm, *1* (Leipzig: Siegfried Lebrecht Crusium, 1790), 272–309.

Gode-von Aesch, Alexander. Natural Science in German Romanticism. Columbia Univ. Germanic Studies, N.S., no. 11. Columbia Univ. Press, 1941.

Goethe, Johann Wolfgang von. See Arber (1946).

Goldsmith, Oliver. A survey of experimental philosophy, considered in its present state of improvement. 2 vols., London: T. Carnan and F. Newberry, 1776.

Goodfield, C. J. The Growth of Scientific Physiology / physiological method and the mechanist-vitalist controversy, illustrated by the problems of respiration and animal heat. London: Hutchinson, 1960.

Grabo, Carl. A Newton among Poets; Shelley's use of science in Prometheus Unbound. Univ. of North Carolina Press, 1930.

——— Prometheus Unbound; an interpretation. Univ. of North Carolina Press, 1935.

——— The Magic Plant; the growth of Shelley's thought. Univ. of North Carolina Press, 1936.

——— "Science and the romantic movement," *Annals of Sci.*, *4* (1939), 191–205.

Graham, James. A short extract from a book just published, intituled, "Medical transactions at the Temple of Health in London, in the course of the years 1781 and 1782. Or an account of upwards of five hundred selected, extraordinary, and well authenticated cures, performed by Dr. Graham's great and most excellent medicines, viz. electrical aether . . ." London [1780?]

——— A sketch: or, short description of Dr. Graham's medical apparatus, &c. erected about the beginning of the year 1780, in his house, on the Royal Terrace, Adelphi, London. London: Almon, Becket, and Richardson and Urquhart, 1780.

s'Gravesande, Laurens Storm van. See Allamand (1758).

Gray, George J. A bibliography of the works of Sir Isaac Newton together with a list of books illustrating his works. 2d ed., Cambridge: Bowes and Bowes, 1907.

Green, J. Reynolds. A History of Botany in the United Kingdom from the Earliest Times to the End of the 19th Century. London: J. M. Dent & Sons, 1914.

Gregory, George. The Economy of Nature Explained and Illustrated on the Principles of Modern Philosophy. 2d ed., 3 vols., London: J. Johnson, 1798.

Gregory, John. Lectures on the duties and qualifications of a physician [1770]. 2d ed., London: W. Strahan and T. Cadell, 1772.

Gregory, Joshua C. The Scientific Achievements of Sir Humphry Davy. Oxford Univ. Press, 1930.

——— A Short History of Atomism from Democritus to Bohr. London: A. & C. Black, 1931.

Grew, Nehemiah. The Anatomy of Vegetables Begun. With a general account of vegetation founded thereon. London: Spencer Hickman, 1672.

——— An Idea of a Phytological History Propounded. Together with a continuation of the anatomy of vegetables, particularly prosecuted upon roots. And an account of the vegetation of roots grounded chiefly thereupon. London: Richard Chiswell, 1673.

——— The Comparative Anatomy of Trunks, together with an account of their vegetation grounded thereupon; in two parts: the former read before the Royal Society, Feb. 25. 1674/5; the latter, June 17, 1675. The whole explicated by several figures in nineteen copper-plates; presented to the Royal Society in the years 1673. and 1674. London: Walter Kettilby, 1675.

Grew, Nehemiah. The Anatomy of Plants. With an idea of a philosophical history of plants. And several other lectures, read before the Royal Society. London: for the author, 1682.

——— Cosmologia Sacra: or a discourse of the universe as it is the creature and kingdom of God. Chiefly written, to demonstrate the truth and excellency of the Bible; which contains the laws of his kingdom in this lower world. In five books. London: W. Rogers, S. Smith, and B. Walford, 1701.

Grinfield, Edward W. Cursory observations upon the "Lectures on physiology, zoology, and the natural history of man, delivered at the Royal College of Surgeons by W. Lawrence, F.R.S. . . ." In a series of letters addressed to that gentleman; with a concluding letter to his pupils. The second edition, to which is added, a congratulatory address to Mr. Lawrence on the suppression of his "Lectures." London: T. Cadell and W. Davies, 1819.

Gronovius, Johann Friedrich. "Extract of a letter from J. F. Gronovius, M.D. at Leyden, November 1742. to Peter Collinson, F.R.S. concerning a water insect, which, being cut into several pieces, becomes so many perfect animals," *Phil. Trans.*, no. 466 (1742), 218–20.

Guye, Philippe-A. "Humphry Davy 1778–1829," Séance solennelle de distribution des prix de concours 28 Janvier 1907 / rapports du recteur et des jurys précédés d'une notice biographique sur Humphry Davy (Geneva: W. Kündig & fils, 1907), pp. 3–18.

Hagberg, Knut. Carl Linnaeus. Trans. Alan Blair. London: Jonathan Cape, 1952.

Hales, Stephen. Vegetable Staticks: or, an account of some statical experiments on the sap in vegetables: being an essay towards a natural history of vegetation. Also, a specimen of an attempt to analyze the air, by a great variety of chymio-statical experiments; which were read at several meetings before the Royal Society. London: W. and J. Innys and T. Woodward, 1727.

——— Statical Essays: containing vegetable staticks; or, an account of some statical experiments on the sap in vegetables. Being an essay towards a natural history of vegetation: of use to those who are curious in the culture and improvement of gardening, &c. Also, a specimen of an attempt to analyse the air, by a great variety of chymio-statical experiments, which were read at several meetings before the Royal Society. 2d ed., Vol. 1 [of Statical essays] London: W. Innys, T. Woodward, and J. Peele, 1731.

——— Statical Essays: containing haemastaticks; or, an account of some hydraulick and hydrostatical experiments made on the blood and blood-vessels of animals. Also an account of some experiments on stones in the kidneys and bladder; with an enquiry into the nature of those anomalous concretions. To which is added, an appendix, containing observations and experiments relating to several subjects in the first volume. The greatest part of which were read at several meetings before the Royal Society. With an index to both volumes. Vol. 2 [of Statical essays], London: W. Innys and R. Manby, and T. Woodward, 1733.

——— "Extract of a letter from the Rev. Dr. Stephen Hales F.R.S. to the Rev. Mr. Westly Hall, concerning some electrical experiments," *Phil. Trans.*, no. 488 (1748), 409–11.

Hall, A. Rupert. The Scientific Revolution 1500–1800 / the formation of the modern scientific attitude. London: Longmans, Green, 1954.

——— *See* Boas (1959).

von Haller, Albrecht. A dissertation on the sensible and irritable parts of animals [London: J. Nourse, 1755]. Introduction by Owsei Temkin. Baltimore: Johns Hopkins Press, 1936.

——— Bibliotheca Botanica. Qua scripta ad rem herbariam facientia a rerum initiis recensentur . . . "Bibliotheca Medicinae . . . ," part 2. Chronological. 2 vols., London [?]: Charles Heydinger, 1771–72.

Hamilton, Sir William. "An account of the late eruption of Mount Vesuvius . . . ," *Phil. Trans., 85* (1795), 73–116.

——— Observations on Mount Vesuvius, Mount Etna, and other volcanos: in a series of letters, addressed to the Royal Society . . . 2d ed., London: T. Cadell, 1773.

Hampden, Renn D. An essay on the philosophical evidence of Christianity; or, the credibility obtained to a scriptural revelation, from its coincidence with the facts of nature. London: John Murray, 1827.

Handley, James. Mechanical essays on the animal oeconomy . . . London: A. Bettesworth and C. Rivington, 1721.

Hansen, Adolph. Goethes Metamorphose der Pflanzen / Geschichte einer botanischen Hypothese. Giessen: Alfred Töpelmann, 1907.

Harmer, Sir Sidney F. "Presidential address, 24th May 1929," *Proc. Linnaean Soc., London,* 141st session (Nov. 1928–May 1929), pp. 68–118. [On John Ellis and the discovery of corallines.]

[*Harrington, Robert*] A New System on Fire and Planetary Life; shewing that the sun and planets are inhabited, and that they enjoy the same temperament as our earth. Also, an elucidation of the phaenomena of electricity and magnetism. London: T. Cadell and W. Davies, 1796.

Harrington, Robert. Some experiments and observations on Sig. Volta's electrical pile, clearly elucidating all the phenomena. Also observations on Dr. Herschel's paper, on light and heat; with other remarks. Carlisle: for Cadell, Jr. and Davies, 1801.

——— The Death-Warrant of the French Theory of Chemistry, signed by truth, reason, common sense, honour and science. With a theory fully, clearly, and rationally accounting for all the phenomena. Also, a full and accurate investigation of all the phenomena of galvanism; and strictures upon the chemical opinions of Messrs. Weigleb, Cruickshanks, Davy, Leslie, Count Rumford, and Dr. Thompson. Likewise, remarks upon Mr. Dalton's late theory, and other observations. London: for the author, 1804.

Harris, John. The atheistical objections, against the being of a God, and his attributes, fairly considered, and fully refuted. In eight sermons, preach'd in the Cathedral-Church of St. Paul, London, 1698. Being the seventh year of the lecture founded by the Honourable Robert Boyle, Esq. London: Richard Wilkin, 1698.

Harris, W. Snow. On the Nature of Thunderstorms; and on the means of protecting buildings and shipping against the destructive effects of lightning. London: John W. Parker, 1843.

Harris, William. A catalogue of the library of the Royal Institution of Great Britain. Methodically arranged, with an alphabetical index of authors. London: by William Savage for T. Payne and R. H. Evans, T. Egerton, J. White and Co., Joseph Johnson, and R. Faulder, 1809.

Hart, Cheney. "Part of a letter from Cheney Hart, M.D. to William Watson, F.R.S. giving some account of the effects of electricity in the county hospital at Shrewsbury," *Phil. Trans., 48* (1754), 786–87.

Hartley, David. Observations on Man, his Frame, his Duty, and his Expectations. 2 vols., London: S. Richardson for James Leake & William Frederick of Bath, and Charles Hitch and Stephen Austen of London, 1749.

Hartog, Sir Philip J. "The newer views of Priestley and Lavoisier," *Annals of Sci., 5* (1941), 1–56.

Harvey, William. Anatomical exercitations concerning the generation of living creatures: to which are added particular discourses, of births, and of conceptions, &c. London: Octavian Pulleyn, 1653.

Haven, Richard. "Coleridge, Hartley, and the mystics," *J. Hist. Ideas, 20* (1959), 476–94.

Heller, John W. "Classical mythology in the *Systema Naturae* of Linnaeus," *Trans. and Proc. Am. Philol. Assoc., 76* (1945), 333–57.

Henkel, Johann Friedrich. Flora saturnisans, ou preuves de l'alliance qui existe entre le regne végétal, et le regne minéral; tirées de l'histoire naturelle et de la chymie: . . . , trans. M. Charas [1722]. Paris: Jean-Thomas Hérissant, 1760.

Henly, William. "Experiments concerning the different efficacy of pointed and blunted rods, in securing buildings against the stroke of lightning," *Phil. Trans., 64* (1774), 133–52.

Heraud, John A. An oration on the death of Samuel Taylor Coleridge, Esq. delivered at the Russell Institution, on Friday, August 8, 1834. London: James Fraser, 1834.

Herford, C. H. "Is there a poetic view of the world," *Proc. Brit. Acad.* 1915–16, pp. 423–53.

Hermann, Johann. Tabula affinitatum animalium olim academico specimine edita nunc oberiore commentario illustrata cum annotationibus ad historiam naturalem animalium augendam facientibus. Strasbourg: J. G. Treuttel, 1783.

Highmore, Nathaniel. The History of Generation. Examining the several opinions of divers authors, especially that of Sir Kenelm Digby, in his discourse of bodies. With a general relation of the manner of generation, as well in plants as in animals: with some figures delineating the first originals of some creatures, evidently demonstrating the rest. To which is joyned a discourse of the cure of wounds by sympathy, or without any real applycation of medicines to the part affected, but especially by that powder, known chiefly by the name of Sir Gilbert Talbots powder. London: John Martin, 1651.

Hill, John. A General Natural History: or, new and accurate descriptions of the animals, vegetables, and minerals, of the different parts of the world: with their virtues and uses, as far as hitherto certainly known, in medicine and mechanics . . . 3 vols., London: Thomas Osborne, 1748–52.

[———] Lucina sine concubitu. A letter humbly address'd to the Royal Society; in which is proved by most incontestible evidence, drawn from reason and practice, that a woman may conceive and be brought to bed without any commerce with man. London: M. Cooper, 1750.
Reprinted: Robert Dodsley, ed., Fugitive pieces on various subjects by several authors, *1* (London: R. and J. Dodsley, 1761), 141–70.

——— A review of the works of the Royal Society of London; containing animadversions on such of the papers as deserve particular observation. In eight parts: under the several heads of arts, antiquities, medicine, miracles, zoophytes, animals, vegetables, minerals. London: R. Griffiths, 1751.

——— Essays in natural history and philosophy. Containing a series of discoveries, by the assistance of microscopes. London: J. Winston and B. White, P. Vaillant, and L. Davis, 1752.

The Inspector. 2 vols., London: R. Griffiths, J. Whiston and B. White, S. Baker, W. Shropshire, L. Davis, and J. Ward, 1753.

——— Thoughts Concerning God and Nature, in answer to Lord Bolingbroke's philosophy. London: for the author, 1755.

——— The sleep of plants, and cause of motion in the sensitive plant, explain'd. In a letter to C. Linnaeus, professor of botany at Upsal. London: R. Baldwin, 1757.

Reprinted: Eden: or, a compleat body of gardening . . . (London: T. Osborne, T. Trye, S. Crowder and Co., and H. Woodgate, 1757), pp. 703–08.

Reprinted: John Hill, Botanical tracts . . . publish'd at various times. Now first collected together. London: R. Baldwin, 1762.

——— Outlines of a system of vegetable generation. London: for the author, 1758.

Reprinted: John Hill, Botanical tracts . . . publish'd at various times. Now first collected together. London: R. Baldwin, 1762.

Hill, John. The Construction of Timber, from its early growth, explained by the microscope, and proved from experiments, in a great variety of kinds. In five books . . . 2d ed., London: for the author, 1774.

Hill, T. G. "John Hill 1716–1775," in F. W. Oliver, ed., Makers of British Botany (Cambridge Univ. Press, 1913), pp. 84–107.

Hillary, William. The Nature, Properties, and Laws of Motion of Fire discovered and demonstrated by observations and experiments. London: L. Davis and G. Reymers, 1760.

Hoadly, B. See Wilson (1756).

Hochdoerfer, Margaret. "The conflict between the religious and scientific views of Albrecht von Haller (1708–1777)," Univ. of Nebraska Studies in Language, Literature, and Criticism, no. 12 (1932).

Hocking, William Ernest. "Analogy and scientific method in philosophy," *J. Philos., Psychol. and Sci. Methods, 7* (1910), 161.

Hoff, Hebbel E. "Galvani and the pre-Galvanian electrophysiologists," *Annals of Sci., 1* (1936), 157–72.

von Hofsten, Nils. "Linnaeus's conception of nature," *Kung. Vetenskaps-Societentens Årsbok,* for 1957, pp. 65–105.

[*d'Holbach, Paul Henri Thierry, Baron*] Système de la nature. Ou des lois du monde physique & du monde moral. Par M. Mirabaud. 2 vols., London [?]: 1770.

Home, Francis. The Principles of Agriculture and Vegetation. Edinburgh: G. Hamilton and J. Balfour, 1757.

Home, Henry. "Of the laws of motion; by the Honourable Henry Home, Esquire, one of the Senators of the College of Justice," [1754] Essays an[d] observations, physical and literary. Read before the Philosophical Society in Edinburgh, and published by them. 2d ed. *1* (1771), 1–78.

Home, Henry, Lord Kames. The Gentleman Farmer. Being an attempt to improve agriculture by subjecting it to the test of rational principles. Edinburgh: W. Creech and T. Cadell, 1776.

Hone, J. M. and *Rossi, M. M.* Bishop Berkeley; his life, writings, and philosophy. London: Faber and Faber, 1931.

Hooke, Robert. Micrographia: or some physiological descriptions of minute bodies made by magnifying glasses. With observations and inquiries thereupon. London: Jo. Martin and Ja. Allestry, 1665.

Hooper, Robert. Observations on the structure and economy of plants: to which is added the analogy between the animal and vegetable kingdom. Oxford: Messrs. Fletcher and Co.; and Rivington and Murray and Highley of London, 1797.

Hosack, David and *Francis, John W.* "Biographical sketch of the late Honourable Cadwallader Colden, formerly Lieutenant-Governor of New-York, with an account of his writings," in *The American Medical and Philosophical Register* . . . , no. 3, 2d ed. (New York, David Hosack and John W. Francis, 1814), pp. 296–303.

Houghton, Walter E. Jr. "The English virtuoso in the seventeenth century," *J. Hist. Ideas, 3* (1942), 51–73, 190–219.

Hulme, T. E. "A critique of satisfaction," in Speculations / essays on humanism and the philosophy of art. Ed. Herbert Read (London: Kegan Paul, Trench, Trubner, 1924), pp. 12–23.

von Humboldt, Friedrich Heinrich Alexander. Florae Fribergensis specimen plantas cryptogamicas praesertim subterraneas exhibens. Edidit Fredericus Alexander ab Humboldt. Accedunt aphorismi ex doctrina physiologiae chemicae plantarum. Berlin: Henr. Augustus Rottman, 1793.

——— "Die Lebenskraft oder der Rhodische Genius. Eine Erzählung," *Die Horen* (eine Monatsschrift herausgegeben von Schiller), *1* (1795), part 5, 90–96.

——— Versuche über die gereizte Muskel- und Nervenfaser nebst Vermuthungen über den chemischen Process des Lebens in der Thier- und Pflanzenwelt. 2 vols., Posen: Decker, and Berlin: Heinrich August Rottmann, 1797.

——— "Extract of a letter from Mr. Humboldt to Mr. Blumenbach, containing new experiments on the irritation caused by the metals with respect to their different impressions on the organs of animals" [Nicholson's] *J. Natural Philos. Chem., Arts, 1* (1797), 256–60.

——— "A letter from Mr. von Humboldt to M. H. van Mons on the chemical process of vitality; together with the extract of a letter from Citizen Fourcroy to Citizen van Mons on the same subject," ibid., pp. 359–64.

——— Versuche über die electrischen Fische. Erfurt: Beyer and Maring, 1806.

Hunter, Alexander. "On vegetation, and the analogy beween plants and animals," in Georgical Essays: in which the food of plants is particularly considered, several new composts recommended, and other important articles of husbandry explained, upon the principles of vegetation. *1* (London: T. Durham, 1770), 79–98.

——— "On vegetation and the motion of the sap," ibid., pp. 121–84.

Hunter, John. "Anatomical observations on the torpedo" [1773], *Phil. Trans., 63* (1774), 481–89.

——— "An account of the Gymnotus electricus," ibid., *65* (1775), 395–407.

——— "Experiments on animals and vegetables, with respect to the power of producing heat," ibid., *65* (1775), 446–58.

——— "Of the heat, &c. of animals and vegetables," ibid., *68* (1778), 7–49.

——— "Experiments and observations on animals, with respect to the power of producing heat," in Observations on Certain Parts of the Animal Œconomy (London: for the author, 1786), pp. 87–113.

Hunter, John. A treatise on the blood, inflammation, and gun-shot wounds, by the late John Hunter. To which is prefixed, a short account of the author's life, by his brother-in-law, Everard Home. London: George Nicol, 1794.

——— The works of John Hunter, F.R.S. with notes, Ed. James F. Palmer. 4 vols., London: Longman, Rees, Orme, Brown, Green, and Longman, 1835–37.

——— Essays and observations on natural history, anatomy, physiology, psychology, and geology. By John Hunter, F.R.S.; being his posthumous papers on those subjects, arranged and revised, with notes: to which are added, the introductory lectures on the Hunterian collection of fossil remains, delivered in the theatre of the Royal College of Surgeons of England, March 8th, 10th, and 12th, 1855. By Richard Owen. 2 vols., London: John van Voorst, 1861.

Hussakov, L. "Benjamin Franklin and Erasmus Darwin: with some unpublished correspondence," *Science,* N.S. *43* (1916), 773–75.

Inchbald, Elizabeth. Animal Magnetism. A farce of three acts as performing at the Theatres-Royal of London and Dublin. London: C. Lewis, 1789.

Ingenhousz, John. "Extract of a letter from Dr. John Ingenhousz, F.R.S. to Sir John Pringle, Bart. P.R.S. containing some experiments on the torpedo, made at Leghorn, January 1, 1773 (after having been informed of those by Mr. Walsh) . . . ," *Phil. Trans., 65* (1775), 1–4.

——— Experiments upon Vegetables, discovering their great power in purifying the common air in the sun-shine, and of injuring it in the shade and at night. To which is joined, a new method of examining the accurate degree of salubrity of the atmosphere. London: P. Elmsley and H. Payne, 1779.

——— "Réflexions sur l'économie des végétaux" [Rozier's] *Observ. sur la physique . . . , 24* (1784), 443–55.

——— Nouvelles expériences et observations sur divers objets de physique. 2 vols., Paris: P. Théophile Barrois le jeune, 1785–89.

——— "An essay on the food of plants and the renovation of soils." Additional appendix to the outlines of the fifteenth chapter of the proposed general report from the Board of Agriculture (London: W. Bulmer and Co., 1796), Paper 3.

Jackson, Benjamin Daydon. Guide to the literature of botany; being a classified selection of botanical works, including nearly 6000 titles not given in Pritzel's 'Thesaurus.' London: for the Index Society by Longmans, Green, & Co., and Dulau & Co., 1881.

——— Catalogue of the library of the Royal Botanic Gardens, Kew. "[Kew Gardens] Bulletin of Miscellaneous Information," Add. ser. 3. London: H.M.S.O., 1899.

——— Linnaeus (afterwards Carl von Linné), The Story of His Life, adapted from the Swedish of Theodor Magnus Fries, emeritus professor of botany in the University of Uppsala, and brought down to the present time in the light of recent research. London: H. F. & G. Witherby, 1923.

Jackson, John. A dissertation on matter and spirit: with some remarks on a book, entitled, An enquiry into the nature of the human soul. London: J. Noon, 1735.

[*Jackson, Maria Elizabeth*] Sketches of the Physiology of Vegetable Life. London: John Hatchard, 1811.

Jallabert, Jean. Theses physicae de electricitate, quas favente Deo, sub praesidio D. D. Joh. Jallabert . . . Geneva: Barrillot & Sons, 1747.

Jansen, Albert. See deBeer (1954).

Jenyns, Soame. "On the chain of universal being," in Disquisitions on Several Subjects. (Dublin: R. Moncrieffe, T. Walker, P. Byrne, and C. Lewis, 1782), pp. 1–10.

Reprinted: Works . . . *3* (London: T. Cadell, 1790), 179–85.

——— "On the analogy between things material and intellectual," Disquisitions on Several Subjects (1782), pp. 75–89. [Reprinted as above, 234–44].

Jessop, Thomas Edmund. A bibliography of George Berkeley with an inventory of Berkeley's manuscript remains by A. A. Luce, D.D. Oxford Univ. Press, 1934.

Johnson, Duncan S. "The evolution of a botanical problem / the history of the discovery of sexuality in plants," *Science,* N.S., *39* (1914), 299–319.

Johnston, George. A History of the British Zoophytes. Edinburgh: W. H. Lizars, 1838.

Jones, W. P. "The vogue of natural history in England 1750–1770," *Annals of Sci.,* 2 (1937), 345–52.

Jones, William. An essay on the first principles of natural philosophy: wherein the use of natural means, or second causes, in the oeconomy of the material world, is demonstrated from reason, experiments of various kinds, and the testimony of antiquity . . . Oxford: Clarendon Press for S. Parker and D. Prince of Oxford, J. Rivington of London, and W. Watson of Dublin, 1762.

Jourdain, Philip E. B. "Newton's hypotheses of ether and of gravitation from 1672 to 1679," *Monist, 25* (1915), 79–106.

——— "Newton's hypotheses of ether and gravitation from 1679 to 1693," ibid., pp. 234–54.

——— "Newton's hypotheses of ether and gravitation from 1693 to 1726," ibid., pp. 418–40.

Jussieu, Antoine de. "The analogy between plants and animals, drawn from the difference of their sexes" [1719] in Richard Bradley, A philosophical account . . . (1721), pp. 25–32.

Jussieu, Bernard de. "De quelques productions marines qui ont été mises au nombre des plantes, & qui sont l'ouvrage d'une sorte d'insectes de mer," *Mém. Acad. Roy. des Sci.* (for 1742), pp. 290–302.

Kellaway, Peter. "The part played by the electric fish in the early history of bioelectricity and electrotherapy," *Bull. Hist. Med., 20* (1946), 112–37.

Kelley, Maurice. Additional chapters on Thomas Cooper. University of Maine Studies, ser. 2, no. 15 (1930).

Kendall, James. Humphrey Davy: "Pilot" of Penzance. London: Faber and Faber, 1954.

Kenrick, William. "On the nature of motion in general," A lecture on the perpetual motion (London: for the author, 1771), part 1, pp. 7–21.

Kentish, Richard. An essay on the method of studying natural history; being an oration delivered to the Societas Naturae Studiosorum at Edinburgh, in the year 1782. London: P. Elmsley and J. Johnson, 1787.

Kerr, Robert. Memoirs of the life, writings, & correspondence of William Smellie . . . 2 vols., Edinburgh: John Anderson, and Longman, Hurst, Rees, Orme, & Brown of London, 1811.

Keynes, Lord John Maynard. "Newton, the man" [1942] in Newton Tercentenary Celebrations 15–19 July 1946 (Cambrige Univ. Press, 1947), pp. 27–34.

Kidd, Jonathan. Catalogue of the works in medicine and natural history contained in the Radcliffe Library. Oxford: S. Collingwood, 1835.

King, William. Divine predestination and fore-knowledg, consistent with the freedom of man's will. A sermon preach'd at Christ-Church, Dublin: May 15, 1709. before His Excellency Thomas Earl of Wharton, Lord Lieutenant of Ireland, and the Right Honourable the House of Lords. London: for J. Baker, 1709.

Knight, G. Wilson. The Starlit Dome / studies in the poetry of vision. London: Methuen, 1959.

Knight, Gowin. An attempt to demonstrate, that all phoenomena in nature may be explained by two simple active principles, attraction and repulsion: wherein the attractions of cohesion, gravity, and magnetism, are shewn to be one and the same; and the phoenomena of the latter are more particularly explained. London: 1748.

Knight, Thomas Andrew. A selection from the philosophical and horticultural papers, published in the transactions of the Royal and Horticultural Societies, by the late Thomas Andrew Knight, Esq. . . . to which is prefixed, a sketch of his life. London: Longman, Orme, Brown, Green, and Longmans, 1841.

Knuth, Paul. Handbook of Flower Pollination / based upon Hermann Müller's work 'The fertilization of flowers by insects' . . . trans. J. R. Ainsworth Davis. Oxford: Clarendon Press, 3 vols., 1906–09.

Koelreuter, Joseph Gottlieb. Vorläufige Nachricht von einigen das Geschlecht der Pflanzen betreffenden Versuchen und Beobachtungen. Leipzig: Gleditschischen Handlung, 1761. [Supplements appeared in 1763, 1764, and 1766.]

Koyré, Alexander. "The significance of the Newtonian synthesis" [1948], *Arch. Internat. Hist. des Sci.* (1950), pp. 291–311.

Krause, Ernst. Erasmus Darwin. Trans. from the German by W. S. Dallas. With a preliminary notice by Charles Darwin. London: John Murray, 1879.

Kuhn, Thomas S. The Structure of Scientific Revolutions. Univ. of Chicago Press, 1962.

LaCondamine, Charles Marie. Relation abrégée d'un voyage fait dans l'interieur de l'Amérique méridionale depuis la côte de la Mer du Sud, jusqu'aux côtes du Brésil & de la Guiane, en descendant la Riviere des Amazones . . . Paris: Veuve Pissot, 1745.

de LaCroix, Demetrius. Connubia Florum / latine carmine demonstrata auctore D. de la Croix, M.D. Cum interpretatione Gallicâ D*******. Paris: Theobustia, 1728.

——— Connubia Florum / latine carmine demonstrata auctore D. de la Croix, M.D. Notas et observationes adjecit Richardus Clayton, Baronettus. Bath: S. Hazard, 1791.

[*Lacy, John*] The Universal System: or mechanical cause of all the appearances and movements of the visible heavens: shewing the true powers which move the earth and planets in their central and annual rotations. With a dissertation on comets, the nature, cause, matter, and use of their tails, and the reasons of their long trajectories: likewise an attempt to prove what it is that moves the sun round its axis. London: J. Buckland, 1779.

Lamarck, Jean Baptiste Pierre Antoine de Monet de. Flore Françoise ou description succincte de toutes les plantes qui croissent naturellement en France. 3 vols., Paris: Imprimerie Royale, 1778.

——— "Mémoire sur les classes les plus convenables à établir parmi les végétaux, & sur l'analogie de leur nombre avec celles déterminées dans le règne animal, ayant égard de part & d'autre à la perfection graduée des organes," *Mém. Acad. Roy. des Sci.* (for 1785), pp. 437–53.

——— Recherches sur les causes des principaux faits physiques, et particulièrement sur celles de la combustion, de l'elévation de l'eau dans l'état de vapeurs; de la chaleur produite par le frottement des corps solides entre eux; de la chaleur qui se rend sensible dans des décompositions subites, dans les effervescences et dans le corps de beaucoup d'animaux pendant la durée de leur vie; de la causticité, de la saveur et de l'odeur de certains composés; de la couleur des corps; de l'origine des composés et de tous les minéraux; enfin l'entretien de la vie des êtres organiques, de leur accroissement, de leur état de vigueur, de leur dépérissement et de leur mort. 2 vols., Paris: Maradan [1793–1794].

——— Réfutation de la théorie pneumatique, ou de la nouvelle doctrine des chimistes modernes, présentée, article par article, dans une suite de résponses aux principes rassemblés et publiés par le Citoyen Fourcroy, dans sa Philosophie chimique . . . Paris: for the author and Agasse [1795–1796].

——— Mémoires de physique et d'histoire naturelle, établis sur des bâses de raisonnement indépendantes de toute théorie; avec l'exposition de nouvelles considérations sur la cause générale des dissolutions; sur la matière du feu; sur la couleur des corps; sur la formation des composés; sur l'origine des minéraux; et sur l'organisation des corps vivans. Paris: Agasse, Maradan, and the author, 1797.

Lamarck, Jean Baptiste Pierre Antoine de Monet de. Philosophie zoologique, ou exposition des considérations relatives à l'histoire naturelle des animaux; à la diversité de leur organisation et des facultés qu'ils en obtiennent; aux causes physiques qui maintiennent en eux la vie et donnent lieu aux mouvemens qu'ils exécutent; enfin, à celles qui produisent, les unes le sentiment, et les autres l'intelligence de ceux qui en sont doués. 2 vols., Paris: Dentu and the author, 1809.
Translated: Zoological Philosophy / an exposition with regard to the natural history of animals / the diversity of their organization and the faculties which they derive from it; the physical causes which maintain life within them and give rise to their various movements; lastly, those which produce feeling and intelligence in some among them. Trans., with an introduction by Hugh Elliott. London: Macmillan, 1914.

——— Histoire naturelle des animaux sans vertèbres, présentant les caractères généraux et particuliers de ces animaux, leur distribution, leurs classes, leurs familles, leur genres, et la citation des principales espèces qui s'y rapportent; récédée d'une Introduction offrant la détermination des caractères essentiels de l'animal, sa distinction du végétal et des autres corps naturels, enfin, l'exposition des principes fondamentaux de la zoologie. *1* (Paris: Verdière, 1815).

——— The Lamarck manuscripts at Harvard, ed. William Morton Wheeler and Thomas Barbour. Harvard Univ. Press, 1933.

——— "Lamarck in 1800. A lecture on the invertebrate animals and a note on fossils taken from the *Systême des animaux sans vertèbres* by J. B. Lamarck. Translated and annotated by D. R. Newth," *Annals of Sci., 8* (1952), 229–54.

Lamettrie, Julien Offray de. Œuvres philosophiques. 2d ed., 2 vols., Berlin: 1764.

Langheinrich, M. George Nicolaus. Q. D. B. V. Dissertationem physicam de sensu plantarum superiorum indultu P. P. Praeses M. Georg. Nicolaus Langheinrich / Curiâ-Variscus, respondens Martinus Haugke / Coldicensis, magisterii candidatus. Ad diem XI. Decembr. A. O. R. M.DC.LXXII. Leipzig: Johann Wittigau [1672?].

Lavoisier, Antoine Laurent. "Réflexions sur la phlogistique, pour servir de développement à la théorie de la combustion & de la calcination, publiée en 1777," *Mém. Acad. Roy. des Sci.* (for 1783), pp. 505–38.

Lawrence, William. An introduction to comparative anatomy and physiology; being the two introductory lectures delivered at the Royal College of Surgeons, on the 21st and 25th of March, 1816. London: J. Callow, 1816.

——— Lectures on physiology, zoology, and the natural history of man, delivered at the Royal College of Surgeons. London: J. Callow, 1819. [Suppressed]

——— "Life," Abraham Rees, ed., The Cyclopaedia; or, universal dictionary of arts, sciences, and literature, *20* (London: Longman, Hurst, Rees, Orme, and Brown . . . 1819).

Lee, Henry. The Vegetable Lamb of Tartary; a curious fable of the cotton plant. To which is added a sketch of the history of cotton and the cotton trade. London: Sampson Low, Marston, Searle, & Rivington, 1887.

Lees, Edwin. The affinities of plants with man and animals, their analogies and associations; a lecture, delivered before the Worcestershire Natural History Society, November 26, 1833. London: William Edwards, 1834.

van Leeuwenhoek, Antony. "A letter from Mr. Anth. van Leeuwenhoek concerning the seeds of plants, with observations on the manner of propagation of plants and animals," *Phil. Trans.*, no. 199 (1693), 700–08 and plate opp. p. 693.

——— "Part of a letter from Mr. Antony van Leeuwenhoek, F.R.S. concerning green weeds growing in water, and some animalcula found about them," ibid., no, 283 (1703 N.S.), 1304–11 and Fig. 6–12 of plate opp. title page.

——— "Microscopical observations on red coral: in a letter to the Royal Society from Mr. Anthony van Leeuwenhoek, F.R.S.," ibid., no. 316 (1708), 126–34.

Lemée, Pierre. Julien Offray de La Mettrie / St-Malo (1709)–Berlin (1751) / Médicin-Philosophe-Polémiste / sa vie / son oeuvre. [Paris?]: Mortain, 1954.

LeSage, Georges Louis. "Lucrèce Newtonien," *Nouveaux Mém. Acad. Royale des Sciences et Belles-lettres* (Berlin) (for 1782), pp. 404–32.

Lindsay, John. "An Inquiry into the nature of the motions of the Mimosa Pudica or Sensative Plant.—" "Jamaica, 15 July 1788." Letters and Papers of the Royal Society, *85* (Decade IX, no. 111). 32 sides. 186 mm. × 231 mm. + 2 pencil drawings signed "J. L. Delint." now bound up with the MS of 1790. The first of these is reproduced in the present study.

——— "An Inquiry into the Nature of the motions of the Sens[i]tive, Sleeping & Moving Plants / Jamaica July 1790" [spelling corrected by a later hand], ibid., *89* (decade IX, no. 199). 65 sides, 150 mm. × 186 mm.

Linnaea, Elisabet Christina. "Om Indianska krassens blickande," *Kongl. Vetenskaps Acad. Handlingar* (Stockholm), *23* (for 1762) 284–87.

Linnaeus, Carl. Systema Naturae, sive regna tria naturae systematice proposita per classes, ordines, genera, & species. Leyden: Theodore Haak, 1735.

——— Classes Plantarum. Seu systemata plantarum omnia a fructificatione desumta, quorum XVI universalia & XIII partiala, compendiose proposita / secundum classes, ordines et nomina genera cum clave cuiusvis methodi et synonymis genericis. Fundamentorum botanicorum Pars II. Leyden: Conrad Wishoff, 1738.

——— Flora Svecica exhibens plantas per regnum Sveciae crescentes, systematice cum differentiis specierum / synonymis autorum / nominibus incolarum / solo locorum / usu pharmacopaeorum. Stockholm: Lars Salvius, 1745.

Linnaeus, Carl. Fauna Svecica sistens animalia Sveciae regni: quadrupedia, aves, amphibia, pisces, insecta, vermes, distributa per classes & ordines, genera & species. Cum differentiis specierum, synonymis autorum, nominibus incolarum, locis habitationum, descriptionibus insectorum. Leyden: Conrad Wishoff and George J. Wishoff, 1746.

——— "Dissertatio de coralliis balticis," Henry Fougt, prop. [1745] *Amoenitates Academicae* [this and following references are to the Leyden edition], *1* (1749), 177–212.

Translated: F. J. Brand, Select dissertations from the *Amoen. Acad.,* a supplement to Mr. Stillingfleet's tracts relating to natural history (London: G. Robinson and J. Robson, 1781), pp. 457–80.

[———] "Sponsalia plantarum," Johann Gustav Wahlbom, prop. [1746] *Amoen. Acad., 1* (1749), 61–109.

Translated: Hugh Rose, The elements of botany . . . (1775), pp. 152–229.

——— Philosophia Botanica in qua explicantur fundamenta botanica cum definitionibus partium, exemplis terminorum, observationibus rariorum, adjectis figuris aeneis. Stockholm: Godfrey Kiesewetter, 1751.

——— "Oeconomia naturae," Isaac J. Biberg, prop. [1749], *Amoen. Acad.* 2 (1752), 1–52.

Translated: Benjamin Stillingfleet, Miscellaneous tracts . . . [1759], 4th ed., 39–126.

[———] "Quaestio historica naturalis, Cui Bono?" Christopher Gedner, prop. [1752], *Amoen. Acad., 3* (1756), 231–75.

Translated: Stillingfleet, Miscellaneous tracts . . . [1759], 4th ed., pp. 161–200.

[———] "Somnus plantarum," [1755] Peter Bremer, prop., *Amoen. Acad. 4* (1759), 333–50.

[———] "Metamorphosis plantarum," Nicholas E. Dahlberg, prop., ibid., pp. 368–86.

[———] "Animalia composita," Albert Bäck, prop. [1759], ibid., *5* (1760), 343–52.

——— Disquisitio de quaestione ab academia imperiali scientarum Petropol. in annum MDCCLIX. pro praemio proposita: sexum plantarum argumentis et experimentis nouis, praeter adhuc iam cognita, vel corrobare, vel impugnare, praemissa expositione historica et physica omnium plantae partium, quae aliquid ad focundationem et perfectionem seminis et fructus conferre creduntur, ab eadem academia die VI. Septembris MDCCLX. in conuentu publico praemio ornata. St. Petersburg: by the academy, 1760.

Translated: A dissertation on the sexes of plants. Trans. James Edward Smith. London: for the translator, 1786.

——— "Prolepsis plantarum," Johann Jacob Ferber, prop. [1763], *Amoen. Acad., 6* (1764), 365–83.

——— Genera morborum in auditorum usum edita a Car. v. Linné. Uppsala: C. E. Steinert, 1763.

——— Philosophia Botanica in qua explicantur fundamenta botanica cum definitionibus partium, exemplis terminorum, observationibus rariorum, adjectis figuris æneis. Editio altera. Vienna: Johann Thomas Trattner, 1763.

——— "Mundus invisibilis," Johann Carl Roos, prop. [1767], *Amoen. Acad.,* 7 (1769), 385–408.

——— Fundamenta Botanica, quae theoriam scientiae botanices aphoristice tradunt [1735].
Madrid: Typographia Regia, 1788.

Translated: Hugh Rose, The elements of botany . . . (1775).

——— A selection of the correspondence of Linnaeus, and other naturalists, from the original manuscripts. Ed. Sir James Edward Smith. 2 vols., London: Longman, Hurst, Rees, Orme, and Brown, 1821.

——— The "Critica Botanica" of Linnaeus, trans. by the late Arthur Hort, Bt., M.A., revised by Miss M. L. Green, B.A., F.L.S. . . . London: Ray Society, 1938.

Liosner, L. D. See Vorontsova (1960).

Lister, Martin. "A letter of Mr. Martyn Lister, written to the publisher from York, Januar.10.1671/2 containing an ingenious account of veins, by him observed in plants, analogous to human veins," *Phil. Trans.,* no. 79 (1672 N.S.), 3053–55.

——— "A further account concerning the existence of veins in all kind of plants; together with a discovery of the membranous substance of those veins, and of some acts in plants resembling those of sense; as also of the agreement of the venal juice in vegetables with the blood of animals, &c. Communicated by Mr. Lister in a letter of Januar 8. 1672/73, and exhibited to the R. Society," ibid., no. 90 (1673 N.S.), 5132–37.

Locy, William A. The Growth of Biology / zoölogy from Aristotle to Cuvier / botany from Theophrastus to Hofmeister / physiology from Harvey to Claude Bernard. London: G. Bell [1926].

Logan, James. "Some experiments concerning the impregnation of the seeds of plants, by James Logan, Esq.; communicated in a letter from him to Mr. Peter Collinson, F.R.S.," *Phil. Trans.,* no. 440 (1736), 192–95.

——— Experimenta et meletemata de plantarum generatione . . . Leyden: Cornelius Haak, 1739.

Translated: Experiments and Considerations on the Generation of Plants. Trans. "J.F." London: C. Davis, 1747.

Logan, James Venable. The Poetry and Aesthetics of Erasmus Darwin. Princeton Studies in English, no. 15. Princeton Univ. Press, 1936.

Lorenzini, Stefano. The curious and accurate observations of Mr. Stephen Lorenzini of Florence, on the dissections of the cramp-fish: containing the comparative anatomy of that and some other fish, with experiments. Dedicated to his Most Serene Highness the Prince of Tuscany. And now done into English from the Italian, with figures after the life. By J. Davis, M.D. London: Jeffery Wale, 1705.

Lorimer, John. A concise essay on magnetism; with an account of the declination and inclination of the magnetic needle; and an attempt to ascertain the cause of the variation thereof. London: for the author, 1795.

van der Lott, Frans. "Kort bericht van den Conger-aal, ofte drilvisch; getrokken uit eenen brief van Frans van der Lott, gedateerd Rio Essequebo den 7 Juny 1761 . . ." *Verhandelingen uitgegeeven door de Hollandsche Maatschappye der Weetenschappen, te Haarlem, 6* (publ. 1762), part 2, supp. 87–95.

Lovejoy, Arthur O. The Great Chain of Being / a study in the history of an idea. Harvard Univ. Press, 1936.

Lovett, Richard. The subtil medium prov'd: or, that wonderful power of nature, so long ago conjectur'd by the most ancient and remarkable philosophers, which they call'd sometimes aether, but oftener elementary fire, verify'd. Shewing that all the distinguishing and essential qualities ascrib'd to aether by them, and the most eminent modern philosophers, are to be found in electrical fire, and that too in the utmost degree of perfection. . . . London: J. Hinton and W. Sandby, and for the author, 1756.

——— Sir Isaac Newton's aether realized: or, the second part of the subtil medium proved, and electricity rendered useful. Being a vindication of that essay, in answer to the animadversions made thereon by the Monthly Review; whereby the electeral fluid, and the subtil aetherial fluid of philosophers are, from the Newtonian principles, clearly demonstrated to be the same thing: with a variety of remarkable observations relative thereto. London: for the author, W. Sandby, J. Waugh, and W. Fenner [1758].

——— The reviewers review'd; or, the bush-fighters exploded: being a reply to the animadversions, made by the authors of the Monthly Review, on a late pamphlet, entitled Sir Isaac Newton's aether realiz'd. To which is added, by way of appendix, electricity render'd useful in medicinal intentions. Illustrated with a variety of remarkable cures perform'd in London. Worcester: by R. Lewis for the author, and S. Mountfort; W. Sandby, W. Fenner, and J. Waugh of London, 1760.

——— Philosophical essays, in three parts. Containing I. An enquiry into the nature and properties of the electrical fluid, in order to explain, illustrate and confirm the truth of Sir Isaac Newton's doctrine of a subtile medium or aether. II. A dissertation on the nature of fire in general, and production of heat in particular. III. A miscellaneous discourse, wherein the fore-mentioned active principle is shewn to be the only probable mechanical cause of motion, cohesion, gravity, magnetism, and other phaenomena of nature . . . Worcester: for the author by R. Lewis; Sandby, and J. Johnson of London; and Fletcher of Oxford, 1766.

——— The electrical philosopher. Containing a new system of physics founded upon the principle of an universal plenum of elementary fire, wherein the nature of elementary fire is explain'd, its office pointed out, its extensive influence and utility in explaining many of the most abstruse phenomena of nature shewn, and the grand desideratum in particular which has been hitherto either entirely given up as inexplicable, or else sought after in vain by the most able naturalists, is at length happily obtain'd, viz. the cause of gravity, the cause of cohesion, &c. &c. . . . Worcester; for the author, R. Lewis, Bew of London, and Fletcher of Oxford, 1774.

Lowndes, Francis. Observations on Medical Electricity, containing a synopsis of all the diseases in which electricity has been recommended or applied, with success; likewise, pointing out a new and more efficaceous method of applying this remedy, by electric vibrations. London: for the author, 1787.

——— The Utility of Medical Electricity Illustrated, in a series of cases, and practical observations: tending to prove the superiority of vibrations to every other mode of applying the electric fluid. London: for the author, 1791.

Lowrie, Walter. See Fechner (1946).

Lyon, John. Experiments and Observations made with a view to point out the errors of the present received theory of electricity; and which tend in their progress to establish a new system, on principles more conformable to the simple operations of nature. London: for the author and J. Dodsley, Joseph Hall of Margate, and Robert Brydone of Dover, 1780.

MacDonald, Margaret. "The philosopher's use of analogy," in Anthony Flew, ed., Logic and Language [1st ser.] (Oxford: Basil Blackwell, 1955), pp. 80–100.

Macfait, Ebeneezer. "Observations on thunder and electricity," Essays an[d] observations, physical and literary. Read before the Philosophical Society in Edinburgh, and published by them, *1* [1754]; 2d ed. (1771), pp. 209–18.

Maclurg, James. Experiments upon the Human Bile: and reflections on the biliary secretion. With an introductory essay. London: T. Cadell, 1772.

Magnus, Rudolf. Goethe als Naturforscher. Leipzig: Johann Ambrosius Barth, 1906.

Major, Johann Daniel. Dissertatio botanica, de planta monstrosa gettorpiensi mensis Junii, Anni MDCLXV, ubi quaedam de coalescentiâ stirpium, & circulatione succi nutritii per easdem, proferuntur: cum figuris æri incisis, & additamento de simili materia. Schleswig: Johann Carstens, 1665.

Malpighi, Marcello. Anatome plantarum, in Opera omnia . . . , *1* (London: Robert Scott, 1686).

——— Anatomes plantarum pars altera. Ibid.

——— "Epistolae quaedam circa has De anatome plantarum auctisq; De ovo incubato observationibus dissertationes, &c. ultro utroque scriptae," "Appendix," ibid., *2*, 13–35.

Mariotte, Edme. Lettre écrite a Monsieur Lantin, Conseiller au Parlement de Bourgogne, sur le sujet des plantes. Œuvres de Mr. Mariotte, de l'Académie Royale des Sciences; . . . , *1* (Leyden, Pieter van der Aa, 1717), [117]–147.

Marsigli, Luigi Ferdinand. Brieve ristretto dell saggio fisico intorne alla storie del mare scritta alla Regia Accademia delle Scienze di Parigi. Ora esposto in una lettera all'eccellentiss. Signor Cristino Martinelli, Nobile Veneto. Venice: Andrea Poletti, 1711.

Martin, Benjamin. An essay on electricity: being an enquiry into the nature cause and properties thereof, on the principles of Sir Isaac Newton's theory of vibrating motion, light, and fire; and the various phaenomena of forty-two capital experiments; with some observations relative to the uses that may be made of this wonderful power of nature. Bath: for the author and Leake and Frederick; Raikes of Gloucester; Collins of Salisbury; and Newbury of London, 1746.

——— A supplement: containing remarks on a rhapsody of adventures of a modern knight-errant in philosophy. Bath: for the author and Leake and Frederick; Raikes of Gloucester; Collins of Salisbury; and Newbury of London, 1746.

——— A Panegyrick on the Newtonian Philosophy. Shewing the nature and dignity of the science, and its absolute necessity to the perfection of human nature; the improvement of arts and sciences, the promotion of true religion, the increase of wealth and honour, and the completion of human felicity. London: W. Owen, and J. Leake and J. Frederick of Bath, 1749.

Mason, S. F. "The scientific revolution and the protestant reformation—II: Lutheranism in relation to iatrochemistry and the German nature-philosophy," *Annals of Sci., 9* (1953), 154–75.

Maty, Paul Henry. A general index to the Philosophical Transactions, from the first to the end of the seventieth volume. London: Lockyer Davis and Peter Elmsly, 1787.

Maupertuis, Pierre Louis Moreau de. Vénus physique [1744]. Œuvres de Maupertuis, 2 (Lyon: Jean-Marie Bruyset, 1768), 1–133.

Mayo, Herbert. "Observations upon the motion of the leaves of the Mimosa pudica," [Royal Institution] *Quart. J. of Sci., Lit., Art,* N.S. 2 (1827), 76–83.

McKillop, Alan Dugald. The background of Thomson's Seasons. Univ. of Minnesota Press, 1942.

McLeay, William Sharp. Horae Entomologicae: or essays on the annulose animals. 2 vols. London: S. Bagster, 1819–21.

——— "Remarks on the identity of certain general laws which have been lately observed to regulate the natural distribution of insects and fungi" [1822]. *Trans. Linnaean Soc.,* London, *14* (1825), 46–68.

——— Number I. of Annulosa Javanica, or an attempt to illustrate the natural affinities and analogies of the insects collected in Java by Thomas Horsfield, M.D.F.L.&G.S. and deposited by him in the museum of the honourable East-India Company. London: Kinsbury, Parbury, and Allen, 1825.

Mendelbaum, Maurice. "The scientific background of evolutionary theory in biology," *J. Hist. Ideas, 18* (1957), 342–62.

Miall, L. C. The Early Naturalists / their lives and work (1530–1789). London: Macmillan, 1912.

Mikan, Johann Christian. Dr. Rud. Jac. Camerarii, . . . opuscula botanici argumenti. Prague: Carl Barth, 1797.

Miles, Josephine. Pathetic Fallacy in the Nineteenth Century / a study of a changing relation between object and emotion. Univ. of California Publications in English, 12 (1942), 183–304.

Mill, John Stuart. "Of analogy," in A System of Logic, ratiocinative and inductive, being a connected view of the principles of evidence, and the methods of scientific investigation. 2 (London: John W. Parker, 1843), 96–106.

Monro, Alexander [second of that name]. Observations on the Structure and Functions of the Nervous System. Illustrated with tables. Edinburgh: William Creech and J. Johnson of London, 1783.

——— "Experiments relating to animal electricity . . ." [Dec. 1792], *Trans. Roy. Soc., Edinburgh, 3* (1794), 231–39.

——— Experiments on the nervous system, with opium and metalline substances; made chiefly with the view of determining the nature and effects of animal electricity. Edinburgh: Adam Neill for Bell & Bradfute, and T. Duncan; and J. Johnson of London, 1793.

More, Louis Trenchard. Isaac Newton / a biography 1642–1727. New York: Charles Scribner's Sons, 1934.

Morgan, George Cadogan. Lectures on Electricity. 2 vols., Norwich: J. March for J. Johnson of London, 1794.

Morland, Samuel. "Some new observations upon the parts and use of the flower in plants," *Phil. Trans.,* no. 287 (1703), 1474–79 and Figs. 23–26 of plate opp. p. 1449.

Mornet, Daniel. Les sciences de la nature en france, au XVIIIe siècle. Paris: Arman Colin, 1911.

Mottelay, Paul Fleury. Bibliographical History of Electricity and Magnetism chronologically arranged . . . London: Charles Griffin, 1922.

Muirhead, John H. Coleridge as Philosopher. London: Allen & Unwin, 1930.

Mustel, Nicholas-Alexandre. "New observations upon vegetation. By Mr. Mustel of the Acad. of Sciences at Rouen; translated from the French," *Phil. Trans., 63* (1773), 126–36.

Nangle, Benjamin Christie. The Monthly Review / first series 1749–1789 / index of contributors and articles. Oxford: Clarendon Press, 1934.

——— The Monthly Review / second series 1790–1815 / indexes of contributors and articles. Oxford: Clarendon Press, 1955.

Needham, John Turbervill. "A letter from Mr. Turbevil Needham, to the president; concerning certain chalky tubulous concretions, called malm: with some microscopical observations on the farina of the red lily, and of worms discovered in smutty corn," *Phil. Trans.*, no. 471 (1743), 634–41.

N.[eedham], [John] T. [urbervill] An account of some new microscopical discoveries founded on . . . observations on the farina foecundans of plants; with a new discovery and description of the action of those minute bodies, analogous to that of the Calamary's milt-vessels. And an examination of the pistil, uterus and stamina of several flowers, with an attempt to shew how the seed is impregnated . . . London: F. Needham, 1745.

——— A letter from Paris, concerning some new electrical experiments made there [4 July 1746]. London: C. Davis and M. Cooper, 1746.

Reprinted: Phil. Trans., no. 481 (1746), 247–63.

Needham, John Turbervill. "A summary of some late observations upon the generation, composition, and decomposition of animal and vegetable substances; communicated in a letter to Martin Folkes Esq; President of the Royal Society, by Mr. Turbervill Needham, Fellow of the same society," *Phil. Trans.*, no. 490 (1748), [615]–666.

Needham, Joseph. "S. T. Coleridge as a philosophical biologist," *Science Progress, 20* (1926), 692–702.

——— A History of Embryology. 2d ed., revised with the assistance of Arthur Hughes. Cambridge Univ. Press, 1959.

Newton, Sir Isaac. Sir Isaac Newton's mathematical principles of natural philosophy and his system of the world / translated into English by Andrew Mott in 1729. The translations revised, and supplied with an historical and explanatory appendix, by Florian Cajori . . . Berkeley: Univ. of California Press, 1934.

——— Opticks or a treatise of the reflections, refractions, inflections & colours of light / based on the fourth edition London, 1730. With a foreword by Albert Einstein / an introduction by Sir Edmund Whittaker / a preface by I. Bernard Cohen and an analytical table of contents prepared by Duane H. D. Roller. New York: Dover Publications, 1952.

——— Isaac Newton's Papers and Letters on Natural Philosophy and Related Documents / ed. with a general introduction by I. Bernard Cohen / assisted by Robert E. Schofield . . . with explanatory prefaces by Marie Boas, Charles Coulston Gillispie, Thomas S. Kuhn, and Perry Miller. Cambridge Univ. Press, 1958.

——— The Correspondence of Isaac Newton, ed. H. W. Turnbull. *1* (1661–75). Cambridge Univ. Press for the Royal Society, 1959.

[*Nicholas of Damascus,* pseudo-Aristotle] "De plantis," ed. E. S. Forster, in The Works of Aristotle. Trans. into English under the editorship of W. D. Ross. *6* (Oxford: Clarendon Press, 1913).

Nicholson, H. Alleyne. Natural History / its rise and progress in Britain as developed in the life and labours of leading naturalists. London and Edinburgh: W. & R. C. Chambers, 1886.

Nicholson, William. "Observations on the electrophore, tending to explain the means by which the torpedo and other fish communicate the electric shock" [Nicholson's] *J. Natural Philos., Chem., Arts, 1* (1797), 355–59.

Nicolson, Marjorie. Newton Demands the Muse / Newton's Opticks and the eighteenth century poets. Princeton Univ. Press, 1946.

——— "The microscope and English imagination," in Science and Imagination. Great Seal Books (Ithaca, N. Y.: Cornell Univ. Press, 1956), pp. 155–234.

Nollet, Jean-Antoine. "Part of a letter from Abbè [*sic*] Nollet, of the Royal Academy of Sciences at Paris, and F.R.S. to Martin Folkes Esq; President of the same, concerning electricity. Translated from the French by T. Stack, M.D.F.R.S.," *Phil. Trans.*, no. 486 (1748), 187–94.

Reprinted: John Ellicott, Several essays toward discovering the laws of electricity . . . (1748), pp. 1–8.

——— "An account of the treatise, presented to the Royal Society, intituled, 'Letters concerning electricity; in which the latest discoveries upon this subject, and the consequences which may be deduced from them, are examined; by the Abbé Nollet, member of the Royal Academy of Sciences of Paris, Fellow of the Royal Society, of the Institute of Bologna, &c.' extracted and translated from the French, by Mr. William Watson, F.R.S.," *Phil. Trans., 48* (1753), 201–16.

Nordenskiold, Erik. The History of Biology / a survey. Trans. Leonard Bucknall Eyre. London: Kegan Paul, Trench, Trubner, 1929.

Öhme, Carl Joseph. De serie corporum naturalium continua disserit . . . d. II. Octobr. MDCCLXXII. Leipzig: Officina Langenhemia [1772].

Reprinted: Christian Friedrich Ludwig, Delectvs opvscvlorvm ad scientiam natvralem spectantivm, *1* (Leipzig: Siegfried Lebrecht Crusius, 1790), 1–22.

Oppenheimer, J Robert. "Analogy in science," *Am. Psychologist, 11* (March 1956), 127–35.

Oppenheimer, Jane M. "William Gilbert: plant grafting and the grand analogy," *J. Hist. Med. Allied Sci., 8* (1953), 165–76.

Oppian. Oppian's Halieuticks of the nature of fishes and fishing of the ancients in V. books. Translated from the Greek with an account of Oppian's life and writings, and a catalogue of his fishes. [Trans. Mr. Diaper and John Jones.] Oxford: at the Theatre, 1722.

d'Ormoy, Abbé. "De l'influence de l'électricité sur la végétation, prouvée Par de nouvelles expériences" [Rozier's] *Observ. sur la physique . . . , 35* (1789), 161–76.

Pallas, Peter Simon. Elenchus Zoophytorum sistens generum adumbrationes cum selectis auctorum synonymis. The Hague: Pieter van Cleef, 1766.

[*Panizzi, Sir Antonio*] Catalogue of the Scientific Books in the Library of the Royal Society. London: Richard and John E. Taylor, 1889.

Paris, John Ayrton. The Life of Sir Humphrey Davy, Bart. LL.D. Late President of the Royal Society, Foreign Associate of the Royal Institute of France, &c. &c. &c. 2 vols., London: Henry Colburn and Richard Bentley, 1831.

Parsons, James. "A letter from James Parsons, M.D.F.R.S. to the Rev. Mr. Birch, Secr.R.S. concerning the formation of corals, corallines, &c," *Phil. Trans.*, *47* (1752), 505–13.

——— Philosophical observations on the analogy between the propagation of animals and that of vegetables: in which are answered some objections against the indivisibility of the soul, which have been inadvertently drawn from the late curious and useful experiments upon the polypus and other animals. With an explanation of the manner in which each piece of a divided polypus become another perfect animal of the same species. London: C. Davis, 1752.

Paterson, William. "An account of a new electric fish. In a letter from Lieutenant William Paterson to Sir Joseph Banks, Bart. F.R.S.," *Phil. Trans.*, *76* (1786), 382–83.

Pearson, Hesketh. Doctor Darwin. London: J. M. Dent & Sons, 1930.

Peart, Edward. The generation of animal heat, investigated with an introduction, in which is an attempt to point out, and ascertain, the elementary principles, and fundamental laws of nature; and apply them to the explanation, of some of the most interesting operations and striking appearances of chemistry. Gainsborough: H. Mozley for J. Edwards of London, 1788.

——— On electricity; with occasional observations on magnetism. Pointing out the inconsistency and fallacy of the doctrine of positive and negative electricity: and investigating and explaining the true principles, composition, and properties of electric atmospheres. Gainsborough: J. M. Mozley for Wm. Millar of London, 1791.

——— On the properties of matter, the principles of chemistry, and the nature and construction of aeriform fluids, or gases. In which the absurdity of the theories hitherto advanced, and generally received, respecting those subjects, are fully exposed; and such an explanation of them given, as reason, naturally, points out; and every observation fully confirms. Gainsborough: Mozley, for W. Millar of London, 1792.

Peirson, R. "On the analogy between plants and animals," in Alexander Hunter, ed., Georgical Essays . . . , *4* (London: T. Durham, 1772), 55–64.

Pemberton, Henry. A View of Sir Isaac Newton's Philosophy. London: S. Palmer, 1728.

Pennant, Thomas. "Cramp ray," in British Zoology: Class III, Reptiles; Class IV, Fish. (Chester: by Eliz. Adams for Benjamin White of London, 1769), pp. 67–69.

——— "Electric ray," in ibid. (London: Benjamin White, 1776), pp. 78–81.

Penrose, Francis. A treatise on electricity: wherein its various phoenomena are accounted for, and the cause of the attraction and gravitation of solids, assigned. To which is added, a short account, how the electrical effluvia act upon the animal frame, and in what disorders the same may probably be applied with success, and in what not. Oxford: at the Theatre for Sackville Parker and W. Owen of London, 1752.

Percival, Thomas. "Miscellaneous observations on the alliance of natural history, and philosophy, with poetry," in Moral and literary dissertations . . . (Warrington: by W. Eyres for J. Johnson of London, 1784), pp. 221–72.

Reprinted: The works, literary, moral, and medical, of Thomas Percival, M.D. . . . , *4* (London: J. Johnson, 1807), 139–71.

——— "Speculations on the perceptive power of vegetables," *Mem. Lit. and Philos. Soc.,* Manchester, 2 (1785), pp. 114–130.

——— "Facts and queries relative to attraction and repulsion," *ibid.,* pp. 429–39.

Perrault, Claude. "Du mouvement peristaltique," in Essais de physique, ou recueil de plusieurs traitez touchant les choses naturelles. *1* (Paris: Jean Baptiste Coignard, 1680), 129–72.

——— "De la circulation de la seve des plantes," in ibid., pp. 173–304.

Peyssonel, Jean André. See Réaumur (1727).

——— Letter to the Royal Society. Dated Guadeloupe, May 1751; read to the Royal Society, 19 March 1752, in Letters and Papers of the Royal Society, *14* (Decade II, no. 279).

——— Traité du Corail Contenant Les nouvelles decouvertes quon a fait sur le Corail, les Pores, madrepores, Scharras, Litophitones, Esponges et autres Corps et productions que la Mer fournit. Pour servir à l'histoire naturelle de la mer. Par le Sr. De Peyssonnel, docteur en Medecine, Correspondant des Academies Royalles des Sciences de Paris, et de Montpelier, et de celle des belles lettres de Marseille.—Medecin, botaniste, entretenu par sa majeste dans lisle Guadeloupe ci elevans Envoyé par le Roy aux Cotes de la Barberie pour les recherches de l'histoire naturelle. BM Add. MS. 4219 ff. 1–113. 224 sides, 163 mm. × 218 mm. [This Ms is only half of that sent by Peyssonel in 1751.]

——— "An account of a manuscript treatise, presented to the Royal Society, intituled, Traité du corail . . . Extracted and translated from the French by Mr. William Watson, F.R.S.," *Phil. Trans., 47* (1752), 445–69.

——— "Dissertation sur les Eponges/ Pour servir à l'histoire naturelle de la mer" [Undated]. BM Add. MSS 4,219, ff. 114–48. 70 sides, 184 mm. × 243 mm.

——— "New observations upon the worms that form sponges. By John Andrew Peyssonel, M.D.F.R.S. Translated from the French" [1757], *Phil. Trans., 50* (1758), 590–94.

——— "Analyse d'un ouvrage manuscrit intitulé: Traité du corail . . ." Par M. Flourens, *Ann. sci. naturelles,* ser. 2, *9* (1838) *Zoologie,* 334–51.

Pfaff, Christoph Heinrich. Über thierische Elektricität und Reizbarkeit. Ein Beytrag zu den neuesten Entdeckungen über diese Gegenstände. Leipzig: Siegfried Lebrecht Crusius, 1795.

——— Sammlung von Briefen gewechselt zwischen Johann Friedrich Pfaff und Herzog Carl von Würtenberg, F. Bouterwek, A. v. Humboldt, A. G. Kästner, und Anderen [incl. C. H. Pfaff]. Ed. Dr. Carl Pfaff (Leipzig: J. C. Hinrichs'sche Buchhandlung, 1853), pp. 75–166.

Pfeffer, W. Die periodische Bewegungen der Blattorgane. Leipzig: Wilhelm Engelmann, 1875.

Pilley, J. P. "Wordsworth's interpretation of nature," *Hibbert J., 19* (1920–21), 537–50.

Piper, Herbert. "The pantheistic sources of Coleridge's early poetry," *J. Hist. Ideas, 20* (1959), 47–59.

Pliny. The Historie of the World. Commonly called, the naturall historie of C. Plinius Secundus. Translated into English by Philemon Holland doctor in physicke. London: Impensis G. B., 1601.

Potter, George Reuben. "Coleridge and the idea of evolution," *Publ., Modern Language Assoc., 40* (1925), 379–97.

——— "Mark Akenside, prophet of evolution," *Modern Philol., 24* (1926–27), 55–64.

——— "Henry Baker, F.R.S. (1698–1774)," ibid., *29* (1932), 301–21.

——— "The significance to the history of English natural science of John Hill's *Review of the works of the Royal Society,*" Univ. of California Publications in English, 14 (1943), 157–80.

Pownall, "Governor" Thomas. "On the ether suggested by Sir Isaac Newton compared with the supposed newly discovered principle of galvanism," [Tilloch's] *Philosophical Mag., 18* (1804), 155–58.

Prichard, James Cowles. A review of the doctrine of a vital principle as maintained by some writers on physiology. With observations on the causes of physical and animal life. London: John and Arthur Arch, 1829.

Priestley, F. E. L. "Newton and the romantic concept of nature," *Univ. of Toronto Quart., 17* (1948), 323–36.

Priestley, Joseph. The History and Present State of Electricity, with Original Experiments. London: J. Dodsley, J. Johnson and B. Davenport, and T. Cadell, 1767.

——— A Familiar Introduction to the Study of Electricity. London: J. Dodsley, T. Cadell, and J. Johnson, 1768.

——— Disquisitions relating to Matter and Spirit. To which is added, the history of the philosophical doctrine concerning the origin of the soul, and the nature of matter; with its influence on Christianity, especially with respect to the doctrine of the pre-existence of Christ. London: J. Johnson, 1777.

Pringle, Sir John. A discourse on the torpedo, delivered at the anniversary meeting of the Royal Society, November 30, 1774. London: for the Royal Society, 1775.

Pritzel, G. A. Thesaurus literaturae botanicae omnium gentium inde a rerum botanicarum initiis ad nostra usque tempora, quindecim millia operum recensens. Leipzig: F. A. Brockhaus, 1872.

Pulos, C. E. The Deep Truth / a study of Shelley's skepticism. Univ. of Nebraska Press, 1954.

Pulteney, Richard. "Some observations upon the sleep of plants; and an account of that faculty, which Linnaeus calls Vigiliae Florum; with an enumeration of several plants, which are subject to that law. Communicated by Wm. Watson, M.D.F.R.S. by Mr. Richard Pultney of Leicester," *Phil. Trans., 50* (1758), 506–17.

——— Historical and Biographical Sketches of the Progress of Botany in England, from its origin to the introduction of the Linnaean system. 2 vols., London: T. Cadell, 1790.

——— A General View of the Writings of Linnaeus, by Richard Pulteney, M.D.F.R.S. The second edition; with corrections, considerable additions, and memoir of the author, by William George Maton, M.D.F.R.S.F.S.A. Fellow of the Royal College of Physicians, and a vice-president of the Linnaean Society of London. To which is annexed the diary of Linnaeus, written by himself, and now translated into English, from the Swedish manuscript in the possession of the editor. [1st ed. 1781] London: J. Mawman, 1805.

Rackstrow, B. Miscellaneous observations, together with a collection of experiments on electricity. With the manner of performing them. Designed to explain the nature and cause of the most remarkable phaenomena thereof: with some remarks on a pamphlet intituled, A sequel to the experiments and observtions tending to illustrate the nature and properties of electricity. To which is annexed, a letter, written by the author to the Academy of Sciences at Bordeaux, relative to the similarity of electricity to lightening and thunder. London: for the author, 1748.

Rader, Melvin A. Presiding Ideas in Wordsworth's Poetry. Univ. of Washington Publications in Language and Literature, 8, no. 2 (1931), 121–26.

Rawlinson MS. See Blair (1724).

Ray, John, and *Willughby, Francis.* "Concerning the motion of the sap in trees, made this spring by Mr. Willugby, and Mr. Wray, Fellowes of the R. Society: and communicated to the publisher of the inquiries touching that subject in Numb. 40," *Phil. Trans.,* no. 48 (1669), 963–65.

Ray, John. Historia plantarum species hactenus editas aliasque insuper multas noviter inventas & descriptas complectens. In qua agitur primò de plantis in genere, earúmque partibus, accidentibus & differentiis; deinde genera omnium tum summa tum subalterna ad species usque infimas, notis suis certis & characteristicis definita, methodo naturae vestigiis insistente desponuntur; species singulae accurate describuntur, obscura illustrantur, omissa supplentur, superflua resecantur, synonyma necessaria adjiciuntur; vires denique & usus recepti compendiò traduntur. 2 vols. London: Henry Faithorne, 1686–87.

——— The Wisdom of God Manifested in the Works of the Creation. London: Samuel Smith, 1691.

——— The Wisdom of God Manifested in the Works of the Creation, in two parts. viz. The heavenly bodies, elements, meteors, fossils, vegetables, animals (beasts, birds, fishes, and insects) more particularly in the body of the earth, its figure, motion, and consistency, and in the admirable structure of the bodies of man, and other animals, as also in their generation, &c. 2d ed., London: Samuel Smith, 1692.

——— "Praefatio," Stirpium Europearum extra Britannias nascentium sylloge . . . London: Samuel Smith and Benjamin Walford, 1694.

Raysor, Thomas M., ed. The English Romantic Poets / a review of research. 2d ed. [Essays by Ernest Bernbaum, Samuel C. Chew, James V. Logan, Jr., Clarence D. Thorpe, Bennett Weaver, and René Wellek] New York: Modern Language Assoc. of America, 1956.

Read, John. "A meteorological journal, principally relating to atmospherical electricity; kept at Knightsbridge, from the 9th of May, 1789 to the 8th of May, 1790. By Mr. John Read; communicated by R. H. A. Bennet, Esq. F.R.S.," *Phil. Trans., 81* (1791), 185–212.

——— "A meteorological journal, principally relating to atmospherical electricity; kept at Knightsbridge, from the 9th of May, 1790, to the 8th of May, 1791. By Mr. John Read; communicated by Richard Henry Alex. Bennet, Esq. F.R.S.," ibid., *82* (1792), 225–56.

——— A summary view of the spontaneous electricity of the earth and atmosphere; wherein the causes of lightning and thunder, as well as the constant electrification of the clouds and vapours, suspended in the air, are explained. With some new experiments and observations tending to illustrate the subject of atmospherical electricity; to which is subjoined the atmospherico-electrical journal, kept during two years, as presented to and published by the Royal Society of London. London: for the author, 1793.

——— "Experiments and observations made with the doubler of electricity, with a view to determine its real utility, in the investigation of the electricity of atmospheric air, in different degrees of purity. By Mr. John Read. Communicated by Richard Henry Alexander Bennet, Esq. F.R.S.," *Phil. Trans., 84* (1794), 266–74.

Réaumur, René Antoine Ferchault de. "Des effets que produit le poisson appellé en françois torpille, ou tremble, sur ceux qui le touchent; et de la cause dont ils dépendent," *Mém. Acad. Roy. des Sci.* (for 1714), pp. 344–60.

——— "Observations sur la formation du corail, & des autres productions appellées plantes pierreuses," ibid. (for 1727), pp. 269–81.

——— "Préface," in Memoires pour servir à l'histoire des insectes. *6* (Paris: Imprimerie Royale, 1742), li–lxxx. *Abstract and Translation: Phil. Trans.*, no. 467 (1743), xii–xvii. *See* Trembley, Abraham (1743).

——— *Also see* Trembley, Maurice (1943).

Reed, Howard S. A Short History of the Plant Sciences. Waltham, Mass.: Chronica Botanica Co., 1942.

——— "Jan Ingenhousz / plant physiologist / with a history of the discovery of photosynthesis," *Chronica Botanica, 11* (1949), 285–393.

Reed, Richard. "Some communications, about an early swarm of bees, as also concerning cyder; descent of sap; the season of transplanting vegetables: sent to the publisher out of Herefordshire by that intelligent gentleman, Richard Reed Esq; in a letter dated March 14. 1670/1, at Lugwardine," *Phil. Trans.*, no. 70 (1671 N.S.), 2128–32.

Reid, Thomas. Essays on the Intellectual Powers of Man. Edinburgh: John Bell & G., G., & J. Robinson of London, 1785.

Rennell, Thomas. Remarks on scepticism, especially as it is concerned with the subjects of organization and life. Being an answer to the views of M. Bichat, Sir T. C. Morgan, and Mr. Lawrence, upon those points. London: F. C. and J. Rivington, 1819.

Richer, Jean. "Observations astronomiques et physiques faites en l'Isle de Caïenne," *Mém. Acad. Roy. des Sci., 7* [1666–99 ser.] (publ. 1729), part 1, 231–326.

Riley, William A. "Erasmus Darwin and the biologic control of insects," *Science*, N.S. *73* (1931), 475–76.

Robertson, Henry. A general view of the natural history of the atmosphere, and of its connection with the sciences of medicine and agriculture; including an essay on the causes of epidemical diseases. 2 vols., Edinburgh: W. Laing, A. Constable & Co., and W. and J. Rees; Cadell & Davies, and Longman, Hurst, Rees & Orme of London, 1808.

Robinet, Jean Baptiste René. De la Nature. 4 vols., Amsterdam: E. van Harrevelt, 1761–66.

——— Considerations philosophiques de la gradation naturelle des formes de l'etre, ou les essais de la nature qui apprend a faire l'homme. Paris: Charles Saillant, 1768.

Robinson, Bryan. A treatise of the animal oeconomy. Dublin: George Grierson, 1732.

——— A dissertation on the aether of Sir Isaac Newton. Dublin: by S. Powell for Geo. Ewing and Wil. Smith, 1743.

——— Sir Isaac Newton's account of the aether, with some additions by way of appendix. Dublin: by S. Powell for G. and A. Ewing and W. Smith, 1745.

——— An appendix to the dissertation on the aether. Dec. 1 1746. [With Robinson, 1745]

Robinson, Eric. "The Derby Philosophical Society," *Annals of Sci., 9* (1953), 359–67.

Ronalds, Sir Francis. Catalogue of books and papers relating to electricity, magnetism, the electric telegraph, &c. including the Ronalds Library. London: Society of Telegraph Engineers, 1880.

Rose, Hugh. The Elements of Botany: containing the history of the science: with accurate definitions of all the terms of art, exemplified in eleven copper-plates; the theory of vegetables; the scientific arrangement of plants, and names used in botany; rules concerning the general history, virtues, and uses of plants. Being a translation of the Philosophia Botanica, and other treatises of the celebrated Linnaeus. To which is added an appendix, wherein are described some plants lately found in Norfolk and Suffolk, illustrated with three additional copper-plates, all taken from the life. By Hugh Rose, apothecary. London: T. Cadell, 1775.

Rosssi, M. M. See Hone (1931).

Rotheram, John. The sexes of plants vindicated: in a letter to Mr. William Smellie, Member of the Antiquarian and Royal Societies of Edinburgh; containing, a refutation of his arguments against the sexes of plants. And remarks on certain passages of his philosophy of natural history. Edinburgh: William Creech, and T. Cadell of London, 1790.

[*Rowbottom, Margaret E.*] "Electricity in the Service of Medicine." An exhibit "until further notice" at the Wellcome Historical Medical Museum, Euston Square, London.

Royal Society, Papers Submitted to. Essays on the earthquake of 1750. "Consisting of several [57] papers laid down before the Royal Society, concerning several earthquakes felt in England, and some neighbouring countries, in the year 1750," *Phil. Trans.*, no. 497 (1750), 601–750.

Royen, Adrien van. Carmen elegiacum de amoribus et connubiis plantarum, quum ordinarium medicinae & botanices professionum in Batava, quae est Leidae, academia auspicaretur, dictum. XIX. Junii MDCCXXXII. Leyden: Samuel Luchtman, 1732.

Russell, Edward Stuart. Form and Function / a contribution to the history of animal morphology. London: John Murray, 1916.

Rutherford, Ernest. "The modern theories of electricity and their relation to the Franklinian theory." [I. Minis Ways, ed.] The record of the celebration of the two hundredth anniversary of the birth of Benjamin Franklin, under the auspices of the American Philosophical Society . . . (Philadelphia: American Philosophical Soc., 1906), pp. 123–57.

von Sachs, Julius. History of Botany [1875]. Trans. Henry E. F. Garnsey. Oxford: Clarendon Press, 1890.

Sarton, George. "The discovery of the electric cell (1800)/ with facsimile reproduction (No. XI) of Alexander Volta's memoir 'On the electricity excited by the mere contact of conducting substances of different kinds' . . . ," *Isis, 15* (1931), 124–57.

Saumarez, Richard. ["On generation and the principle of life"] [T. Bradley's and A. F. M. Willich's] *Medical and Physical J. . . . ,* 2 (1799), 242–47, 321–26.

——— A new system of physiology, comprehending the laws by which animated beings in general, and the human species in particular, are governed, in their several states of health and disease. 2d ed., 2 vols., London: by J. Davis for T. Cox . . . , 1799.

——— The principles of physiological and physical science; comprehending the ends for which animated beings were created; and an examination of the unnatural and artificial systems of philosophy which now prevail. London: T. Egerton; J. Murray; Sherwood, Neely, and Jones; E. Cox; and T. Underwood, 1812.

Savage, Spencer. See Ellis (1948).

Sawyer, F. C. "Books of reference in zoology, chiefly bibliographical," *J. Soc. for Bibliog. of Natural Hist., 3* (1955), 72–91.

Scharrer, Ernst. "Anatomy and the concept of analogy," *Science,* N.S. *103* (1946), 578–79.

——— "The concept of analogy," *Pubblicazioni Stazione Zoologica, Napoli, 28* (1956), 204–13.

Schelling, Friedrich Wilhelm J. Ideen zu einer Philosophie der Natur. Als Einleitung in das Studium dieser Wissenschaft. 2d ed. Landeshut: Philipp Krüll, 1803.

——— The Ages of the World. Trans. with introduction and notes by Frederick de Wolfe Bolman, Jr. Columbia Univ. Press, 1942.

Schonland, B. F. J. The Flight of Thunderbolts. Oxford: Clarendon Press, 1950.

——— "The work of Benjamin Franklin on thunderstorms and the development of the lightning rod," *J. Franklin Inst., 253* (1952), 375–92.

Schrank, Franz von Paula. Vom Pflanzenschlafe und von anverwandten Erscheinungen bey Pflanzen. Ingolstadt: Johann Wilhelm Krüll, 1792.

Seward, Anna. Memoirs of the Life of Dr. Darwin, chiefly during his residence at Lichfield, with anecdotes of his friends, and criticisms on his writings. London: J. Johnson, 1804.

Sewell, Elizabeth. The Orphic Voice: Poetry and Natural History. Yale University Press, 1960. [A Bergen Lecture in Yale Univ., 26 April 1957.]

Sharrock, Robert. The history of the propagation and improvement of vegetables by the concurrence of art and nature: shewing the several ways for the propagation of plants usually cultivated in England, as they are increased by seed, off sets, suckers, truncheons, cuttings, slips, laying, circumposition, the several ways of graftings and inoculations; as likewise the methods for improvement and best culture of field, orchard, and garden plants, the means used for remedy of annoyances incident to them; with the effect of nature, and her manner of working upon the several endeavors and operations of the artist. Written according to observations made from experience and practice. Oxford: Thomas Robinson, 1660.

Shelley, Percy Bysshe. The Complete Poetical Works of Percy Bysshe Shelley. Ed. Thomas Hutchinson [1905]. Oxford Univ. Press, 1956.

Sherrington, Charles Scott. Goethe on Nature & on Science. Cambridge Univ. Press, 1942.

——— Goethe on Nature and on Science. 2d ed., Cambridge Univ. Press, 1949.

Sherwood, Margaret. Coleridge's Imaginative Conception of the imagination. Wellesley College [Mass.] Press, 1937.

Simpson, George Gaylord. "Lamarck, Darwin and Butler/ three approaches to evolution," *Am. Scholar, 30* (1961), 238–49.

Smart, Christopher. The Hilliad: an Epic Poem. London: J. Newbery, 1753.

Smellie, William. "Aether," in Encyclopedia Britannica, *1* (London: John Donaldson, 1773), 31–34.

Reprinted: Kerr, Memoirs of Smellie, *1* (1811), 370–86.

——— The Philosophy of Natural History. Vol. 1. Edinburgh: for the heirs of Charles Elliott . . . and G. G. and J. Robinsons of London, 1790. Vol. 2. Edinburgh: Bell and Bradfute, J. Dickson, W. Creech, . . . and G. G. and J. Robinson, T. Cadell, Jun. and W. Davies, and T. Kay of London, 1799.

Smith, James Edward. "Some observations on the irritability of vegetables," *Phil. Trans., 78* (1788), 158–65.

Reprinted: Smith, Tracts Relating to Natural History. (London: for the author, 1798), pp. 165–178.

——— An Introduction to Physiological and Systematical Botany. London: Longman, Hurst, Rees, and Orme, and J. White, 1807.

Smith, Sir James Edward. See Linnaeus (1821).

Snow, Adolph Judah. Matter and Gravity in Newton's Physical Philosophy; a study in the natural philosophy of Newton's time. Oxford Univ. Press, 1926.

Solander, Daniel. See Ellis (1786).

Spallanzani, Abbé Lazzaro. "A dissertation concerning the generation of certain plants," in Dissertations Relative to the Natural History of Animals and Vegetables, 2 (London: J. Murray, 1784), 249–347.

Spemann, Hans. "Zur Geschichte und Kritik des Begriffs der Homologie," in Allgemeine Biologie. "Die Kultur der Gegenwart / ihre Entwicklung und ihre Ziele," ed. Paul Hinneberg, Teil 3, Abt. 4, *1* (Leipzig and Berlin: B. G. Teubner, 1915), 63–86.

Sprat, Thomas. The History of the Royal-Society of London, for the Improving of Natural Knowledge. London: J. Martyn and J. Allestry, 1667.

Sprengel, Christian Konrad. Das entdeckte Geheimniss der Natur im Bau und in der Befruchtung der Blumen / von Christian Konrad Sprengel, mit 25 Kupfertafeln. Berlin: Friedrich Vieweg der älter, 1793.

Sprengel, Kurt Polycarp Joachim. Historia rei herbariae. 2 vols., Paris and Strasbourg: Treuttel et Würtz; Amsterdam: In Taberna Libraria et Artium, 1808.

——— and *deCandolle, A. P.* Elements of the Philosophy of Plants: containing the principles of scientific botany; nomenclature, theory of classification, phytography; anatomy, chemistry, physiology, geography, and diseases of plants, and practical illustrations. Edinburgh: William Blackwood, 1821.

Stallknecht, Newton P. Strange Seas of Thought / studies in William Wordsworth's philosophy of man and nature. Duke Univ. Press, 1945.

Stanhope, Charles [Viscount Stanhope of Mahon]. Principles of Electricity, containing divers new theorems and experiments, together with an analysis of the superior advantages of high and pointed conductors. The treatise comprehends an explanation of an electrical returning stroke, by which, fatal effects may be produced, even at a vast distance from the place where the lightning falls. London: P. Elmsly, 1779.

Stearn, W. T. "The background of Linnaeus's contributions to the nomen clature and methods of systematic biology," *Systematic Zool., 8* (1959), 4–22.

Stewart, John. "Some remarks on the laws of motion, and the inertia of matter," Essays an[d] observations physical and literary. Read before the Philosophical Society in Edinburgh, and published by them. 2d ed., *1* [1754], (1771), 79–156.

[*Stewart, John*] The revelation of nature, with the prophesy [*sic*] of reason. New York: for the author, "In the fifth year of intellectual existence, or the publication of the apocalypse of nature, 3000 years from the Grecian olympiads, and 4800 from recorded knowledge in the Chinese table of eclipses, beyond which chronology is lost in fable."

Stiles, Sir F. H. Eyles. "Extracts of three letters of Sir F. H. Eyles Stiles, F.R.S. to Daniel Wray, Esq; F.R.S. concerning some new microscopes made at Naples, and their use in viewing the smallest objects. Naples, 11 August 1761," *Phil. Trans., 55* (1765), 246–70.

Stillingfleet, Benjamin. Miscellaneous tracts relating to natural history, husbandry, and physick. To which is added the calendar of flora. [1759] 4th ed., London: J. Dodsley, Leigh and Sotheby, and T. Payne, 1791.

Stoever, D. H. The Life of Sir Charles Linnaeus, Knight of the Swedish Order of the Polar Star, &c. &c. to which is added, a copious list of his works, and a biographical sketch of the life of his son: by D. H. Stoever, Ph.D. Translated from the original German by Joseph Trapp, A. M. London: B. and J. White, 1794.

Stukeley, William. "The philosophy of earthquakes; by the Rev. William Stukeley, M.D.F.R.S. &c. in a letter to Martin Folkes, Esq; LL.D. and President of the Royal Society, &c.," *Phil. Trans.,* no. 497 (1750), 731–50.

——— "On corals & corallines; ater [a letter?] to Mr. Collison. May 13, 1752." "Read at R.S. May 14th 1752," in Letters and Papers of the Royal Society, *14* (Decade II, no. 296). 10 pp. 153 mm × 184 mm.

——— "On Corals, Corallines &c." "Read at R. S. May 28 1752," in ibid., no. 301. 5 pp. 153 mm. × 184 mm.

——— "On Corals &c." Read to the Royal Society, 11 June 1752, in ibid., *15* (Decade II, no. 309). 16 pp. 153 mm. × 184 mm.

Swainson, William. A preliminary discourse on the study of natural history, in Dionysius Lardner, ed., The Cabinet Cyclopaedia. London: Longman, Rees, Orme, Brown, Green, and Longman; and John Taylor, 1834.

Teilhard de Chardin, Pierre. The Phenomenon of Man [1947]. Trans. Bernard Wall. London: Collins, 1959.

Temkin, Owsei. "Metaphors of human biology," in Robert C. Stauffer, ed., Science and Civilization (Univ. of Wisconsin Press, 1949), pp. 167–94.

Theophrastus. Enquiry into plants and minor works on odours and weather signs. Trans. Sir Arthur Hort, Bart. Loeb Classical Library, 2 vols., London: William Heinemann, 1916.

Thienemann, August. "Die Stufenfolge der Dinge, der Versuch eines natürlichen Systems der Naturkörper aus dem achzehnten Jahrhundert," *Zool. Annalen, 3* (1910), 185–274.

Thomas, Friedrich A. W. Das Elisabeth Linné-Phänomen (sogennantes Blitzen der Blüten) und seine Deutungen / Zur Anregung und Aufklärung, zunächst für Botaniker und Blumenfreunde. Jena: Gustav Fischer, 1914.

Thomas, H. Hamshaw. "Richard Bradley, an early eighteenth-century biologist," *Bull. Brit. Soc. for Hist. of Sci., 1* (1952), 176–78.

——— "Experimental plant biology in pre-Linnaean times," ibid., *2* (1955), 15–22.

Thompson, Sir Benjamin. "Experiments on the production of dephlogisticated air from water with various substances . . . ," *Phil. Trans., 77* (1787), 84–124.

Thompson, John V. "On Polyzoa, a new animal discovered as an inhabitant of some zoophites—with a description of the newly instituted genera of Pedicellaria and Vesicularia, and their species." Zoological researches, and illustrations; or, natural history of nondescript or imperfectly known animals . . . *1,* part 1 (Cork: King and Ridings [1830]), 89–100.

Thompson, Silvanus Phillips. Hand List of the Magnetic and Electrical Books in the Library of Silvanus Phillips Thompson. London: for the author, 1914.

Thornton, John L. John Abernethy / a biography. London: for the author, 1953.

Thorpe, T. E. Humphrey Davy: Poet and Philosopher. Century Science Series, London: Cassell, 1896.

[*Tilloch, Alexander?*] "A correct and more particular account than any that has yet appeared of the galvanic experiments made by Mr. Carpue on the body of Michael Carney," [Tilloch's] *Philosophical Mag., 18* (1804), 90–92.

Tinker, Chauncey Brewster. Nature's Simple Plan: a phase of radical thought in the mid-eighteenth century. Princeton Univ. Press, 1922.

Todd, John T. "Some observations and experiments made on the torpedo of the Cape of Good Hope in the year 1812. By John T. Todd, late surgeon of His Majesty's ship Lion. Communicated by Sir Everard Home, Bart. V.P.R.S.," *Phil. Trans., 106* (1816), 120–26.

——— "Account of some experiments on the Torpedo electricus at La Rochelle . . . ," ibid., *107* (1817), 32–35.

Toland, John. Christianity Not Mysterious: or, a treatise shewing, that there is nothing in the gospel contrary to reason, nor above it: and that no Christian doctrine can be properly call'd a mystery. London: for the author, 1696.

Tonge, Israel. "Some observations, directions and inquiries concerning the motion of sap in trees, in pursuance of what was formerly begun therein, about the latter end of 1668. And the next following spring, by Dr. Ezerel Tonge, and Francis Willoughby Esq," *Phil. Trans.,* no. 57, (1670 N.S.) 1165–67.

Townson, Robert. "Objections against the perceptivity of plants, so far as is evinced by their external motions, in answer to Dr. Percival's memoir in the Manchester Transactions" [1792]. *Trans. Linnaean Soc., London, 2* (1794), 267–72.

Reprinted: "Objections against the perceptivity of plants, so far as it is evinced by their external motions,"—Tracts and Observations in Natural History and Physiology. (London: for the author, 1799), pp. 137–46.

Trembley, Abraham. Réaumur, René-Antoine Ferchault de; and *Bentinck, William.* Some papers lately read before the Royal Society concerning the fresh-water polypus; an insect, which hath this surprising property, that being cut into several pieces, each piece becomes a perfect animal, as complete as that of which it was originally only a part. Cromwell Mortimer, ed. London: T. Woodward and C. Davis, 1743.

Inserted: in *Phil. Trans.* the pamphlet appears as no. 467 (Jan. 1743), succeeding p. 280 of no. 466.

Trembley, Abraham. Mémoires, pour servir à l'histoire d'un genre de polypes d'eau douce, à bras en forme de cornes. Leyden: Jean and Herman Verbeck, 1744.

——— "Translation of a letter from Mr. Abraham Trembley, F.R.S. to the president with observations upon several newly discover'd species of fresh-water polypi," *Phil. Trans.*, no. 474 (1744) 169–83 and Pl. II (opp. p. 159) Fig. 5–7.

Trembley, Abraham. "Observations upon several species of small water insects of the Polypus kind communicated in a letter to the president, from Mr. Abraham Trembley, F.R.S. Translated from the French," ibid., *44*, supp. (1747), 627–55 and Pl. I (opp. p. 575), Fig. 4–10.

——— "Extract of a letter of Mr. Abraham Trembley, F.R.S. to Tho. Birch, D.D. Secret. R.S. Translated from the French," ibid., *50* (1757), 59–62.

Trembley, Maurice. Correspondence inédite entre Reaumur et Abraham Trembley comprenant 113 lettres recueilles et annotées par Maurice Trembley. Introduction par Emile Guyénot. Geneva: Georg, 1943.

Treviranus, G. R. "On the organized bodies found in the seminal fluid of animals, and their analogy to the pollen of plants," *Edinburgh New Philosophical J.*, 22 (1837), 330–43. [1835] [Also a commentary on the article, apparently by Robert Jameson, pp. 343–45].

[*Tull, Jethro*] The new horse-houghing husbandry: or, an essay on the principles of tillage and vegetation. Wherein is shewn, a method of introducing a sort of vineyard-culture into the corn-fields. in order to increase their product, and diminish the common expence, by the use of instruments lately invented. London: for the author, 1731.

Tupper, James Perchard. An essay on the probability of sensation in vegetables; with additional observations on instinct, sensation, irritability, &c. London: White, Cochrane, 1811.

——— "Additional observations on the general analogies between animals and vegetables; and also on instinct, sensation, and irritability," An essay on the probability of sensation in vegetables . . . 2d ed. (London: Longman, Hurst, Rees, Orme, and Brown, 1817), pp. 89–127.

Turnbull, H. W. See Newton (1959).

Turner, Robert. Electricology: or, a discourse upon electricity. Being an enquiry into the nature; causes; properties; and effects thereof, upon the principles of the aether. Illustrated by a series of surprizing experiments. Containing every thing curious in this branch of philosophy, that has been communicated by Professor Muschenbroek; LeMonier; L'Abbe Nolet &c. abroad; and by Messieurs Watson, Martin, and other literati at home: with several new and conclusive ones; and particularly, the surprizing phoenomenon of the sensitive plant, and wonderful benumbing property of the torpedo, are herein explain'd and accounted for. 2d ed., Worcester: by Thomas Olivers for the author; S. Austen and J. Hodges of London, and T. Warren of Birmingham, 1746.

Turrill, W. B. et al. "Differences in the systematics of plants and animals and their dependence on differences in structure, function, and behaviour in the two groups" *Proc. Linnaean Soc., London,* 133d session (1940–41), part 3, pp. 272–87.

Uggla, Arvid H. J. Linnaeus. Trans. Alan Blair. Stockholm: Swedish Institute for Cultural Relations with Foreign Counties, 1957.

Vaillant, Sebastian. Discours sur la structure des fleurs, leurs differences et l'usage de leurs parties; prononcé a l'ouverture du Jardin Royale de Paris, le Xe jour de mois de Juin 1717 . . . Leyden: Pieter van der Aa, 1718.

[*Vallemont, Pierre le Lorrain de.*] Curiosities of Nature and Art in Husbandry and Gardening. Containing several new experiments in the improvement of land, trees, fruits, &c. And also nice and useful observations in the vegetation and propagation of plants; with choice secrets to make plants, flowers and fruits larger, more beautiful, and to ripen quicker than usual [1703]. Trans W. Fleetwood. London: D. Brown, A. Roper, and Fran. Coggin, 1707.

Valli, Eusebius. Experiments on Animal Electricity, with their application to physiology. And some pathological and medical observations. London: J. Johnson, 1793.

Vartamian, Aram. "Trembley's polyp, LaMettrie, and eighteenth-century French materialism," *J. Hist. Ideas, 11* (1950), 259–86.

Vivenzio, Giovanni. Istoria e teoria de'tremuoti in generale ed in particolare di quelli della Calabria, e di Messina del MDCCXXXIII. Naples: Stamperia Royale, 1783.

Volta, Alessandro. "Account of some discoveries made by Mr. Galvani, of Bologna; with experiments and observations on them. In two letters from Mr. Alexander Volta, F.R.S. Professor of Natural Philosophy in the University of Pavia, to Mr. Tiberius Cavallo, F.R.S." [Sept. 13 and Oct. 25, 1792], *Phil. Trans., 83* (1793), 10–44.

——— "Observations on animal electricity; being the substance of two letters from A. Volta to Professor Greu [from *Neues J. Physik, 3,* p. 4, and *4,* p. 1.]." [Tilloch's] *Philosophical Mag.,* 4 (1799), 59–68, 163–71, 306–12.

——— "On the electricity excited by the mere contact of conducting substances of two different kinds. In a letter from Mr. Alexander Volta, F.R.S. Professor of Natural Philosophy in the University of Pavia . . . ," *Phil. Trans., 90* (1800), 403–31. *Translated:* [Tilloch's] *Philosophical Mag.,* 7 (Sept. 1800), 289–311.

Vorontsova, M. A. and *Liosner, L. D.* Asexual Propagation and Regeneration. Trans. P. M. Allen,/ edited F. Billett. London: Pergamon Press, 1960.

W., J. R. "Reply to T.C.'s essay on vegetable life," *Port Folio,* ser III [IV], *5* (1815), 19–37.

Walker, Adam. A system of familiar philosophy: in twelve lectures, being the course usually read by Mr. A. Walker . . . London: for the author, G. Kearsley, and Bell and Bradfute of Edinburgh, 1799.

Walker, W. Cameron. "The detection and estimation of electric charges in the eighteenth century," *Annals of Sci., 1* (1936), 66–100.

——— "Animal electricity before Galvani," ibid., 2 (1937), 84–113.

Wall, Dr. [*William?*] "Experiments of the luminous qualities of amber diamonds, and gum lac . . . ," *Phil. Trans.*, no. 314 (1708), 69–76.

Walsh, John. "Of the electric property of the torpedo. In a letter from John Walsh, Esq; F.R.S. to Benjamin Franklin, Esq; LL.D., F.R.S., Ac.R. Par. Soc. Ext., &c." [1773], ibid., *63* (1774), 461–80.

——— "Of torpedos found on the coast of England. In a letter from John Walsh, Esq; F.R.S. to Thomas Pennant, Esq; F.R.S.," ibid., *64* (1774), 464–73.

Watson, Richard. "On the subjects of chemistry, and their general division" [1765?—Watson remarked on p. 103 that the essay was written "nearly twenty years ago"; some copies were printed, but not published, in 1771], in Chemical Essays, 3d ed., *5* (London: T. Evans 1787), 103–75.

Watson, William. Experiments and Observations Tending to Illustrate the Nature and Properties of Electricity. London: C. Davis, 1746.

——— A sequel to the experiments and observations tending to illustrate the nature and properties of electricity: wherein it is presumed, by a series of experiments expressly for that purpose, that the source of the electrical power, and its manner of acting are demonstrated. Addressed to the Royal Society. London: C. Davis, 1746.

——— MS report of a paper read to the Royal Society on the subject of corals on 28 May 1752, in Letters and Papers of the Royal Society, *14* (Decade II, no. 300). 3 pp. 193 mm. x 312 mm.

——— "An account of the insect called the vegetable fly: by William Watson, M.D.F.R.S.," *Phil. Trans.*, *53* (1763), 271–74 and Pl. XXIII (p. 448).

——— *See* Nollet (1753).

——— "An answer to Dr. Lining's query relating to the death of Professor Richman," *Phil. Trans.*, *48* (1754), 765–72 and Fig. 1–3 of Pl. 31.

——— Observations upon the effects of electricity applied to a tetanus, or muscular rigidity, of four months' continuance. In a letter to the Royal Society. London: W. Richardson and S. Clark, 1763.

——— "Observations upon the effects of lightning with an account of the apparatus proposed to prevent its mischiefs to buildings, more particularly to powder magazines; being answers to certain questions proposed by M. Calandrini, of Geneva, to William Watson, M.D.F.R.S.," *Phil. Trans.*, *54* (1764), 201–27.

Weekes, W. H. "Details of an experiment in which certain insects, known as the Acarus crossi, appeared incident to the long-continued operation of a voltaic current upon silicate of potass, within a close atmosphere over mercury," *Proc. London Electrical Soc.* (1843), pp. 240–53 and Pl. VI, Fig. 24, 25.

Wells, William Charles. "Observations on the influence, which incites the muscles of animals to contract in Mr. Galvani's experiments," *Phil. Trans.*, *85* (1795), 246–62.

——— An Essay on Dew, and several appearances connected with it. London: Taylor and Hessey, 1814.

Welsh, David. Account of the Life and Writings of Thomas Brown, M.D. Edinburgh. W. & C. Tait, and Longman, Hurst, Rees, Orme, Brown, & Green of London, 1825.

[*Wesley, John*] The Desideratum: or, electricity made plain and useful. By a lover of mankind, and of common sense [1759]. London: W. Flexney, E. Cae, George Clark, George Keith, and T. Smith, 1760.

Wheeler, Leonard Richmond. Vitalism: Its History and Validity. Univ. of London, D. Phil. Thesis. London: H. F. & G. Witherby, 1939.

Whicher, Olive. See Adams (1949).

White, Charles. "On the regeneration of animal substances," *Mem. Lit. and Philos. Soc., Manchester, 1* (1785), 325–41.

——— An account of the regular gradation in man, and in different animals and vegetables; and from the former to the latter. Illustrated with engravings adapted to the subject. Read to the Literary and Philosophical Society of Manchester, at different meetings, in the year 1795. London: C. Dilly, 1799.

White, Gilbert. The Natural History and Antiquities of Selborne . . . London: T. Bensley for B. White and Son, 1789.

White, Newman Ivey. Shelley. 2 vols., London. Secker and Warburg, 1947.

Whitehead, Alfred North. Science and the Modern World. Lowell Lectures 1925. Cambridge Univ. Press, 1926.

Whittaker, E. T. "The aether: past and present," *Endeavour, 2* (1943), 117–20.

——— "Classical Theories," A history of the theories of aether and electricity, *1* (2d ed. London: Thomas Nelson, 1951).

Whytt, Robert. An essay on the vital and other involuntary motions of animals. Edinburgh: Hamilton, Balfour, and Neill, 1751.

Wiesner, Julius. Jan Ingen-Housz / sein Leben und sein Wirken als Naturforscher and Arzt. Vienna: Carl Konegen, 1905.

Wild, John. George Berkeley, A Study of his Life and Philosophy. Harvard Univ. Press, 1936.

Wilkinson, Charles Henry. An analysis of a course of lectures on the principles of natural philosophy . . . To which is prefixed, an essay on electricity, with a view of explaining the phenomena of the Leyden phial, etc. on mechanical principles. London: M. Aleen, 1799.

——— Elements of Galvanism, in theory and practice; with a comprehensive view of its history, from the first experiments of Galvani to the present time . . . 2 vols., London: John Murray, 1804.

Willey, Basil. The Eighteenth Century Background / studies in the idea of nature in the thought of the period. London: Chatto & Windus, 1940.

Willey, Basil. "Samuel Taylor Coleridge," in Nineteenth Century Studies / Coleridge to Matthew Arnold (London: Chatto & Windus, 1949), pp. 1–50.

——— The Seventeenth Century Background / studies in the thought of the age in relation to poetry and religion [1934]. London: Chatto and Windus, 1950.

Williams, George. "The beginnings of nature poetry in the eighteenth century," *Studies in Philol.,* *27* (1930), 583–608.

Williamson, Hugh. "Experiments and observations on the Gymnotus electricus, or electrical eel. By Hugh Williamson, M.D. Communicated by John Walsh, Esq. F.R.S.," *Phil. Trans.,* *65* (1775), 94–101.

Willughby, Francis. ". . . the letter of that worthy and observing gentlemen, Mr. VVilloughby, containing an answer to such of the precedent remarks and inquiries, as concerned him, and therefore were imparted to him," ibid., no. 57 (1670 N.S.), 1166–67.

Wilson, Benjamin. An essay towards an explication of the phaenomena of electricity, deduced from the aether of Sir Isaac Newton, contained in three papers which were read before the Royal-Society. London: C. Davis and M. Cooper, 1746.

——— and *Hoadly, Dr. B.* Observations on a Series of Electrical Experiments. London: T. Payne, 1756.

——— An Account of Experiments Made at the Pantheon, on the nature and use of conductors: to which are added, some new experiments with the Leyden Phial. London: J. Nourse, 1778.

——— A Short View of Electricity. London: C. Nourse, 1780.

Wilson, J. Walter. "Cellular tissue and the dawn of the cell theory," *Isis,* *35* (1944), 168–73.

Wimsatt, William K., Jr. "The structure of romantic nature imagery" [1949] in The Verbal Icon / studies in the meaning of poetry [1954] (New York: Noonday Press, 1958), pp. 103–16.

Wodehouse, R. P. Pollen Grains: their structure, identification and significance in science and medicine. London: McGraw-Hill, 1935.

Woodward, B. B. Catalogue of the books, manuscripts, maps and drawings in the British Museum (Natural History). 5 vols., London: by the Trustees, and sold by Longmans & Co., B. Quaritch, and Kegan Paul, Trench, Trübner & Co., 1903–1915.

Woodward, John. An essay toward a natural history of the earth: and terrestrial bodies, especially minerals: as also of the sea, rivers, and springs. With an account of the universal deluge: and of the effects that it had upon the earth. London: Ric. Wilkin, 1695.

——— "Some thoughts and experiments concerning vegetation. By John Woodward, M.D. of the College of Physicians, & R.S. & Professor of Physick in Gresham College," *Phil. Trans.,* no. 253 (1699), 193–227.

Wordsworth, William. The Poetical Works of William Wordsworth, ed. Ernest de Selincourt [and Helen Darbishire]. 5 vols., Oxford: Clarendon Press, 1940–49.

——— The Prelude or Growth of a Poet's Mind / edited from the manuscripts with introduction, textual and critical notes by Ernest de Selincourt. 2d ed. rev. by Helen Darbinshire. Oxford: Clarendon Press, 1959.

Young, Thomas. "A catalogue of works relating to natural philosophy, and the mechanical arts," A course of lectures on natural philosophy and the mechanical arts. 2 (London: Joseph Johnson, 1807), 105–503.

Zirkle, Conway. "Some forgotten records of hybridization and sex in plants 1716–1739," *J. Heredity, 23* (1932), 433–48.

Index

Abernethy, John, 64 n., 189 f., 192 n., 197
Abrus, 143
Acari, electrical, 199
Accademia del Cimento, 35
Achard, 34 n.
Acid principle, electric, 21
Adams, George [the elder], 93 n.
Adams, George [the younger], Pl. 2, 47 f., 105 n.
Adanson, Michel, 36 n., 106
Addison, Joseph, 62, 149 n.
Aeschynomene, 142
Aether. *See* Ether
Affinities, 195 f.
Agriculture, 64, 78
Aikin, John, 64 n., 160 n.
Akenside, Mark, 165 f., 204
Aldini, Giovanni, 45 n.
Algae: "vegetable matter," 78; difficult to distinguish from corallines, 113; calcareous, 136, 138 n.; "polypary" constructed by animals, 139 ff.
Allamand, J. N. S., 36
Allen, B. Sprague, 151 n.
Alston, Charles, 118 f., 121
"Altar of science," 1
Amici, Giovanni Battista, 107
Amphibia, 195
Analogue, 197
Analogy, and scientific method, 57–70, 184 f.; and empiricism, 65 ff., 131, 153, 165, 175, 190; tested by experiment, Hales, 85; Trembley, 123; Davy, 185; Lindsay, 193; and consonance of nature, 92, 153 n.; zoophytes, 137; Berdoe, 139 n.; courtroom scene, 155 n.; philosophical vs. popular, 165, 169 f.; romantic feeling for nature, 166 n.; of all existence, 183; and comparative anatomy, 186. *See also* Botanical analogy, idea of; Circulation of sap; Generation of plants
Analogy of seed and egg, Pl. 3; budding and regeneration, Pl. 4; plants and minerals, 58 f., 72 ff., 81 f., 156; mineral formation and animal embryos, 60; plant grafts and magnetic field of the earth, 60; plants and animals, 65n.; plant growth and *arbor Dianae,* 72; plant grafts and inoculation of humans, 82; style and Fallopian tubes, 94; flowers and insects, 116; prolepsis and essential parts of animals, 116; regeneration in polyp and starfish, 125 n.; plants and shellfish, 126; swarm-spores and ants, 141 n.; courtiers and hothouse plants, 142; leaves and lungs, 146; seeds and spiders, 163; fungi and animals, 163; seed and earth, 172; silica and bones, 182 n.
Anatomy, comparative, 194–97
Anaxagoras, 58
Anderson, F. H., 61 n.
Andry, Nicholas, 90
Animal heat, E. Darwin, 170; John Hunter, 187 f.
Animalculist thesis, 90, 94 f.; denial of seminal animalcules by Linnaeus, 101, 118
"Animate phial," 39
Anthoxanthum, 163
Apollodorus, 145 n.
Apreece, Mrs., 185 n.
Aquinas, Thomas, 66 n.
Arber, Agnes, vii, 60 n., 185 n.
Aristotle, 58 ff., 98, 149 n.
Armadillo, 195
Artificial system. *See* Systematics
Ascanius, Peter, 63 n.
Aurora borealis, electrical, 25

Index

Autogamy, Fig. 1, 99; orthodoxy of graded function, 98 ff., 117 ff., 162 n.
Autotrophic nutrition, 177 f.
Avenarius, Richard, 200 n.
Averrhoa, sensitive, 151
Avicularium. *See* Coralline

Bacon, Francis, 57 f., 61 f., 74, 76 n., 89 n., 145 n., 172 n.
Baker, Carlos, 207
Baker, Henry, 46, 82 n., 90 f., 125, 134 n., 172 n.
Baker, John R., viii, 63 n., 125, 127 n., 149 n.
Bancroft, Edward, 39 f.
Banks, Sir Joseph, 32, 153 n., 174
Barclay, John, 191
Barlow, Lady, viii
Barometz. *See* Tartarian lamb
Barton, Richard, 9 n., 66
Bartram, John, 126, 134 n.
Baster, Job, 136 n.
Bat, 195
Bate, Walter Jackson, 208 n.
Bates, Marston, 61 n.
Baumé, Antoine, 177 n.
Bazin, Gilles Augustin, 69 n.
Beach, Joseph Warren, 201, 204 n.
Beale, John, 80, 116 n.
Beament, J. W. L., 186 n.
Beattie, James, 161, 209
Beaumont, John, 72 f.
Beccaria, Giovanni Battista, 26 f., 49
Beck, Hanno, 189 n.
Becket, John Brice, 46 f.
Beddoes, Thomas, 180
Bell, George, 68, 151, 153
Bell, Peter R., viii, 142 n., 144 n.
Bennet, Richard Henry Alexander, 26 n., 28, 29 n.
Bentley, Richard, 6
Berdoe, Marmaduke, 33 f., 47, 106, 139 n., 166
Bergson, Henri, 189
Berkeley, George, 11 ff., 19 f., 43, 46, 50, 66 n., 83 n.
Bernbaum, Ernst, 203
Bertholon, Abbé Pierre, 26 n., 29
Bewley, William, 25 n., 39, 40 n.
Bianchi, 46
Bichat, Marie François Xavier, 188, 190, 192
Bignon, Abbé, 128
Birch, John, 47
Blackstone, Bernard, viii, 200 n., 207
Blagden, Sir Charles, 26
Blair, Patrick, 82 f., 87, 89, 95 f., 99, 117, 120, 121 n.
Blake, William, 200
Bleeding, of plants, 79
Bleeker, P., 42 n.
Blind, Mathilde, 203 n.
Blood, shaken to produce electricity, 16 n.
Bloom, Harold, 207
Blumenbach, J. F., 107 n., 184, 195 n.
Boas, Marie, 5, 6 n.
Bobart, Jacob, 98, 111
Boerhaave, Hermann, 101, 124, 128
Boerman, A. J., 109 n.
Bohr atom, 11
Bondaroy, Fougeroux de, 122 n., 139 n.
Bonnet, Charles, 34 n., Table 1, 71; 84 n., 106 n., 122, 127, 132, 147, 152, 179, 195 n., 197
Borelli, Alfonso, 3, 35
Boscovich, Rogerio, 9, 184
Bose, Caspar, 145
Bose, G. M., 29, 39
Bose, Sir Jagadis C., 200 n.
Boston, earthquake explained by electricity, 27 n.
Bot fly, 33
Botanical analogy: idea of, 59; plants and minerals, 72–73; circulation of sap, 78–84; generation in plants and animals, 88–108; keystone of Linnaean botany, 110 f.; problematical organisms, 122–38; sensitive plant, 144, 151; observations of irritability and sensitivity in plants, 144–56; rejection of analogies with minerals in favor of analogies with animals, 156; guiding principle in Erasmus Darwin's poetry, 161–65; criticism by Lamarck, 177–80; Davy, 182 ff.; Wordsworth, 203; poetry, 208
Bourguet, Louis, 100
Bowdoin, James, 24 n.
Boyd, James, 116 n.
Boyle, Robert, 2, 4, 6, 15
Bradley, Richard, 69, 81, 83 n., 93 n., 96–100, 103, 117, 121, 128, 142, 146, 179, 197
Breyn, Johann Philipp, 145 n.
Brisseau-Mirbel, C. F., 107 n., 176 n., 178 f., 194
Bromine, 186
Bromley, John S., viii

Index

Broussonet, Pierre Marie Auguste, 42 n., 151 n.
Brown, Thomas, 174 f.
Browne, Peter, 5 n., 65 f.
Browne, Sir Thomas, 66 n.
Browning, John, 31 n.
Bruce, Robert, 151
Bruguière, Jean Guillaume, 195 n.
"Brush realized," 200
Brydone, Patrick, 26 n.
Buds, analogous to polyzoa or corallines, 163 f.
Büchner, Andreas Elias, 139 n.
Buffon, Georges Louis Leclerc, comte de, 22 f., 105 n., 126 f., 155 n., 161, 195 n.
Butler, Joseph, 66 n.
Bywater, John, 29 n., 182 n.

Cabæus, 15 n.
Cain, Arthur J., viii, 115
Camerarius, Rudolph Jacob, 98, 117, 120 f., 160
Campanella, Tommaso, 145
Campanula, 118 f.
Camper, Peter, Pl. 7, 147 n., 154
Candolle, Augustin Pyrame de, 29 n.
Canning, George, 174
Canthigaster janthinopterus, 42
Canton, John, 24 n., 41
Capacitance, 41
Capillaries, vegetable, 82
Capillarity, principle of electrical action in organisms, 28
Carlisle, Sir Anthony, 155 n.
Cassava, prickly, 117
Castor-oil plant, 119
Causation: pretensions to explain, 3, 18 f., 67; Brown's criticism of Darwin, 174; "beyond our reach," 190
Cavallo, Tiberius, 20 n., 22, 26 n., 27, 34 n., 41 n., 42 n., 45, 47, 54 f., 68, 182
Cavendish, Henry, 41 f.
Cellular tissue, 175
Cesalpino, Andrea, 89, 116
Chain of being, 58 f., 137 n. *See also* Scale of being
Chambers, Ephraim, 83, 173 n., 199 f.
Chance, Burton, 12 n.
Chaos, 140
Chardin, Pierre Teilhard de, 200 n.
Charles II, 74 f.
Chénier, André, 161, 209
Chickens, cured by electricity, 38
Chlorine, 186
Chondrilla, 163
Circulation of sap in plants, 78–88; peristaltic motion, 80; capillaries, 82 f.; veins and arteries, 82; systole and diastole, 83; disproved for gross fluids, survival for subtle fluids, 86
Clark-Kennedy, A. E., 83 n.
Clover, 142
Coelenterates. *See* Polyp
Cohen, I. Bernard, 4 n., 5, 27 n.
Cohen, Morris, 186
Coins, compared to polyp, 126
Colden, Cadwallader, 9, 16 n., 26 n., 64 n., 113 n., 126
Cole, Francis J., 107 n.
Coleridge, Samuel Taylor, 166 n., 167 n., 174, 179, 184, 192 n., 208 n.
Collinson, Peter, 16, 22, 33 n., 126 n.
Collinsonia, 163
Controls, experimental, 29
Cook, John, 7 f.
Cooper, Thomas, 155 n.
Coral. *See* Polyp
Corallines, 133–38; Pl. 5; difficulty of distinguishing from algae, 113; plants with animated flowers, 136 f.; analogous to budding plants, 163
Cornut, Jacques Philippe, 141 f.
Cosmic synthesis. *See* Forces, synthesis of
"Cosmic Tories," 152 n.
Cotugno, Domenico, 34
Covolo, dal, Giambattista, 147, 163
Coxe, Daniel, 72, 81
Crabbe, George, Pl. 5
Cramp ray, 39
Crocodile, 195
Crombie, Alistair C., viii
Crop rotation, 77 f.
Crosse, Andrew, 199
Cryptograms, seeds of, 110 f.
Cudworth, Ralph, 191
Cullen, William, 177 n., 187
Cuvier, Georges Léopold Chrétien Frédéric Dagobert, 188 ff., 192, 195
Cycles of electricity, 27
"Cypher of nature," 10

Dale, Samuel, 128
Dalenpatius, 90
Darlington, C. D., 104 n.
Darlington, William, 119 n.
Darstellung, 209
Darwin, Charles, 150 n., 197 n., 201
Darwin, Erasmus, Pl. 1, 2, 6 n., 21, 26 n., 29, 32, 127 n., 190, 203 f., 206 ff., 208 n.; electric fish, 42 n.; Tartarian lamb,

Darwin, Erasmus (*continued*)
145 n.; notion of plant sensitivity as a subject for poetry, 162; Linnaean systematics in verse, 162; poet of botanical analogy, 162–65; evolution, 165–68; theory of life, 168–73; reaction to his writings, 174 f., 179 f.; and Davy, 182 f.
Darwin, Robert Waring [brother of Erasmus], 145 n.
Darwin, Robert Waring [son of Erasmus], 165 n.
Date palms, sexes in, 89
Daudin, Henri, 138 n.
Davy, Sir Humphry, 1 n., 88, 156 n., 166 n., 180–86, 193, 203; early writings, 180 f.; criticism of idea of immanence, 181 f.; criticism of idea of botanical analogy, 182 f.; evolution, 183; analogy and scientific method, 184 ff.; Neoplatonic mysticism, 206 n.; 209
Day, Joy, viii
deBeer, Sir Gavin R., viii, 115 n.
Dedu, N., 75 n., 92 f., 145
deGraaf, René, 92
Deists, 65
d'Azyr, Felix Vicq, 195
Delage, Yves, 133 n.
Deleuze, J. F. P., 182 n.
Delille, Jacques, 126 n.
Demainbray, Stephen, 28 f.
Democritus, 58
Descartes, René, 2 f.; reaction against, 6, 15 n.
Desfontaines, René Louiche, 196
deVallemont, Pierre le Lorrain, 73 n., 75 n., 168 n., 173 n.
Diana of Ephesus cult figure, Frontispiece, 173
Dichogamy, 117 f.
Dickson, Adam, 64
Digby, Sir Kenelm, 15 n., 73 f.
Dillenius, John James, 135
Dioecious plants, 98
Diseases cured by electricity, 38, 43–48
D'Israeli, Isaac, 63 n.
Doig, David, 173 n.
Dollard, John, 154 n.
Donati, Vitaliano, 132 ff., 136
d'Ormoy, Abbé, 29
Doubler of electricity, 55
Dove, John, 64
Draba, 142
"Dual affinity," 115
Dualism: John Harris, 6 f.; resolved by notions of subtle fluids, 6 ff., 75; 168 f.
Dudley, Paul, 97 n.
du Fay, Charles François de Cisternay, 193 n.
Duhamel du Monceau, Henri Louis, 102 n., 106, 122 n.
Duncan, J. S., 156 n.
Dunn, S. G., 201
du Phanjas, Abbé François Para, 127 n.
Dutrochet, Henri Joachim, 144 n., 194

Earthquakes, electrical, 25 ff.
Edwards, George, 139
Eeles, Henry, 21, 44
Eggs, hatching, Pl. 3, 172; by electricity, 34 n.
Electric fish: mechanist notions, 35; Robert Turner's flounder, 35 f.; and Leyden jar, 35–43; early accounts, 36 f.; cures effected with shocks, 38, 43; recognition of electricity, 39 f.; capacitance, 41 f.; electric toby, 42 f.; nervous action, 50 f.; claimed as example of galvanic electricity, 53; electrochemistry, 55
Electricity, atmospheric, 16–27, 19 f., Pl. 1; resemblance of sparks to lightning, 16; Stephen Hales, 16; Bryan Robinson, 16; Benjamin Wilson, 17; prime cause, 19; secondary cause, 20; acid principle, 21; planetary motion, 21; transmission of light, 21; Franklin, 24 f.; aurora borealis, 25; meteors, 25 f.; earthquakes, 25 ff.; hurricanes, 26; whirlwinds and waterspouts, 26 n.; volcanoes, 27; "ferilli," 27; dethroned as master of the cosmos, 56; discovered at same time as the polyp, 126 n.
Electricity, medical, 43–48, Pl. 2; electric fish, 38, 43; benevolence, 44 f.; revival of the dead, 45; penetration of bodies, 46; as a remedy, 46 f.
Electricity, organic, 19, 20, 25 f., 28–35, 180, 191; capillarity and circulation promoted by, 28; development of silkworms, 29; growth promoted by, 29; growth retarded by negative electricity, 29 n.; "fairy rings" of mushrooms, 29 n.; "heavenly manure," 29 n.; sensitivity in plants, 30 f.; pollination of flowers, 31; luminous flowers, 31 f.; development and evolution, 33; rapid flight of bot fly, 33; jellyfish, 33; incubation, 34 n.; nervous action, 48–56; generation of plants, 106; static in lower animals and electrochemical in

higher ones, 176; Crosse and the creation of "insects," 199; Chambers, 199 f.
Electrochemistry, 52–56; higher animals, 176
Electrophore, 55
Eleusinian mysteries, 172
Ellicott, John, 125
Elliott, Hugh, 176 n.
Ellis, George, 174
Ellis, John, Pl. 5, 24 n., 63 n., 132 n., 135–38, 140 n., 150
Empiric-dogmatic dispute, 63 f.
Empiricism: Haller, 50 n.; Trembley, 124; Haller and Newton, 156; Davy, 181 f., 190; Shelley, 205
Equilibrium, concept of, 23
Erklärung, 209
Essequibo, 36
Ether, 191, 201; to justify Newton's intuitions, 4; cause of phenomena, 4–8; resolution of dualism, 7 f.; Hartley's indirect evidence for, 10; criticized by Berkeley, 11 ff.; identified with electricity, 15; electric fish, 36; universal, 66; hot and cold, 87–88 n.; and light, 144; Erasmus Darwin, 169 ff. *See also* Forces, synthesis of
Euler, Leonhard, 8 n.
Euphrates lily, 145
Evelyn, John, 145 n.
Evolution, Berdoe, 33 f.; Darwin, 165–68; Lamarck, 175 n.; Davy, 183; 199 f.
Exell, A. W., 145 n.
Explanation, ambitions for total, 2 f., 198; Newton, 5; Newtonian speculation, 8–11; deplored by Davy, 181
Explanation, principle of limited, 6; Newton, 2; ignored by Lovett, 18 f.; Barclay, 191; Brisseau-Mirbel, 194
Explanation, refinement of, 3, 5 f., 75 f., 195
"Exploring wire," 26

Fearing, Francis, 188 n.
Fechner, Gustav Theodor, 200 n.
Feijoo y Montenegro, Benito Jerónimo, 154 n.
"Ferilli," 27
Fermin, Philippe, 38 n.
Feuer, L. S., 198 n., 206 n.
Field, George, 156 n.
Fielding, Henry, 126
"Flakes of fire," 20
Fletcher, Phineas, 60 n.
Flounder, electrified, 35
Flowers, 109–12; essential parts of plants, 115 ff.; analogous to insects, 116; hermaphrodites, 117 f.; of coral and other sea animals, 128 ff., 133 n., 136 f.; irritability, 147; said to be real animals, 164; evolution into insects, 167. *See also* Generation of plants; Pollen
Folkes, Martin, 125
Fontana, Felix, 50 f., 140 f., 176 n.
Forces, 15, 166; synthesis of, intuitions of Newton, 3, 18, 204; as a cosmic synthesis, 6; post-Newtonian speculation, 8 ff.; in *Siris,* 13; criticized by Hunter, 188. *See also* Electricity; Subtle fluids; Vital forces
Forster, Edward, 32
Fothergill, John, 25
Fourcroy, Antoine de, 178
Fowler, Richard, 54
Fragonard, Jean Honoré, Pl. 1
Franklin, Benjamin, Pl. 1, 21 n., 22 ff., 27, 39 f., 84 n.
Franklin, Mark L., viii
Fraser, Alexander, 13
Freke, John, 19, 21, 30 f., 47
Frere, John, 174
Frog, motions excited by electricity, 51 f.
Fulton, John Farquhar, 43 n.
Functions, scale of, classical notions, 58 f.; Hooke, 70 ff. *See also* Graded function, orthodoxy of

Galen, 43
Galvani, Luigi, 51–56, 169
Galvanism. *See* Electricity, organic
Garden, Alexander, 26 n.
Garden, George, 89
Gardens and sensitive plant, 151
Garfinkle, Norton, 174
Garstang, Walter, 201
Generation of plants, 88–108, Pl. 2; sex of plants denied, 89, 118–22; analogies drawn to animal generation without reference to sexuality, 98 ff.; sexual theories, 91–108; counterparts to animalculists and ovists in animal generation, 92–96; male influence, how transmitted, 92–108; subtle fluids in, 96–108; self-fertilization (autogamy) and orthodoxy of graded function, 98 ff.; Fig. 1, 99, 117 ff.; Linnaeus's theories of, 101 ff. *See also* Linnaeus; Pollen
Geoffroy, Étienne François, 95, 98, 103, 128
Georges-Berthier, Auguste, 6 n.

Geotropism, 148
Gerould, John H., 176 n.
Gesner, Johann, 101 n., 111 n., 114, 121
Gibbon, Edward, 173 n.
Gilbert, William, 60
Gillispie, Charles Coulston, 13 n., 116 n., 176 n., 199
Gimcrack, Sir Nicholas, 62
Girod-Chantrans, Justin, 141
Girtanner, 188 n.
Glow-worm, electrical, 34
Gmelin, Johann Friedrich, 147
Goatsucker, 195
Gode-von Aesch, Alexander, 154 n., 161, 173 n.
Godwin, William, 201
Goethe, Johann Wolfgang von, Frontispiece, 116, 208
Goguet, Antoine, 173 n.
Goldsmith, Oliver, 63, 155 n.
Gould, Rupert T., 199 n.
Grabo, Carl, 203 f., 206 n.
Graded function: orthodoxy of, 59 f., 78; denial of plant sexuality, 89, 118–22; self-fertilization of plants, 98 ff., 117 ff., 162, 167; denial of animal nature of corals, 129–32; denial of free motion to leaves, 142; denial of sensation to plants, 153
Graham, James, 44
Gravesande, van s' Laurens Storm, 36 f., 40 n., 43
Gray, Stephen [?], 39
Gregory, George, 34 n.
Gregory, James, 64 n., 188 n.
Gregory, John, 64 n., 67 n., 68 n., 166 n., 187
Gregory, Joshua C., 186 n.
Greville, C. F., 164 n.
Grew, Nehemiah, 3, 73–76, 80 ff., 91–95, 98, 117, 132, 142
Gronovius, J. F., 113 n., 125
Grundfest, Harry, 37 n.
Guerlac, Henri, 84 n.
Guthrie, W. K. C., 172 n.
Gymnotus. *See* Electric fish

Haeckel, Ernst Heinrich, 200 n.
Hagberg, Knut, 109 n.
Haggren, 31 f.
Hales, Stephen, 16, 83–87, 100 f., 106 n., 142, 206
Hall, A. Rupert, 6 n., 81 n.
Haller, Albrecht von, 49 f., 112, 121, 146 f., 156
Hamilton, Sir William, 27
Hampden, Renn, 156 n.
Hansen, Adolph, 116
Harmer, Sir Sidney, 136 n.
Harrington, Robert, 198 f.
Harris, J., 11
Harris, John, 6 f., 65 n.
Harris, W. Snow, 24 n.
Hart, Cheney, 45
Hartley, David, 10, 33, 65, 67, 180, 201
Hartsoeker, N., 90
Harvey, William, 78 f., 81 n., 82, 91 f.
Hauksbee, Francis, 16
Hawkins, Sir John, 63 n.
Hazard, Paul, 105 n.
"Heavenly manure," 29 n.
Heliotropism, 142, 163
Helmont, Jean Baptiste Van, 76, 190
Hemp, 121
Henkel, J. F., 82 n.
Henly, William, 20 n., 41
Henslow, John Stevens, 201
Hermann, Johann, 195
Herschel, Sir John, 185 f.
Herschel, Sir William, 170, 199, 203
Herodotus, 89
Hickman, Dom Robert, 21 n.
Hieroglyphics, 173
Hill, "Sir" John, 43, 46, 62 f., 99, 105, 134, 139, 143 f.
Hill, T. G., 63 n.
Hippocrates, 89
Hoadly, B., 17 n.
Hobbes, Thomas, 3
Hochdoerfer, Margaret, 50 n.
Hocking, W. E., 186 n.
Hofsten, Nils, von, 115
Hogg, Thomas Jefferson, 206
Holbach, Paul Henri Thierry, Baron d', 9 f., 166, 172 n., 204
Home, Sir Everard, 192, 197 n.
Home, Francis, 86 n.
Homologue, 197
Hooke, Robert, 3, 70 ff., 138 n., 145 f.
Hooper, Robert, 153
Houghton, John, 76 n.
Hughes, Griffith, 133 n., 134 n.
Hulme, T. E., 198 n.
Humboldt, Friedrich Heinrich Alexander von, Frontispiece, 53, 189, 192
Humean skepticism: Thomas Brown, 174; P. B. Shelley, 205
Hummingbird, 195
Hunter, Alexander, 148
Hunter, John, 143 n., 148, 153, 177, 186–

97; electric fish, 41, 50; hypodermic injections, 46 n.; theory of life, 186–90; experimental method, 192; comparative anatomy, 194–97
Hurricanes, electrical, 26
Hutchinson, G. Evelyn, viii
Hybrids, 95 f., 106 n.; explained by Leeuwenhoek, 90
Hydra. *See* Polyp
Hydroid. *See* Coralline
Hypodermic syringe and electricity, 46
Hypotheses: without a place in experimental philosophy, 2; of the ether, 13 f.

Imagination in science, 184 f.
Immanence: idea of, and electricity, 15–22, 21 n.; defined, 17; Richard Lovett, 17 ff.; Robert Turner and electricity of the torpedo, 35 f.; E. Darwin, 169, 171, 174; Lamarck, 175 f.; criticism and rejection, 181–92; Shelley, 203, 206; poetic ground of physics, 204 n.; poetry, 208
Imperato, Ferrante, 127
Ingenhousz, Jan, 88, 140, 178 n., 182
Injury currents, 54
Instinct in plants, 148, 155
Iodine, 186
Iris, 118 f.
Irritability, 144, 146 ff., 177, 193

Jackson, Maria Elizabeth, 150 n., 154 f.
Jallabert, Jean, 29
Jenyns, Soame, 66 n., 149 f.
John-go-to-bed-at-noon, 142
Johnson, Rev. Samuel, 9 n.
Jones, Howard Mumford, 50 n.
Jones, Rev. William, 20 n.
Jupiter, 172 n.
Jurin, James, 62 n.
Jussieu, Antoine de, 128 n.
Jussieu, Bernard de, 102, 106, 110 f., 129 f., 132, 134, 136

Kalmia, 117
Kames, Henry Home, Lord, 64, 119 n., 151 n., 154 n.
Keats, John, 207 f.
Keir, James, 165
Keith, Patrick, 178
Kellaway, Peter, 35 n., 43 n.
Kenrick, William, 9 n., 17 n., 144
Kentish, Richard, 61 n.
Kerr, Robert, 119 n.
King, William, 65
King-Hele, Desmond, 159 n., 204 n.
Kircher, Athanasius, 60 n.
Kirkpatrick, Thomas, 17 n.
Kite experiment, 24
Knight, G. Wilson, 202 n., 204, 207
Knight, Gowin, 21 n.
Knight, Thomas Andrew, 88, 117, 148, 153 n., 174, 182, 193 f.
Knuth, Paul, 121 n.
Koelreuter, Joseph Gottlieb, 106, 121 n.
Koestlin, Carl Heinrich, 29 n.
Kooymans, Johanna, viii
Kuhn, Thomas, 158
Keynes, John Maynard, 7 n.

LaCondamine, Charles Marie de, 36 n.
Lacroix, Demetrius, de, 145 n., 160
Lacy, John, 21
Lamarck, Jean Baptiste Pierre Antoine de Monet de, 175–80, 190 n., 191, 196, 200, 205; subtle fluids and life, 175 f.; scale of beings, 176 f.; autotrophic nutrition, 177 f.; denial of sensitivity in plants, 178 f.; essential difference of plants from animals, 179
Lamettrie, Julien Offray de, Pl. 3, 81 n., 126, 127 n., 166, 200 n., 203 f.
Lang, Andrew, 172 n.
Largus, Scribonius, 43
Larval development, electrical stimulation of, 29
Lavater, Johann Caspar, 154
Lavoisier, 175, 181
Lawrence, William, 6 n., 188 n., 189 f., 192
Leaf-mining insects, 134
Lee, Henry, 145 n.
Lees, Edwin, 156 n.
Leeuwenhoek, Antony van, 3, 89 f., 94, 103, 106 n., 172 n.; observation of polyp, 123; coral, 127 f.
leGrise, Claude, viii
Leibniz, Gottfried Wilhelm, 9, 13, 100, 137 n., 166 n., 204
Lemmi, Charles A., 173 n.
Lemur, 195
LeSage, Georges Louis, 8 n.
Leyden jar, 22–28, 67, Pl. 2; popularity of electricity, 22; earthquake machine, 27; sting of jellyfish, 33; electric fish, 35–43; basis of Galvani's notion of muscular motion, 51–54; criticism of that notion, 53–56; facilitated mathematical concepts, 84 n.; rejection by Darwin as a model for muscular motion, 168 f.

Lieberkühn, Johann Nathanael, 102
Life, theory of: E. Darwin, 168–73; Hunter and others, 186–92
Lightning. *See* Electricity, atmospheric
Lightning rod, 24 f.
Lily, luminous, 31
Limited explanation, principle of. *See* Explanation, scientific
Lind, James, 41 n.
Lindsay, John, Pl. 6, 148, 192 f.
Linnaea, Elisabet Christina, 31
Linnaeus, Carl, Pl. 3, 24 n., 32 ff., 40, 63 n., 69, 87, 109–22, 138, 155 n., 156, 164, 173 n., 196 f.; and pollen, 101 ff., 106 n.; notion of sexuality, 109 ff.; systematics, 111 ff.; scale of beings, 113 ff.; prolepsis, 116 f.; "rhapsodist of nature," compared to Goethe, 116 n.; orthodoxy of graded function, 117 ff.; classification of corals, 128, 132, 134, 138 n.; flowers in corallines, 136 f.; notion of animated flowers, 136 ff.; vegetating fly, 139; "chaos," 140; movement of leaves, 142; sleep of plants, 142 ff., 145 n.; Venus' fly trap, 150
Linnaeus, Carl [the younger], 150
Lion, 196
Lister, Martin, 79 f., 145
Locke, John, 65
Logan, James, 118 n.
Lorenzini, Stefano, 35
Lott, Frans, van der, 37 f., 43
Louis, XV, 22
Love, Frontispiece, 205; spirit of life, 170 ff.; evolution, 183
Love-in-the-mist, 117
Lovejoy, Arthur O., 13, 59 n., 154 n.
Lovett, Richard, 17 ff., 22, 47, 169
Lowndes, Francis, 44
"Luce electricum," 32
Lucretian epics of science, 161
Ludolf, Job, 43
Luminescence: of the sea, Francis Penrose, 20; Franklin, 24; Berdoe, 34; of flowers, 29 n., 31 f.
Lychnis, 120
Lyell, Charles, 186, 191 f.
Lyon, Rev. John, 21
Lyonnet, Pierre, 65 n., 69

Macfait, Ebeneezer, 26 n.
Mach, Ernst, 200 n.
Maclaine, Archibald, 21 n., 40 n.
Maclurg, James, 49, 64 n., 154 n.
Macrocosm, 60
Maize, Turkish, 121
Major, Johann David, 79
Malebranche, Nicolas, 92, 100
Malpighi, Marcello, 81 n., 82, 89, 92, 94, 160
Man, 195
Marigold, luminous, 31
Marilaun, A. Kerner von, 121 n.
Mariotte, Edme, 81 n., 145
Marmot, 195
Marsigli, 128
Martin, Benjamin, 16 f.
Martyn, John, 82 n., 83 n., 96
Materialism, 6–11, 127, 151, 155 n., 174, 180, 190, 204 f.
Mather, Cotton, 96 n.
Maty, Matthew, 27, 84 n.
Maucauco, the flying, 195
Maupertuis, Pierre Louis Moreau de, 72 n.
McKillop, Alan Dugald, 160 n.
McLeay, William, 178, 196
McNair, Philip, viii
Mechanism, 74, 90 n., 145; corpuscularian, explanations not satisfactory, 2 f.; electricity, 15; electric fish, 35; water transformed to plant substance, 76; plant generation, 97; plant motion, 141 f.
Menon, Abbé, 29
Mercury, French, 121
Metamorphosis of plants, Frontispiece, 116
Meteors, electrical, 25 f.
Miall, L. C., 112 n.
Micheli, Pierantonio, 110
Microcosm, 60
Microscopes, 3, 104 n., 105 n.
Miles, Henry, 125
Mill, John Stuart, 67
Miller, Philip, 88
Millington, Sir Thomas, 91 n.
Milton, John, 185
Mimicry, 168
Mimosa. See Sensitive plant
Monboddo, James Burnet, Lord, 173 n.
Monism. *See* Forces, synthesis of
Monkey, white-eyelid, 195; colobus, 196
Monks, convulsed by electric shock, 22
Monro, Alexander, 50, 53 ff.
Montgomery, James, Pl. 5
More, Hannah, 161
Morgan, Augustus de, 4
Morgan, George Cadogan, 53
Morison, Robert, 135

Morland, Samuel, 94 f., 98, 102 f.
Mornet, Daniel, 10 n.
Morris brothers, 61 n.
"Mundus invisibilis," 140
Murray, Mr. and Mrs. J. J., Jr., viii
Muschenbroek, Pieter van, 38
Muscular motion, 163, 168 f.; Stephen Hales, Bryan Robinson, 16
Mussels, 126
Mylonas, George E., 172 n.
Myth, Prometheus and electricity, 25; allegorical theory of, creation of Eve from Adam's rib, to explain evolution of monosexual from hermaphrodite forms, 162 n.; Pluto and Persephone, to explain relation of matter to spirit, 172; birth of Venus, to explain marine origins of life, 172; Orphic symbol of egg of night, to explain vital energy, 172; Jupiter as personification of attraction, 172 n.; Psyche, to explain attraction in living and dead matter, 189

Nasturtium, luminous, 31 f.
Natural history, 61–71
Natural system. *See* Systematics
Naturphilosophie, 208
Needham, John Turbervill, 22, 34 n., 68, 72, 103, 106, 139, 172 n.
Needham, Joseph, viii
Neoplatonism, in Newton and Henry More, 13; visions of "more than human" figures, 166; Shelley, 206
Nervous action, theory of, role of ether, 4, 5, 7, 180; role of electricity, 16, 48 ff.; Galvani, 51–56
Newton, Sir Isaac, 1, 100, 106 n., 143, 156, 161, 170, 180, 185, 191, 199, 203, 206; statement of principle of limited explanation, 2; ambiguous scientific legacy, 3; ethereal hypothesis, 4 ff.; resolution of dualism, 7; influence upon later speculation, 7 ff., 13; electricity, 15, 16–21; opinion of natural history, 62 n.; plant physiology, 85 ff.
Nicholas of Damascus, 59, 78 n.
Nicholson, William, 41
Nicol, J. A. Colin, 42 n.
Nicolson, Marjorie, 6, 160 n.
Nollet, Abbé Jean-Antoine, 22 ff., 28
Nordenskiold, Eric, 188 n., 200 n.

Occult qualities, 11, 15, 74
Öhme, C. J., 194 f.
Oldenburg, Henry, 13, 80 n.
Opium, use by Monro, 53; use by Lindsay, 193
Oppenheimer, Jane M., 60 n.
Oppian, 35 n.
Opuntia tuna, 152
Orang-outang, 195
Orphic cosmology, 172
Ovist hypothesis, 92 f.
Ovulist hypothesis, 92–97
Owen, Richard, 197, 199 n.
Oxalis, 146
Oxygen and carbon dioxide in plant respiration, 178
Oyster, 126

"Pain at a distance," 35
Pallas, Peter Simon, 136 n., 138, 179, 196
Pangolin, 195
Parkinsonia, 142
Parsons, George, 177 n.
Parsons, James, Pl. 4, 106, 127, 131 f., 135
Paterson, William, 42
Peart, Edward, 198 f.
Pelham, Edgar, 203 n.
Pemberton, Henry, 6
Pennant, Thomas, 39 f., 160, 161 n.
Penrose, Francis, 20, 46, 88 n.
Percival, Thomas, 8 n., 63 n., 68, 151 ff., 160 ff.
Perrault, Claude, 3, 35, 81 n., 83 n., 188 n.
Peyssonel, Jean André, 128 ff., 134 ff., 138
Pfaff, Christoph Heinrich, 182
Pfeffer, W., 142 n.
Phlogiston, analogous to electricity, 20 f.; analogous to organic substance, 149; E. Darwin, 170; Lavoisier, 181; J. Priestley, 198
"Phosoxygen," 180
Pike, Samuel, 13 n.
"Piscine electricity," 39
Pistil, mistaken for a male sex organ, 91
Pius II, and barnacle tree, 139
Pivati, Giovanni, 46
Planetary motion, electrical, 21
Plant-animal. *See* Polyp; Coralline; Vegetable fly
Plantain, 117
"Plastic nature," 93
Plato, 58, 77. *See also* Neoplatonism
Pleasure principle, 149; Percival, 151 f.; Smellie, 152 f.; James P. Tupper, 155 f.
Plenitude, principle of, 13
Pliny, 89, 145 n.
Pluche, Nöel Antoine, 111 n., 128 n.
Plutarch, 58, 172 n.

Pluto and Persephone, 172
Pollen, carried by electricity, 31; cause of luminous flowers, 32; spermatic fluid, 91, 94; fertilizes female flower parts without contact, 92–95, Fig. 1, 99; action explained, 94; color disappears before fertilization, 94; penetrates to ovules, 94 ff., 97, 160; burst in water, 98, 102 ff., Fig. 2, 104; magnetic virtue, 98; carried by insects, 99 n., 106, 120, 168 n.; subtle fluids, 100–08; Linnaeus, 101 f.; Jussieu, 102; Needham, 102 ff., tube, 103–07; of sea animals, 105, 134; spermatophore, 105; analogous to insects, 163
Pollenist hypothesis, 94 f., 97, 107; disputed by Linnaeus, 102 f.
Polyp, 16, 117, 122–38, Pl. 4; coral, 111, 113, 127–34; thought to be an animal in *1703*, 123; investigations of Trembley, 122–25; "fresh-water starfish," 125. *See also* Corallines; Sponges
Polypide. *See* Coralline
Polyzoa. *See* Coralline
Pontano, Giovanni, 95 n.
Poole, Thomas, 184 n.
Pope, Alexander, 62, 68 n.
Portland vase, 173 n.
Potter, George Reuben, 62 f., 91 n., 166
Pownall, Governor Thomas, 20 n.
Preformation, 97 n., 121 f.; Henry Baker, 91; Darwin, 172
Price, Derek J. deSolla, viii
Prichard, James Cowles, 191 f.
Priestley, Joseph, 9, 20 ff., 24, 25 n., 38 f., 62 n., 86 ff., 105 n., 149 n., 151, 180, 198; earthquake machine, 27; algae, 140
Priestley, Joseph [fils], 156 n.
Pringle, Sir John, 9 n.
Prior, Matthew, 30
"Problematical organisms," 122–41
Prolepsis, 116 f.; Hill's notion and life cycle of sea animals, 134; Erasmus Darwin, 164
Prometheus, experiments on electricity, 25
Protandry, 117 f.
Proterogyny, 117 f.
Pulos, C. E., 205
Pulteney, Richard, 32, 144 n.
Pumpkin, citron, 121

Quack physicians, electrical nostrums, 44
Quantum theory, 11

Rackstrow, B., 19 f.
Raspé, Rudolph Erich, 139
Rawlinson, Richard, 83, 96 n.
Ray, John, 79, 80 n., 93 ff., 98, 117, 127, 135, 145 n., 146, 160
Read, John, 26 f., 48
Réaumur, René Antoine Ferchault de, 34 f., 37, 39 f., 63 f., 65 n., 106 n., 111, 123 f., 129 f., 134, 172
Recapitulation, 100
Reed, Richard, 80 f.
Regeneration. *See* Polyp
Reid, Thomas, 66 n.
Remington, Charles L., viii
Rennel, Thomas, 191 n.
Reproduction. *See* Generation
Return stroke, 26 n.
Reynolds, Sir Joshua, 197
"Rhodische Genius," 189
Richards, I. A., 185 n.
Richer, Jean, 36 n.
Richmann, George Wilhelm, 25
Ritterbush, P. C., 29 n., 162 n., 193 n.
Robertson, Henry, 29 n.
Robinson, Bryan, 8, 17
Robinson, Thomas, 60 n.
Robison, John, 55
Romantic protest, 197–210
Ronayne, 41
Rotheram, John, 120
Rothman, Dr., 109
Rougier, Francis L., 200 n.
Rousseau, Jean-Jacques, 110 n.
Rowbottom, Margaret, 47 n.
Royal Humane Society, 45 n.
Royen, Adrien, van, 160

Sachs, Julius, von, 106 n., 144 n.
St. Clare, Dr., 43 f.
St. Elmo's fire, 20
St. Hilaire, Geoffroy, 196
Santorio, Santorio, 83
Sap. *See* Circulation of sap
Saumarez, Richard, 189
Saussure, Théodore de, 178, 181
Scale of beings, Pl. 7, 34, 120, 149 f., 198; distinguished from chain of beings, 59 n.; basis for analogies between plants and animals, 67; Hartley, 67; Stillingfleet, 68 f., 198; loss of a single link impossible, 69, 156; Bonnet, 70 ff.; diagram, 71; embryos ascend, 100; Linnaeus, 113–15; natural system, 113–15, 176; polyp, 125–38; marine and

terrestrial, 132 f.; vegetating fly, 138 f.; algae will climb, 141; Charles White, 153 f.; Hunter, 153, 197; notions of racial inferiority, 154; Darwin, 166 f., 171; Lamarck, 176 f.; rejection of, 179 f., 194–97. *See also* Chain of being; Functions, scale of; Graded function, orthodoxy of
Scharrer, Ernst, 186
Schonland, B. J. F., 24 n.
Schwann, Theodor, 176 n.
Sea fan, 137
Sea moss. *See* Coralline
Segregation experiments: on plants, 98, 121 f.; on the polyp, 123
Selection, sexual, 167 f.
Selectivity in plant nutrition, 58 f., 77
Senebier, Jean, 68 n., 141, 178
Sensitive plant, 59 f., 144–56, 162, 182, Pl. 6; and electricity, 30 f.; analogous to polyp, 123, 127, 133 n., 136 ff.; *Dionaea,* 150 f.; differences from animals, 177–80; John Lindsay, 192 f.; Shelley, 206 f.
Sexual system. *See* Systematics
Shakespeare, William, 185
Sharrock, Robert, 142
Shaw, Thomas, 128
Shelley, Mary, 45 n.
Shelley, Percy Bysshe, 166 n., 203–07
Sherard, William, 88
Siegesbeck, Johann Georg, 119 n.
Silkworm. *See* Larval development
Simpson, George Gaylord, 176 n., 198 n.
Skene, David, 136, 150 n.
"Skeptics, modern," 190
Sleep of plants, 141–44, 192 ff.; based on a voluntary faculty, 163 f., 175
Sloane, Sir Hans, 88, 145 n.
Smellie, William, 119 f., 152 f., 188
Smith, Sir James Edward, 117 n., 152 f., 178
Smith, James L. B., viii, 42
Smith, Robert A., viii
Smith, Samuel Stanhope, 154 n.
Snow, Adolph Judah, 13 n.
Solander, Daniel, 138 n., 143 n.
Sorrel, 142
Spallanzani, Lazzaro, 106, 121 f., 139 n., 182
Spark gap, electric fish, 40 f.
Spemann, Hans, 197 n.
Spermatophore, 105
Sphinx moth, 195
Sponges, 133 f., 138
Spores of mushrooms, thought to be animals, 139 f.
Sprat, Bishop Thomas, 60 f.
Sprengel, Christian Konrad, 106 f., 117
Sprengel, Kurt Polycarp Joachim, 29 n., 80 n., 107
Spurge, 117
Stahl, Georg Ernst, 190
Stallknecht, Newton P., 201, 202 n.
Stanhope, Hon. Charles, 26 n., 27
Stearn, W. T., viii, 63 n.
Stensen, Nicholas, 92
Stewart, Dugald, 174 n.
Stewart, John "Walking," 204 n.
Stiles, Sir F. H. Eyles, 105 n.
Stillingfleet, Benjamin, 68 f., 147, 198
Sting-cup, 33
Stone-plants, 73
Storge, 163
Stuckey, Johanna, viii
Stukeley, William, 34, 130 f., 135; electricity of earthquakes, 27; electricity the very soul of the world, 33
Subtle fluids, 20, 21, 201, 204 f.; refinement of explanatory texture by Newton, 6; key to the cypher of nature, 10 f.; vitalized by Berkeley, 13; raised by the heart and rubbed glass, 15; plant life, 75; Stephen Hales and circulation in plants, 82–88; plant generation, 93–108, 118; evolution, 166, 168 ff.; Erasmus Darwin's spirit of life, 170–74; Lamarck, 175 f., 177 n.; criticism of, 182; theory of life, 187–92
Swainson, William, 196
Swallows, migration, 120 n.
Swammerdam, Jan, 49, 54, 92, 98, 105, 116
Swarm-spores, 141 n.
Swedenborg, Emanuel, 20 n.
Sweet, Henry, 203 n.
Swift, Jonathan, 62
Swordfish, 195
Synthesis of forces. *See* Forces, synthesis of
Systematics, 111–15, 118, 162, 176 f.

Tamarind, 142 f.
Tartarian lamb, 145
Tar-water, 12, and electricity, 43
Taylor, Thomas, 173 n.
Telegraph plant, 150 f.
Temkin, Owsei, 186 n.
Temple of Health, 44

Thames, River, shock transmitted across, 22
Theophrastus, 59
Thienemann, August, 72, 115, 132 n., 179 n.
Thiersch, Hermann, 173 n.
Thomas, Friedrich A. W., 31 n.
Thomas H. Hamshaw, 85
Thompson, Sir Benjamin, Count Rumford, 140
Thompson, John V., 138 n.
Thomson, James, 160
Tidwell, Pat, viii, 99, 104
Tiger, 196
Tilloch, Alexander, 45 n.
Tilton, Eleanor, 27 n.
Timiriazeff, C. A., 192 n.
Toby, electrical, 42 f.
Toland, John, 65
Torpedo. *See* Electric fish
Torre, Giovanni Maria, della, 105
Total explanation, ambitions for. *See* Explanation, scientific
Tournefoil, luminous, 31
Tournefort, Joseph Pitton de, 73 n., 111, 135
Townson, Robert, 177
"Tragedy of Flora," 161
Trembley, Abraham, 65 n., 122–25, 127 n., 129 f., 138
Treviranus, Gottfried Reinhold, 107 f.
Tressan, Louis Elisabeth, de, comte de LaVergne, 21 n.
Tucker, Abraham, 173 n.
Tull, Jethro, 60 n., 78
Tupper, James Perchard, 155 f.
Turner, Robert, 169; electricity of the sensitive plant, 30; of the torpedo, 35
Turrill, W. B., viii
Turtle, 195

Uggla, Arvid H. J., 110 n.
Ungar, Franz, 141 n.
Ur-fleisch, 33
Urphänomen, 208

Vaillant, Sebastian, 94 f., 101 n., 109, 160
Valli, Eusebius, 20 n., 53 ff.
Vallisneri, A., 110
Vartamian, Aram, 127
Vegetable fly, 138 f.
Vegetable matter, 78, 140
Venus, 172
Venus' fly trap, 150
Verati, 46
Vesuvius, 27
"Vigilant flowers," 143
Vince, S., 8 n.
Vital spirits, 202, 204 f.; Berkeley, 12 f.; electricity, 19 f.
"Vivacity," as a name for electricity, 19
Vivenzio, Giovanni, 27 n., 34
Volcanoes, electrical, 27
Volta, Alessandro, 53–56
Voltaire, François Marie Arouet de, 195 n.
Vorontsova, M. A., 127 n.

Walker, Adam, 204
Walker, Jeremy D. B., viii
Walker, W. Cameron, 36 n.
Wall, Dr., 16
Walsh, John, 39 ff.
Warburton, William, 173 n.
Waterspouts, electrical, 26 n.
Watson, J. Steven, viii
Watson, Richard, 205
Watson, Sir William, 22 f., 25, 45 n., 63 n., 130 f., 135 f., 139, 148 f.
Watt, Gregory, 1
Webb, Philip, 135 f.
Weekes, W. H., 199
Wells, William Charles, 54, 185
Wesley, John, 20, 27, 83 n.; electricity of sensitive plant, 31
Whale, 195
Whirlwinds, electrical, 26 n.
White, Andrew D., 24 n.
White, Charles, Pl. 7, 153 f.
White, Gilbert, 160
White, Newman Ivey, 205 n.
Whitehead, Alfred North, 203, 207
Whittaker, Sir Edmund, 4 n.
Whytt, Robert, 50, 63 f.
Wieland, Christoph Martin, 161 n.
Wiesner, Julius, 178 n.
Wilkinson, C. H., 182 n.
Willey, Basil, 149 n.
Williamson, Hugh, 41
Willow-herb, 117
Willow tree, electrified, 30; analogous to polyp, Pl. 4, 127
Willughby, Francis, 79
Wilson, Benjamin, 17
Wilson, J. Walter, 176 n.
Wimsatt, William K., Jr., viii, 201

Wind, Edgar, viii
Winkler, Johann Heinrich, 24 n., 46
Wodehouse, R. P., 107 n.
Wood, Alexander, 46 n.
Woodward, John, 60 n., 76 ff., 87, 90 n., 140
Wordsworth, 166 n., 200–03
Worms, regeneration, 127, 132; nerves, 155

Young, Arthur, 64 n.
Young, William, 150

Zakon, Samuel J., 46 n.
Zea, 117
Zirkle, Conway, 96 n., 119 n.
Zooecium. *See* Coralline
Zoophyte. *See* Coralline; Polyp; Scale of being; Sponge